P9-BZD-726

The Illustrated Natural History of Canada/**The Western Plains**

THE ILLUSTRATED NATURAL HISTORY

Scientific Consultants to the Serie

Aspen Grove Prairie

ƆF CANADA # The Western Plains MAX BRAITHWAITE

arth *Science Consultant* WALTER TOVELL, Curator, Department of Geology, Royal Ontario Museum. *Life Science Consultant* J. MURRAY SPEIRS, Department of Zoology, University of Toronto

Library of Congress Catalog Card Number: 79-105929

Natural Science of Canada Limited
58 Northline Road, Toronto 16, Ontario, Canada

Publisher: Jack McClelland
Editor-in-Chief: Peter Crabtree
Senior Editor: Michael Worek
Art Director: Peter Moulding
Visual Editor: Bill Brooks

Editorial Consultant: Pierre Berton

THE WESTERN PLAINS

Editors: Gerd Grossman / Michael Worek
Art Directors: Bill Fox / Peter Moulding
Picture Editor: Bill Brooks
Artists: Vlasta van Kampen / Jerry Kozoriz / Gordon McLean

*Northern Canadian muskeg–
breeding ground of the whooping crane*

Contents

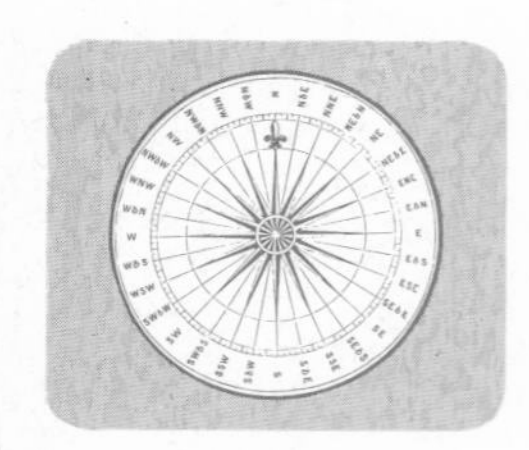

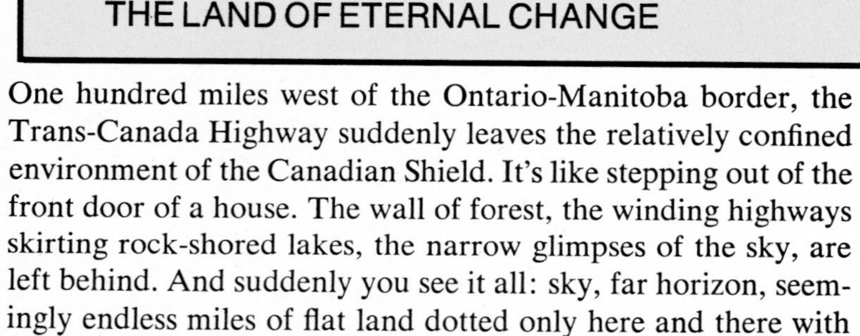

Prologue

THE LAND OF ETERNAL CHANGE

The Author enjoying one of his frequent field trips.

One hundred miles west of the Ontario-Manitoba border, the Trans-Canada Highway suddenly leaves the relatively confined environment of the Canadian Shield. It's like stepping out of the front door of a house. The wall of forest, the winding highways skirting rock-shored lakes, the narrow glimpses of the sky, are left behind. And suddenly you see it all: sky, far horizon, seemingly endless miles of flat land dotted only here and there with aspen groves. These are the great western plains of Canada.

This is the part of Canada that stretches westerly from the Canadian Shield eight hundred miles to the foothills of the Rocky Mountains. A continuation of the interior plains of the United States, the region runs 1,600 miles north in a narrowing band to the Arctic Ocean. Altogether, it occupies an area of 775,000 square miles, which is roughly one-fifth of the total area of Canada. The 375,000 square miles that lie within the three prairie regions of Manitoba, Saskatchewan and Alberta comprise just about half the total area of those provinces.

The southern portion of the plains usually referred to as "the prairies," is unique in the settled area of the country. It possesses the country's best soils and the worst climate. Much of the area is semi-arid and only the fortunate timing of the rainfall prevents it from being a barren, wind-swept desert. It is the home of innumerable animals, many of which are found nowhere else in the country; before man invaded the area with his ploughs, it was the range of the greatest herds of grazers that ever inhabited the earth. About half of North America's ducks breed on its wetlands and at least two species of giant birds fight a losing battle against civilization's intrusion of its territory.

Most of all, out on the plains there is a feeling of bigness. Big sky, stretching from far horizon to far horizon, with big white clouds scudding across it; big road reaching far, far ahead in a straight line with the telephone poles coming together on the skyline. Big fields, mostly without fences, lie flat and level on both sides of the road. Big flocks of ducks are in the sky. Big rivers, when you come to them, cut wide deep banks. Everything is big, except the trees, and they seem remarkably spindly and short after the great forests of the shield.

It soon becomes monotonous, this straightness and flatness, so that the land seems barren and almost uninhabited. But leave the highway, turn up a sideroad and look around. The place becomes alive. Nearby, a small brown and grey gopher sits up beside his burrow. Mice scurry through the dry grass and a red-tailed hawk swoops from a telephone pole to end the scurrying. A meadowlark sings from a fence post. The dusty roadside is alive with grasshoppers. What seemed like a drab collection of weeds and grasses is in fact a mass of delicate bloom, yellow, red and blue.

Back on the highway, going west, although the land seems flat it actually rises steadily. The southern plains rise from an altitude of less than 800 feet above sea level at Winnipeg, to 4,000 feet in the foothills of Alberta. A novelist once called it "the land of eternal change" – and it takes much more than a single exploration to attempt to gauge the infinite surprise and variety of the harsh, yet bountiful, "breadbasket of the world."

THE WESTERN PLAINS: AN ALBUM OF MAPS

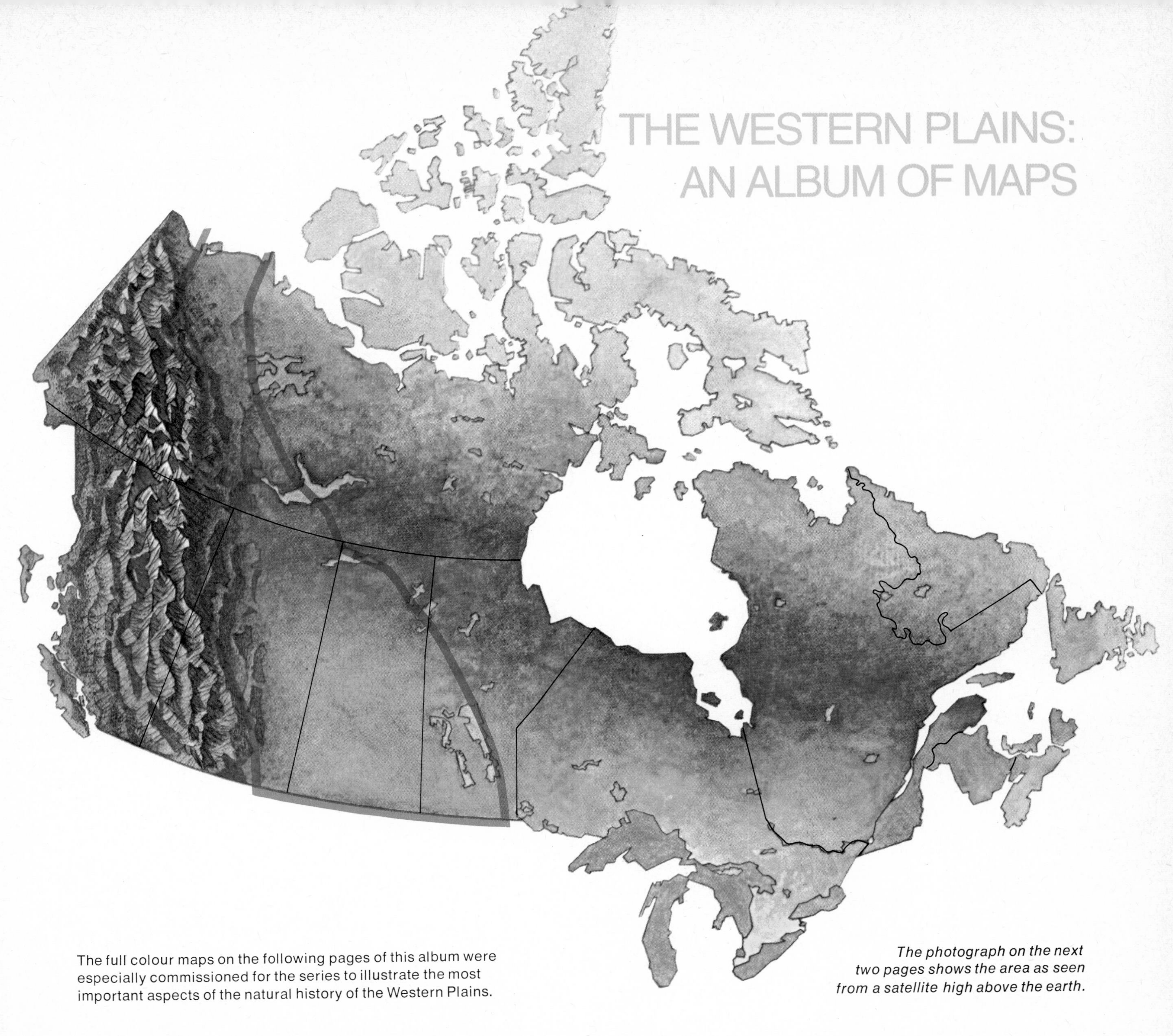

The full colour maps on the following pages of this album were especially commissioned for the series to illustrate the most important aspects of the natural history of the Western Plains.

The photograph on the next two pages shows the area as seen from a satellite high above the earth.

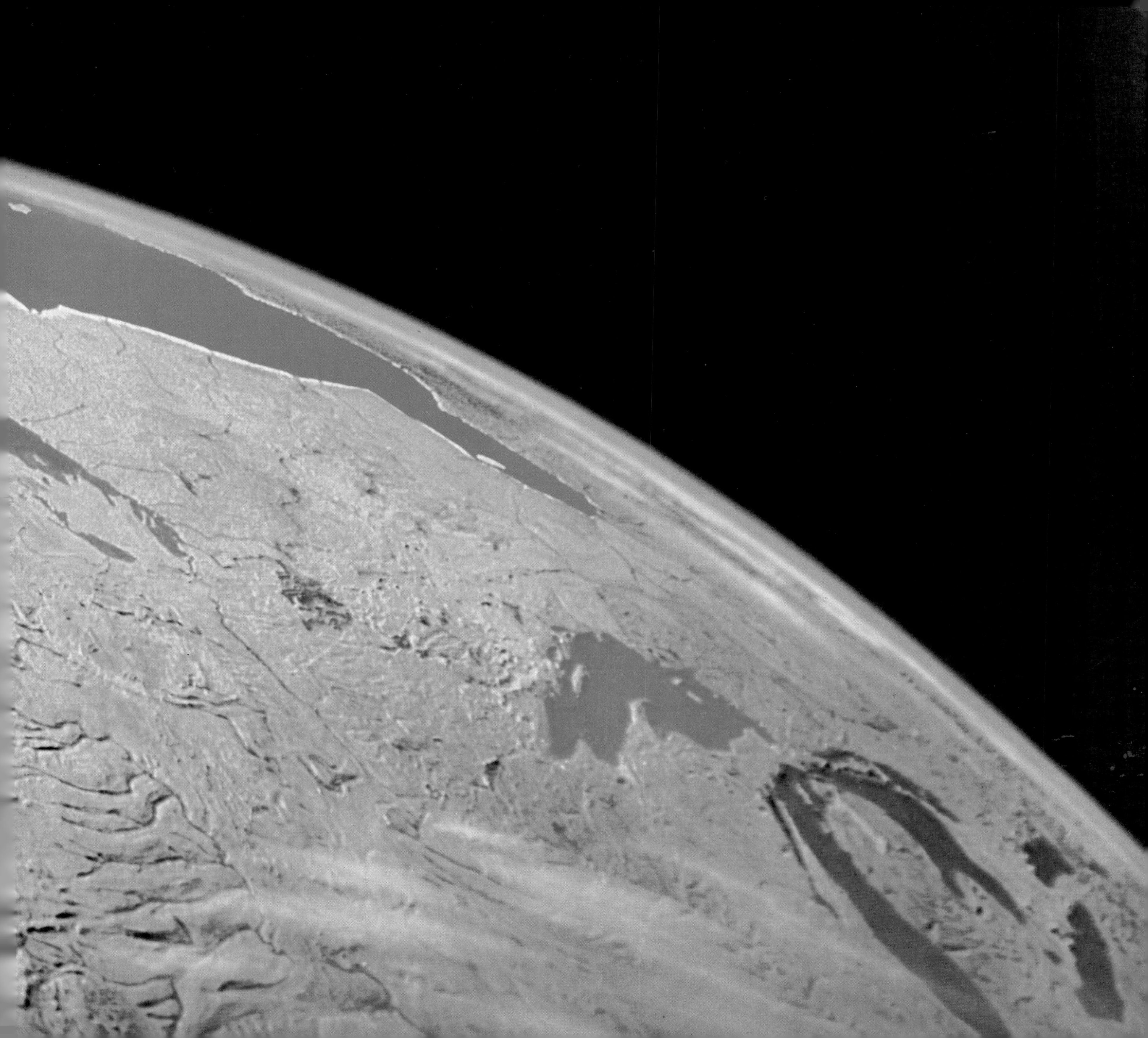

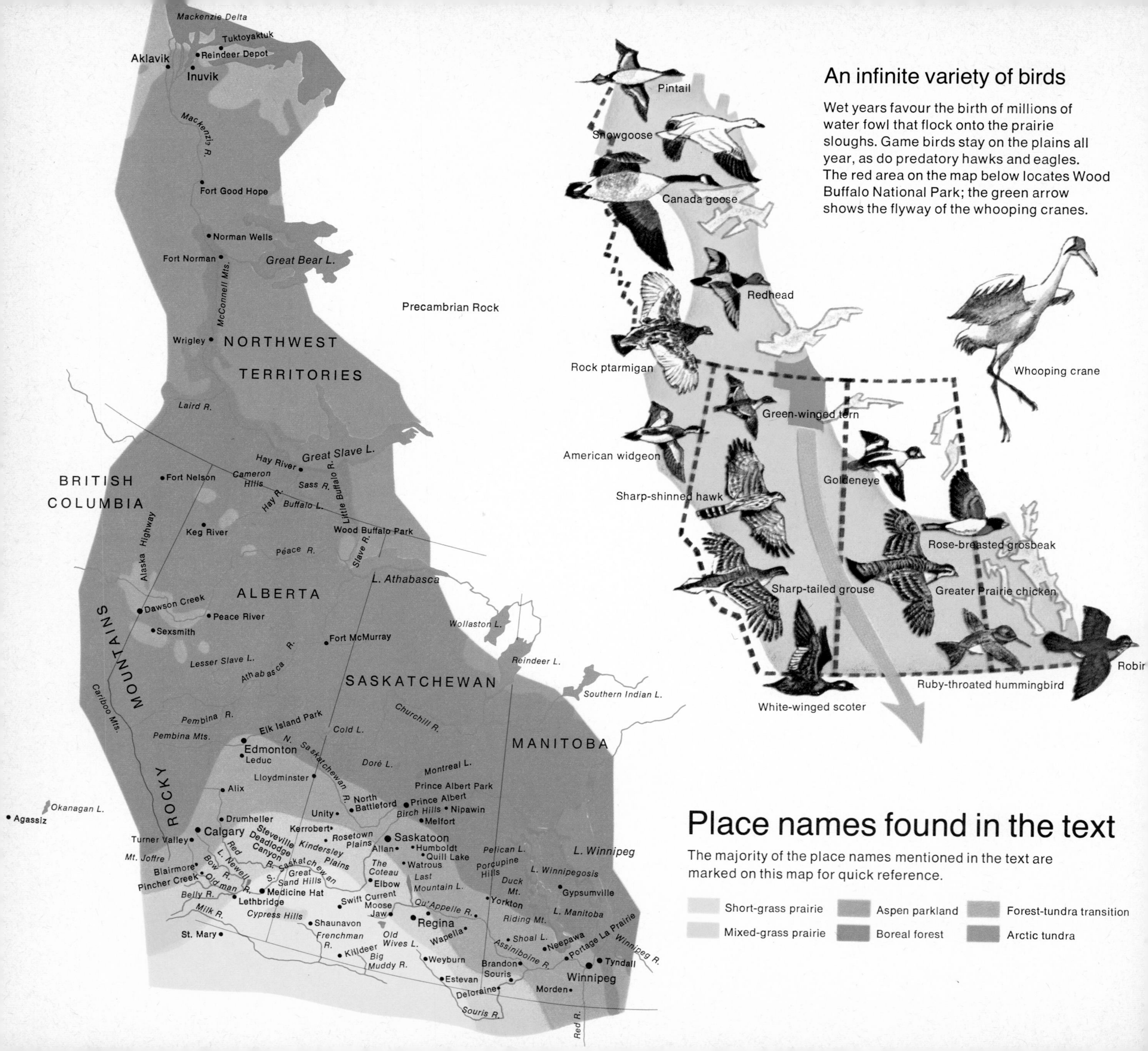

An infinite variety of birds

Wet years favour the birth of millions of water fowl that flock onto the prairie sloughs. Game birds stay on the plains all year, as do predatory hawks and eagles. The red area on the map below locates Wood Buffalo National Park; the green arrow shows the flyway of the whooping cranes.

Place names found in the text

The majority of the place names mentioned in the text are marked on this map for quick reference.

Short-grass prairie	Aspen parkland	Forest-tundra transition
Mixed-grass prairie	Boreal forest	Arctic tundra

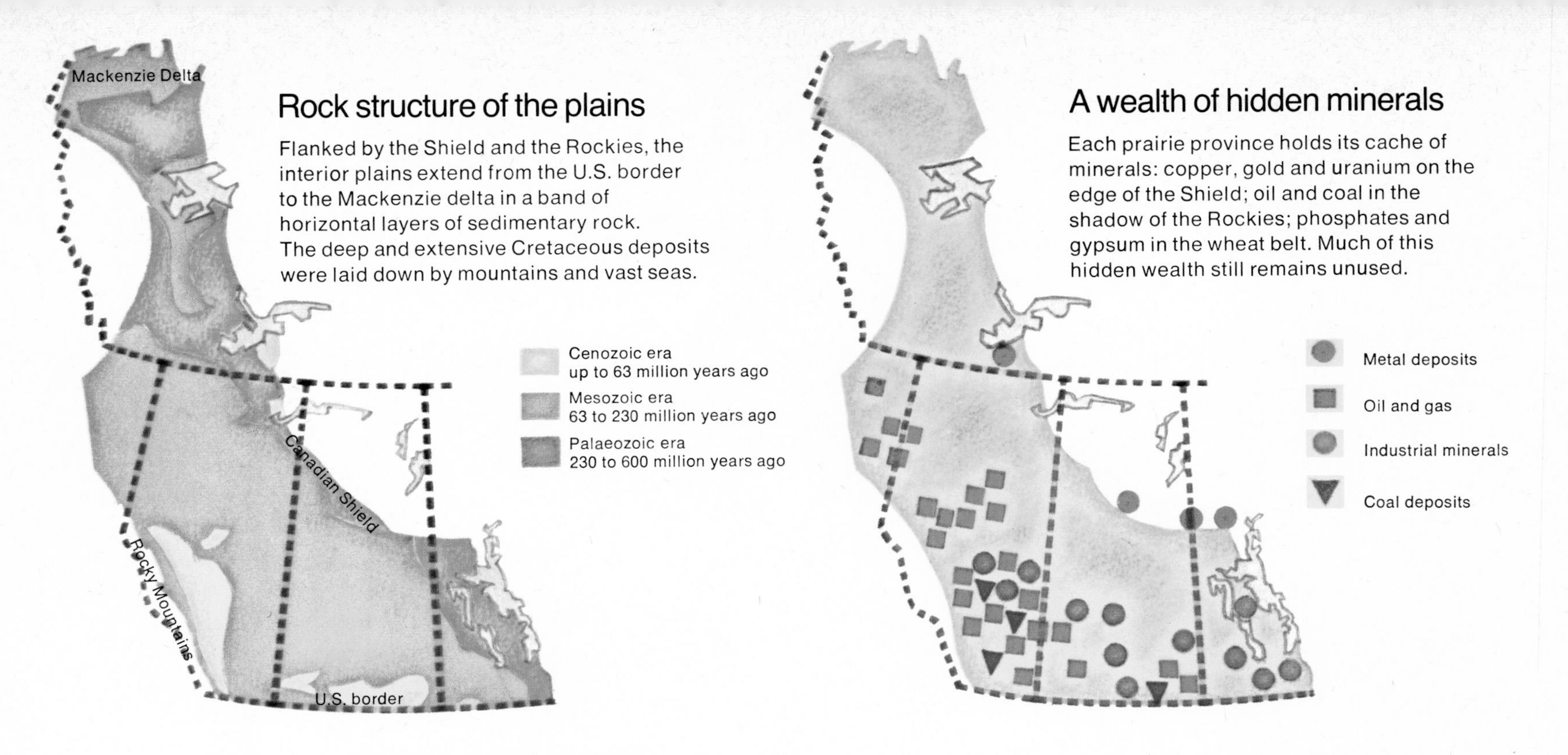

Rock structure of the plains

Flanked by the Shield and the Rockies, the interior plains extend from the U.S. border to the Mackenzie delta in a band of horizontal layers of sedimentary rock. The deep and extensive Cretaceous deposits were laid down by mountains and vast seas.

A wealth of hidden minerals

Each prairie province holds its cache of minerals: copper, gold and uranium on the edge of the Shield; oil and coal in the shadow of the Rockies; phosphates and gypsum in the wheat belt. Much of this hidden wealth still remains unused.

How animal life developed

The sediments of the plains contain an almost undisturbed record of life covering a period of 600 million years. Emerging from the sea, dinosaurs and other reptiles ruled supreme for 100 million years, until the emergence of mammals.

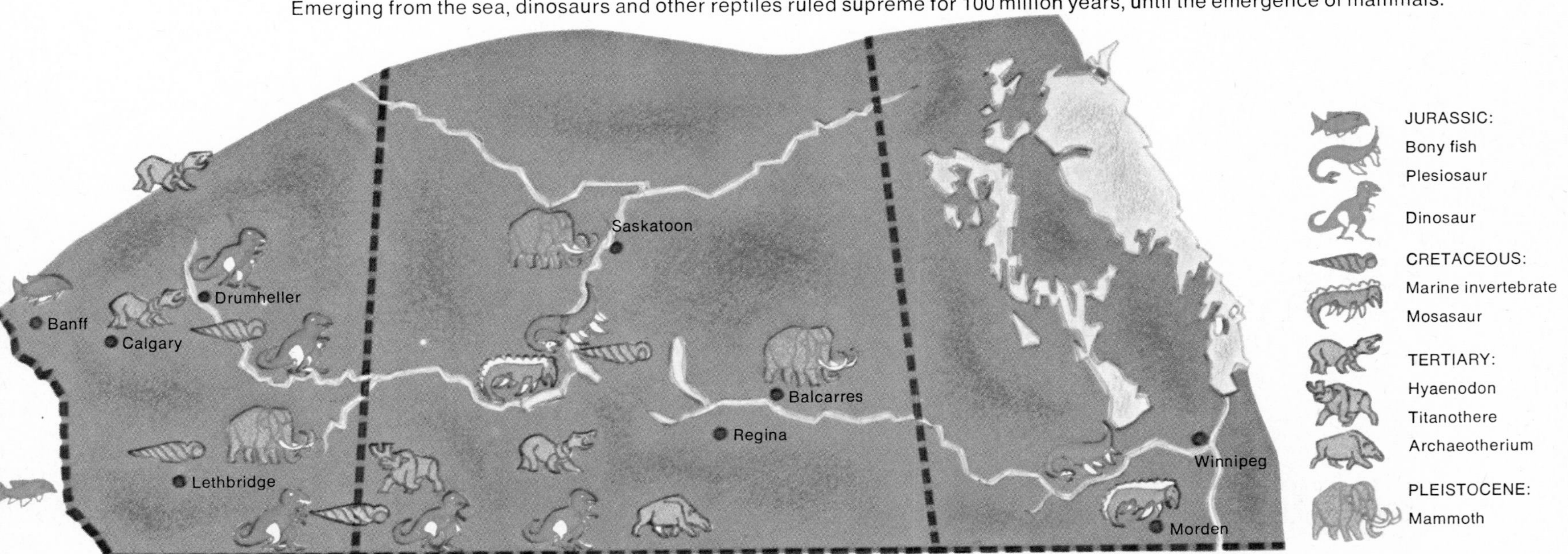

to Medicine Hat 41 miles

A naturalist's tour

To the naturalist emerging from rugged pine forests in the east along the Trans-Canada Highway, the prairies are not a mere desert of grass, but rather a platform for the unobstructed observation of wildlife. Many parks shelter species that no longer run free on the southern prairies. The grey wolf and lynx can be seen at Riding Mountain; moose and deer at Elk Island and Moose Mountain; and grizzlies at Swan Hills. Museum and park specialists will guide travellers to sanctuaries and reserves. The round-trip indicated on the map should fit into a two-week vacation.

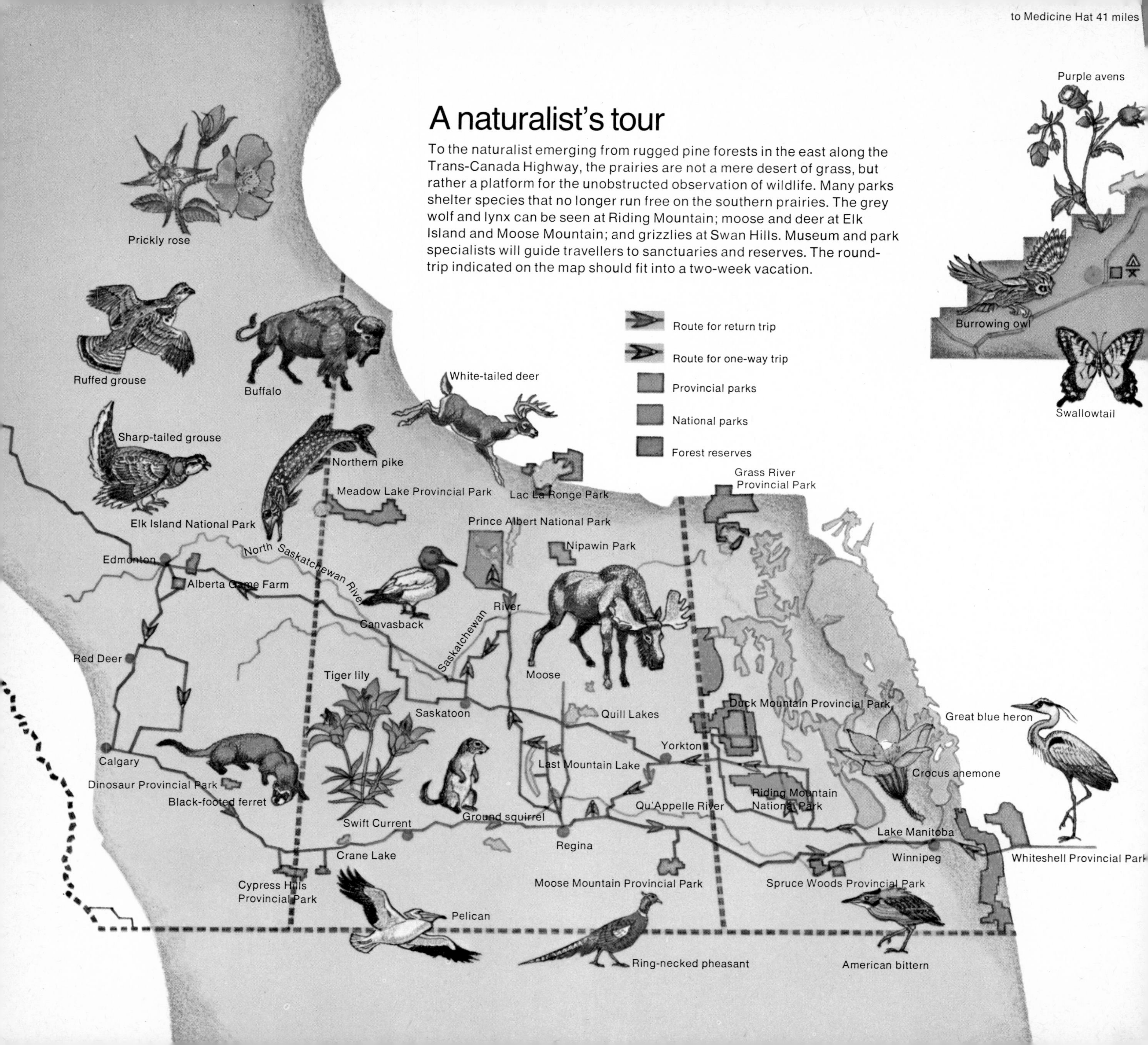

Route for return trip
Route for one-way trip
Provincial parks
National parks
Forest reserves

Prickly rose
Ruffed grouse
Buffalo
Sharp-tailed grouse
White-tailed deer
Northern pike
Meadow Lake Provincial Park
Lac La Ronge Park
Grass River Provincial Park
Prince Albert National Park
Nipawin Park
Elk Island National Park
Edmonton
North Saskatchewan River
Alberta Game Farm
Canvasback
Saskatchewan River
Moose
Red Deer
Tiger lily
Saskatoon
Quill Lakes
Duck Mountain Provincial Park
Great blue heron
Yorkton
Last Mountain Lake
Crocus anemone
Calgary
Dinosaur Provincial Park
Black-footed ferret
Riding Mountain National Park
Qu'Appelle River
Swift Current
Ground squirrel
Regina
Lake Manitoba
Winnipeg
Whiteshell Provincial Park
Crane Lake
Cypress Hills Provincial Park
Moose Mountain Provincial Park
Spruce Woods Provincial Park
Pelican
Ring-necked pheasant
American bittern
Purple avens
Burrowing owl
Swallowtail

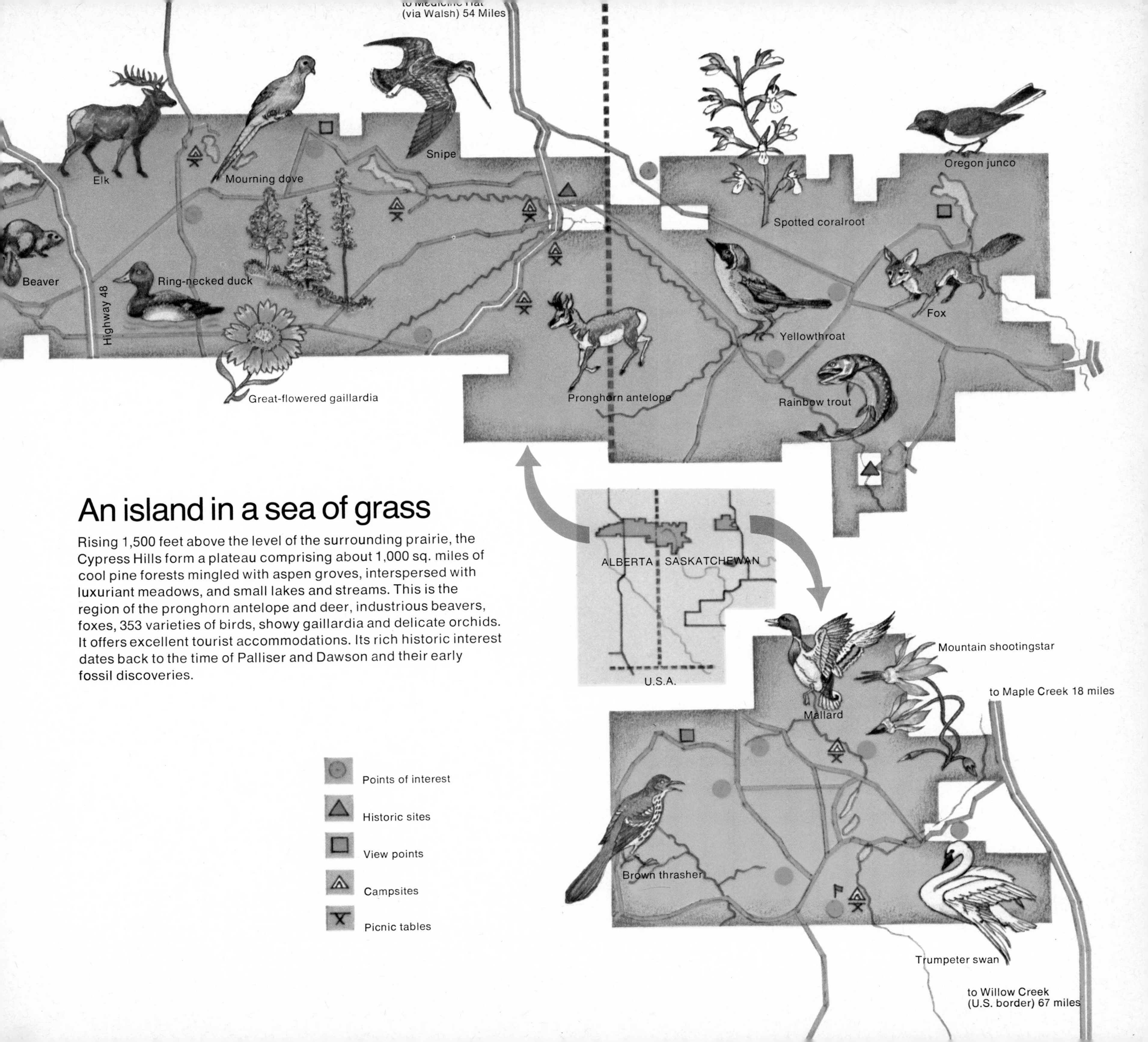

An island in a sea of grass

Rising 1,500 feet above the level of the surrounding prairie, the Cypress Hills form a plateau comprising about 1,000 sq. miles of cool pine forests mingled with aspen groves, interspersed with luxuriant meadows, and small lakes and streams. This is the region of the pronghorn antelope and deer, industrious beavers, foxes, 353 varieties of birds, showy gaillardia and delicate orchids. It offers excellent tourist accommodations. Its rich historic interest dates back to the time of Palliser and Dawson and their early fossil discoveries.

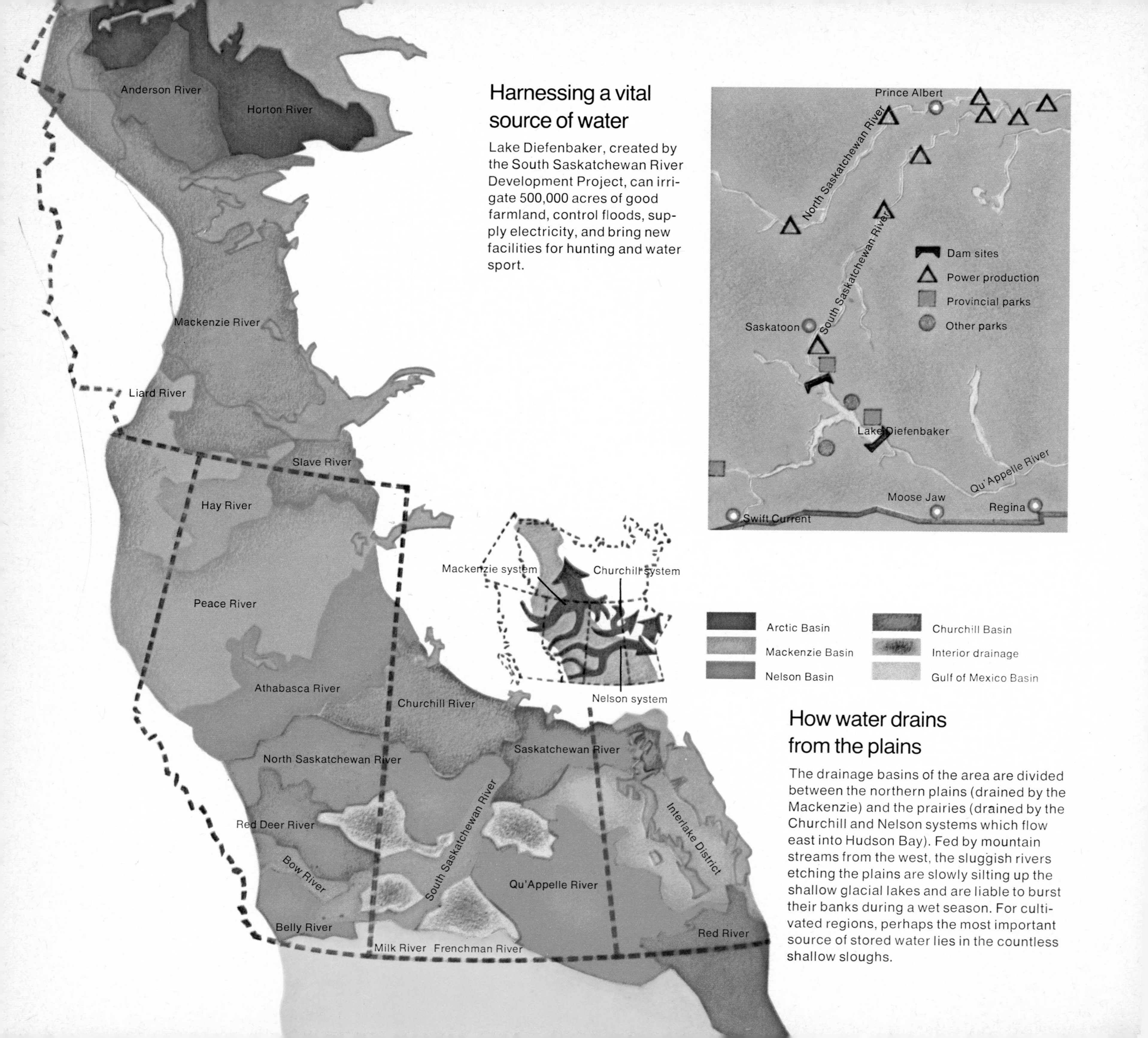

Harnessing a vital source of water

Lake Diefenbaker, created by the South Saskatchewan River Development Project, can irrigate 500,000 acres of good farmland, control floods, supply electricity, and bring new facilities for hunting and water sport.

How water drains from the plains

The drainage basins of the area are divided between the northern plains (drained by the Mackenzie) and the prairies (drained by the Churchill and Nelson systems which flow east into Hudson Bay). Fed by mountain streams from the west, the sluggish rivers etching the plains are slowly silting up the shallow glacial lakes and are liable to burst their banks during a wet season. For cultivated regions, perhaps the most important source of stored water lies in the countless shallow sloughs.

PART ONE / **THE REGION**

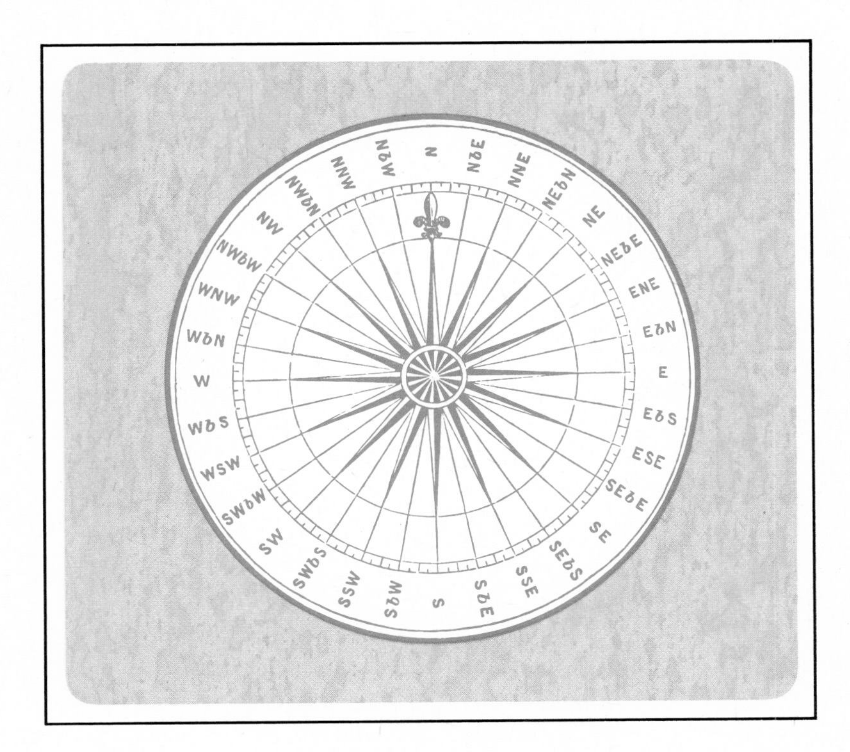

1 CROSSING THE PLAINS

The start of the journey westward is across the first wide prairie level – the bed of Agassiz, an ancient glacial lake – drained by the Red River that flows leisurely from across the U.S. border northward to the city of Winnipeg. There the Red is joined from the west by the Assiniboine which has previously been joined by the Souris. Together they flow at a faster rate to empty into Lake Winnipeg, the largest lake that lies completely within the plains region.

Lake Winnipeg along with its associated lakes, Winnipegosis, Manitoba and a group of smaller ones, are the remains of an immense glacial lake that covered most of southern Manitoba. Today they are shallow lakes, with ridges of sand representing old beaches between them. They are much used for commercial fishing and recreation, and their marshy shores support innumerable water birds. But like all glacial lakes they are gradually drying up and filling in, and some thousands of years hence will be like the land to the south of them, large lacustrine plains.

The Red is the villain river of the plains. Slow running with low banks and a wide, flat valley, it is subject to flooding. Each year the farmers and townspeople of the valley, including the citizens of Winnipeg where, in 1950, more than eight thousand homes were flooded, watch the snow-melting conditions with deep concern. If the snowfall has been moderate and the thaw is early and gradual the river can handle the runoff. But if the snow is deep and it thaws late the water and ice suddenly spill over the low banks onto the valley, carrying away buildings and livestock and filling basements with the fine silt that the river always carries.

Going west over the first prairie level on Highway 14, approaching the town of Morden, a range of hills comes into sight. They are known as the Pembina Mountains which are not really mountains but high moraines piled here by the continental glacier. They mark the Manitoba Escarpment which is a ridge along the edge of the Cretaceous bedrock that underlies the plains from this point west. The escarpment is cut by river valleys into a series of hills. Besides the Pembina Mountains, these include Riding Mountain, Duck Mountain and Porcupine Mountain. The first is a national park and the others are provincial parks.

The second prairie level is even flatter than the first and is also drier, with fewer trees. The road crosses the shallow and muddy Pembina River which, together with the Qu'Appelle, Souris and Assiniboine drains the southern portion of this level. They meander their slow, twisting, muddy ways eastward to join the Red River system. Often almost without water in the dry seasons, they spill over their banks after heavy rain. All are partly controlled by a system of reservoirs, and the Qu'Appelle has recently been revived with water from the Saskatchewan River Project.

Farther west the sameness and monotony grows. High-winging hawks beneath the fleece of the sky and snatches of meadowlark song become common. Ducks rise from the sloughs that polka-dot the fields, and now and then a black and white magpie lifts from beside the remains of a gopher and wings heavily to the side of the road to wait patiently before resuming its feast.

Northwest from the town of Weyburn the aspens and willows become scarcer, the fields flatter and wider, and the disciplined grain crops as even as the bristles on a brush. There are fewer sloughs now, for precipitation decreases as you go westward. But when it does rain the mud is unbelievably thick and sticky, for this is the region of dark brown clay soil with the remarkable water-retaining ability that makes this area, when enough rainfall comes at the right time, the world's best wheat-growing land.

This is the famous Regina Plain which, more than any area of the plains, symbolizes the term "bald-headed prairie." The big farms with their red barns and solid white frame houses reveal that the farmers are prosperous. The men go about their work with great skill using the most modern equipment. Tiller-combines cultivate and sow the seeds in one operation. Harvesting-combines take off the crop with equal efficiency. Chemical sprayers control weeds and insects that once plagued farmers, and mechanical fertilizer spreaders replenish the land with the best fertility formula as laid down by the University of Saskatchewan extension department. This is truly a wheat factory of great efficiency.

On the outskirts of Regina, a traveller may be startled by a pair of Canada geese that rise from the roadside and wing low over the highway. He is passing through the most unique establishment of its kind in Canada, the Wascana Bird Sanctuary. Here in 360 acres of man-made marshes, right within the city limits, hundreds of species of birds from yellow-headed blackbirds to whistling swans live and raise their young in the wild state. The sanctuary is part of the Saskatchewan Museum of Natural History, one of the best of its kind on the continent.

Regina itself, the capital city of Saskatchewan with 130,000 inhabitants, is unusual from a natural history point of view. Like the city of Lethbridge farther west, is a model of how to make the most use of the least water. By damming tiny Wascana Creek and supplementing it from deep wells, a lake was constructed in the middle of town, in front of the parliament buildings. Water drawn directly from this lake keeps the trees and grass of the city green. Every straight street and avenue is lined with elms, box elders and ash trees and throughout the city are parks full of these trees, along with innumerable shrubs and flower beds and green lawns. Many parts of Regina conjure the feeling of being in a forest of eastern Canada.

West of Regina, past the city of Moose Jaw, the rolling country is characteristic of the plains. Terminal moraines, piled up by the great continental glacier, have been weathered down to even rounded hills. Then the second step up on the plains, the Missouri Coteau, comes into view, cutting diagonally across southern Saskatchewan, marking the eastern edge of the third prairie level. This level is a plateau stretching to the foothills of the Rockies. It rises gradually from about 2,500 feet above sea level to 4,000 feet on the western side.

Continuing west, there are fewer big, prosperous wheat farms. Here the rolling land is unbroken with the short grass growing in clumps. And here and there, usually around man-made hollows, called dugouts, filled with muddy water, white-faced beef cattle stare at the passing traffic. This is the short-grass country where the shortage of rainfall and the poorer brown soil dictate that agriculture shall be ranching rather than wheat growing. And now, far to the south but plainly visible from the Trans-Canada Highway, the flat horizon is broken by a line of rounded hills. These are the famous Cypress Hills, a geological freak which will be described later.

Farther west, the traveller can sometimes see – towards the south – a series of pointed hills that stand up like sandpiles on a flat floor. These misplaced elevations, which are just south of the U.S. border, are called the Sweetgrass Hills, just as the surrounding country is called the Sweetgrass Country. What makes them so unusual is that they are intrusions of igneous rock – on the plains igneous rock is almost always buried many hundreds, even thousands of feet below the sedimentary rocks.

2 THE VITAL WATERWAYS

Down the southern slopes of the Cypress Hills run the only streams of the plains that don't flow east or north. They are the Frenchman and the Big Muddy and other smaller creeks that flow into the Milk River whose grey waters have come from the mountains to join the Missouri at Fort Peck, Montana, and ultimately end up in the Gulf of Mexico.

Farther on, at Medicine Hat, the road crosses another stream, the South Saskatchewan. The murky water beneath the bridge, carrying floating sticks and other debris, is heading for an equally distant destination – Hudson Bay. It is part of the Saskatchewan-Nelson River system that dominates the plains. The network is made up of two branches of the Saskatchewan that flows across the plains to the north end of Lake Winnipeg where the now-combined river joins with waters of the Red River system and flows into the Nelson River, which carries all the water into Hudson Bay.

The two main branches of the Saskatchewan drain a total watershed of about 150,000 sq. miles. The South Saskatchewan draws most of its water from glaciers on the east side of the Rockies. Tiny rivulets join into dashing mountain streams which join five main tributaries – the Red Deer, the Bow, the Oldman, the Belly and the St. Mary. These twist their way out of the foothills, eastward across the dry ground of southern Alberta, ultimately coming together at the Saskatchewan border. After flowing sixty miles east the river widens into Lake Diefenbaker, the result of the Gardiner Dam, just past the "elbow" that turns the river north. This T-shaped, 440-mile lake will inevitably alter the ecology and agriculture of its immediate surroundings. Beyond the dam the river runs north to meet the North Saskatchewan a few miles east of Prince Albert. In the course of its

1,300-mile journey from the Rockies to Lake Winnipeg, the South Saskatchewan drops more than a mile.

The waters that feed the North Saskatchewan come from glaciers a few miles from the source of the Red Deer and Bow. The Brazeau is its principal tributary. In its 1,100-mile run to Lake Winnipeg the northern branch drops seven thousand feet. The Saskatchewan is a wide, shallow and muddy river with a current so strong that only a powerful swimmer can make headway against it. Treacherous undercurrents swirl and eddy, building and washing away sandbars; they eat away at the unconsolidated material of the river's banks and carry it along to build a huge delta near the border with Manitoba. Then the river gathers itself into one full, mighty stream and dashes over the Manitoba Escarpment in a series of wild rapids that caused the early voyageurs to name it Kisikatchewin, which in the Cree language means "rapid water."

Unlike its unruly cousin, the Red, the Saskatchewan is not a flooding river. Its banks are steep and high, casting a twisting ribbon of greenery across the parched land. Here birch, poplar, elm, chokecherry, saskatoon, willows and countless shrubs thrive on the moisture from the river, making a home for thousands of birds and a playground for children. Once the principal highway into the West for fur traders and freighters, the Saskatchewan today is little used for transportation. No freighters or pleasure ships ply its waters. Only here and there a current-driven ferry carries cars and trucks from one side to the other. Ranchers water their stock along its muddy margins, but to pioneer farmers it was more of an obstruction than a help.

Unlike the pattern of settlement in eastern Canada, few towns were built on the rivers. Instead, the settlements sprang up along the railway lines that were laid away from the rivers. Nor was the current used, as with Ontario streams, to power sawmills or grist-mills. Only the largest cities, Edmonton, Calgary, Lethbridge, Medicine Hat, Saskatoon and Prince Albert, draw water from the river and dump their sewage back into it farther down stream. Not far north of where glacier waters gather to form the North Saskatchewan River, other similar

North of Swift Current, the silt-laden South Saskatchewan River slowly winds its way eastward draining 65,000 square miles of semi-arid prairie through its broad 300 foot channel.

waters are forming streams that run into the Athabasca River. The Athabasca runs parallel with the Saskatchewan for about a hundred miles as though heading for the same destination. Then, north of Edmonton it encounters high ground that turns it abruptly north to become a tributary of the great Mackenzie River system which drains the whole northern slope of the great plains into the Arctic Ocean.

The Mackenzie is the biggest river system in Canada, draining an area of half a million square miles. Its tributaries, the Peace, the Hay and the Liard, are immense rivers in their own right. And the lakes – Athabasca, Great Slave and Great Bear – are veritable inland seas. Great Bear with an area of 12,275 square miles is the largest lake lying wholly within Canada. The broad, straight Mackenzie River has a total length from its most distant source to the Arctic of 2,635 miles.

Unlike the Saskatchewan, the Mackenzie is used extensively for transportation. It offers the only surface route to the large northern section of the plains, rich in oil, metals and furs. Throughout the short summer season heavy barges burdened with household appliances, machinery, furniture, food, medicines and equipment ply the Mackenzie, pushed by diesel-driven tugs, to supply the settlements along the banks of the river. Apart from the large lakes that have been mentioned, there are relatively few lakes on the plains compared with the Canadian Shield. Except for lakes impounded in coulees, such as Pelican Lake in Alberta, the majority of lakes tend to be shallow and marshy. The crystal-clear water of the shield lakes, where a sandy or rock bottom can be seen at depths of six to ten feet, are almost unknown on the plains.

One body of water unique to the area is the salt-water lake. It is fed by ground water which, in the process of winding its way from level to level, picks up great quantities of mineral salts. Since no streams drain the lake, constant evaporation year after year increases the salt content almost to saturation point.

The best-known salt-water lake is Little Manitou, near the town of Watrous, Saskatchewan. The salinity of this prairie lake is much greater than that of the ocean. The water is consequently so buoyant that a non-swimmer can paddle about without danger of sinking. When he comes out and dries off, ridges of white salt cling to his body. People come considerable distances – from Texas, for example – to bathe in these waters

SIMPLE CREATURES OF THE SLOUGHS

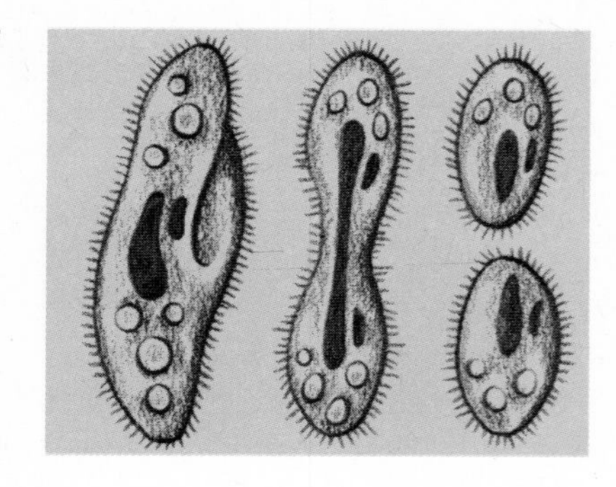

The white Paramecium, *almost too small to see, reproduces by simply dividing into two. It propels itself rapidly through the water by waving its hair-like cilia.*

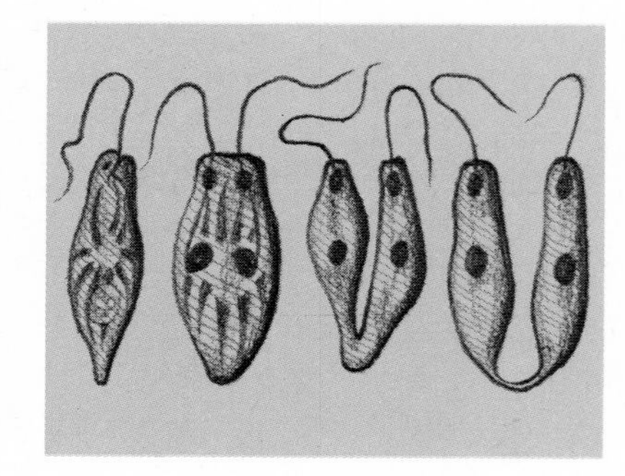

Green whale-shaped Euglenas *produce chlorophyll like a plant, multiply by fission, and use a whip for movement.*

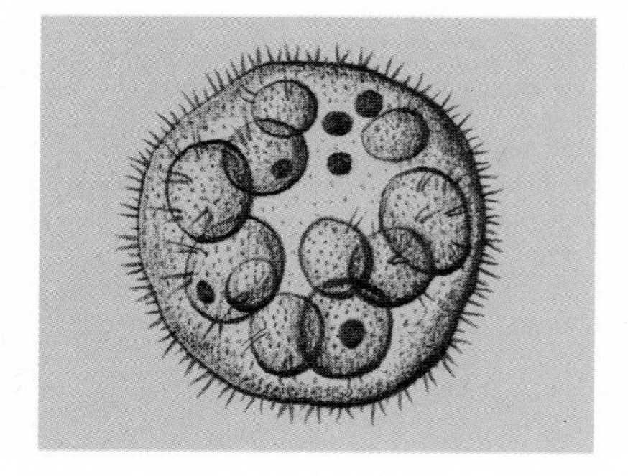

The hollow, spherical Volvox *rolls near the surface through its miniature green world, bearing daughter cells within.*

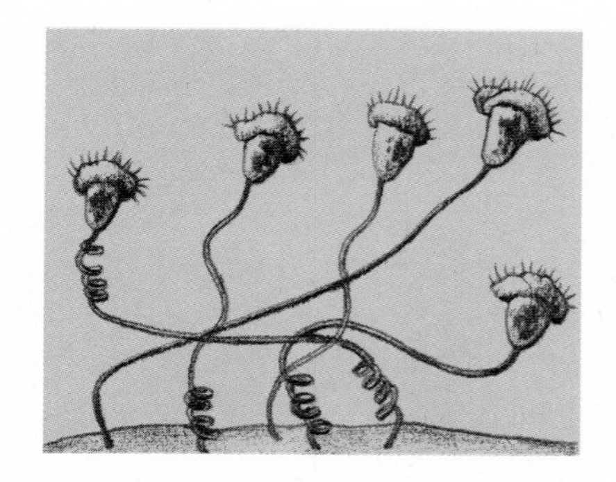

Bell-shaped Vorticelli, *often seen as fluffy white patches, hitch a ride on the bodies of water insects or crustaceans.*

which they consider a cure-all for muscular and skin ailments.

The best-known body of water on the plains and the one with the greatest effect on plant and animal life is the slough. A slough (pronounced *slew*) is simply a low place – often a result of the passing of the continental glacier – that fills up with water from melting snow or rain. It may be as small as a barnyard or a mile or more across. It may remain all year or dry up in early summer. Its shores may be crowded with willow, snowberry, aspen and brambles, or barren and encrusted with dirty-white sodium sulphate, known locally as "alkali." One thing all sloughs have in common – no stream runs into them or out of them.

Most sloughs contain great quantities of aquatic plants from bulrushes to filamentous algae, as well as molluscs, crustacea, tadpoles, mosquito larvae, dragonfly nymphs, and billions of protozoa too small to be seen. They are the homes of muskrats, mink, frogs, snakes and lizards. Blackbirds, terns, coots, pelicans, and millions of ducks nest near or in them. But they never contain fish.

In dry years the sloughs of the southern plains dry up and revert to pasture land or are planted with grain. In wet years they spread out over the surrounding land, flooding wheat fields, changing the course of roads, and killing trees. Farmers rarely bother to drain sloughs for the simple reason that they are in the lowest land of the area, and land is plentiful but water desperately scarce.

3 A CLIMATE OF EXTREMES

Nowhere else in Canada does weather distress people so much, or stimulate so much conversation, as it does on the plains. Every waking moment of the day the grain farmer squints into the sky for signs of rain, hail, frost, blizzards or dust storms. When he's not watching the weather he is talking about it. It dominates his life and makes him the fatalist he is. The climate of the plains is capricious and cruel. Winters are long and unbearably cold; summers are short and often unbearably hot. The winds blow unceasingly; in the winter howling blizzards block the roads, bury cattle and can cause a man to be lost and perish within distances as short as from his house to his barn.

Only central Russia has a climate as extreme as that of the Canadian plains. Lacking the moderating influences of oceans, the average temperature of the plains is far below that of many other regions of similar latitude. Regina, for instance, has an annual average temperature of 34.5 degrees Fahrenheit compared with forty-eight degrees at Ocean Falls, B.C. – and Ocean Falls is farther north. An even more drastic comparison can be drawn between Winnipeg and London, England, which is actually farther north. Winnipeg's average January temperature is three degrees "below" zero while London has an average January temperature of forty degrees "above," but Winnipeg's average July temperature of sixty-seven degrees is higher than that of London. Only the southwestern corner of the plains enjoys some relief from these extremes. Although average temperatures are about the same as in other parts of the plains, the winters are alleviated by chinook winds. Without any notice these warm winds from the region of Mount Baker come wafting over the foothills, turning winter into summer. Overnight two-foot snowdrifts melt away, leaving bare ground wet and steaming. After the wind, winter returns, but on the Canadian plains any break in the long winter is welcome.

Along with the miserable extremes in temperature the plains are dry. Average precipitation is far below that generally required for agriculture and much of the south is classed as "semi-arid" with total annual precipitation as low as twelve inches. The highly productive Regina plain receives on the average only 14.7 inches annually, compared with thirty-eight inches at London, Ontario.

To further complicate the water problem, the rainfall fluctuates from year to year with periodic droughts that may last as long as ten years. The worst of these in living memory was the 1930-39 drought that literally drove thousands of farmers off the land. Each year there was less rain than the previous year, until 1937, when the Regina plain received a total of 9.41 inches for the entire year (compared with 22.53 inches in 1927), and neighbouring regions suffered similar conditions. Many firmly believed that as a wheat growing area the plains were finished.

Associated with the drought were three other destroyers – dust storms, grasshoppers and Russian thistle. Farmers still cringe when they think of them. Sloughs dried up completely and water fowl perished by the thousands. Howling winds filled the air with choking dust for days on end, and swept precious top soil in drifts half-way up telephone poles. Russian thistle, a persistent branching weed, covered the land like a fungus and, when ripe, broke off and tumbled across the fields scattering millions of seeds and piling high against fences. Grasshoppers ate everything that grew, and even attacked clothing hung on the line to dry.

The reason for the lack of moisture is closely related to the reason for the extremes in temperature. It is due to the mountains in the west. Without them the climate of the plains would be as moist as that of British Columbia. But the prevailing westerly winds, moistened and warmed by the Pacific Ocean and its Japanese Current, are forced up and cooled by the mountains so that they lose moisture before they reach the plains, where they are dry and warm. Furthermore, many winter weather-systems build up in the Arctic and swoop down over the southern plains with full force.

In summer the opposite often happens. Winds from the south bring unduly hot weather to the plains, accompanied by sudden destructive storms. On a hot July or August day, dark, white-capped thunder-heads build up on the horizon. Like messengers of doom they roll and broil, while the farmer with a fine stand of wheat on his summer fallow stands in the yard watching helplessly. Then the terrible calm before the storm is followed by a howling rush of wind that flattens the fields. Too often this is accompanied by the roaring beat of hailstones, as big as golf balls, that bounce off the hard clay in the yard, smash windows, and within minutes beat a crop worth more than ten thousand dollars into soggy pulp.

Then there are tornadoes – thunderstorms that suddenly take a turn for the worse, producing a howling, twisting funnel that rearranges the landscape like a blast of dynamite. Tornadoes are so common on the plains that the Queen's Printer has issued a booklet giving precise dates and descriptions of hundreds of them. An eye-witness account states: "Suddenly a huge black cloud which overhung the western horizon burst and fell to the ground in the shape of a cone. There was a noise like an express train and large pieces of timber and trees were twisting round like matches. The barn was picked up and dashed to the ground, smashed to bits. No sooner was this done than the very

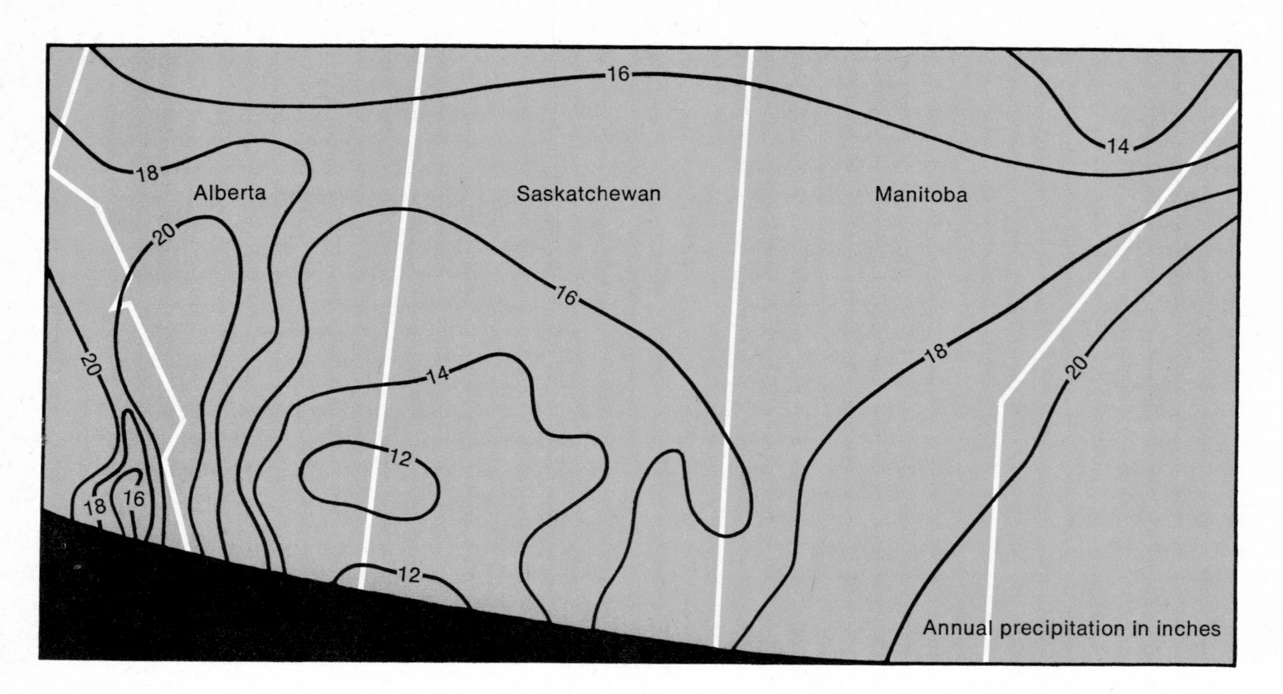

THE DRY INTERIOR: Three-quarters of Canada's crop lands lie isolated in the semi-arid continental interior. Intense activity is crowded into the brief period when the temperature soars above 42° Fahrenheit, the minimum temperature required for growth. Fortunately the heaviest rainfall comes during June when the crops need it most. The total annual precipitation is between eleven and twenty inches; on the Pacific coast, 500 miles to the west, it is more than 100 inches.

house was torn from its foundations, lifted overhead and rolled over and over."

During the worst tornado on record, the one that demolished several streets in Regina and killed twenty-eight people in 1912, a rowboat with a man in it was picked up off Wascana Lake and deposited in a field almost a mile away. The damage to wildlife during these storms is incalculable. Nests of meadowlarks and other ground-nesting birds float away and fledglings are drowned. Mallards' nests are battered to pieces along with their helpless tenants. One of the great fears of naturalists working to save whooping cranes from extinction is that the few remaining nesting pairs may be killed by storms.

The mitigating circumstance that saves the plains as an agricultural area is that the rain which does fall usually comes in May and June when the developing grasses, including grain, need it most. The remarkable moisture-holding capacity of the clay soils, the great depths of the subsoils, coupled with the extensive deep-seeking roots of the grasses make it possible for the plants to thrive during a July and August season that is completely without rain. In 1937, a year when exactly this condition prevailed in Saskatchewan, the heavy-land crop reached twenty bushels to the acre.

4 THE RICH BLACK SOIL

The western Canadian plains have been divided by geographers into a number of subregions according to precipitation, vegetation and soils. Among these divisions there is a great deal of overlapping of characteristics and confusion of names. To simplify matters, the plains can be divided into two main divisions – the southern prairie and the northern bushland. The dividing line runs unevenly from the base of Lake Winnipeg northwest to the city of Edmonton. But having drawn the line it must be explained that there are deviations. Some prairie lies north of the line, notably the great agricultural land of the Peace River country and there is plenty of bush in the southern section, such as the Cypress Hills, not far from the U.S. border.

The prairie is a good starting point. Some dictionaries define it as "a large treeless tract of level or undulating grassland." Actually there is no such land in Canada, as every region has some trees. However, it can be defined as predominantly grassland with a few trees. This is the region where most of the plains-people live and work, where the typical plant and animal

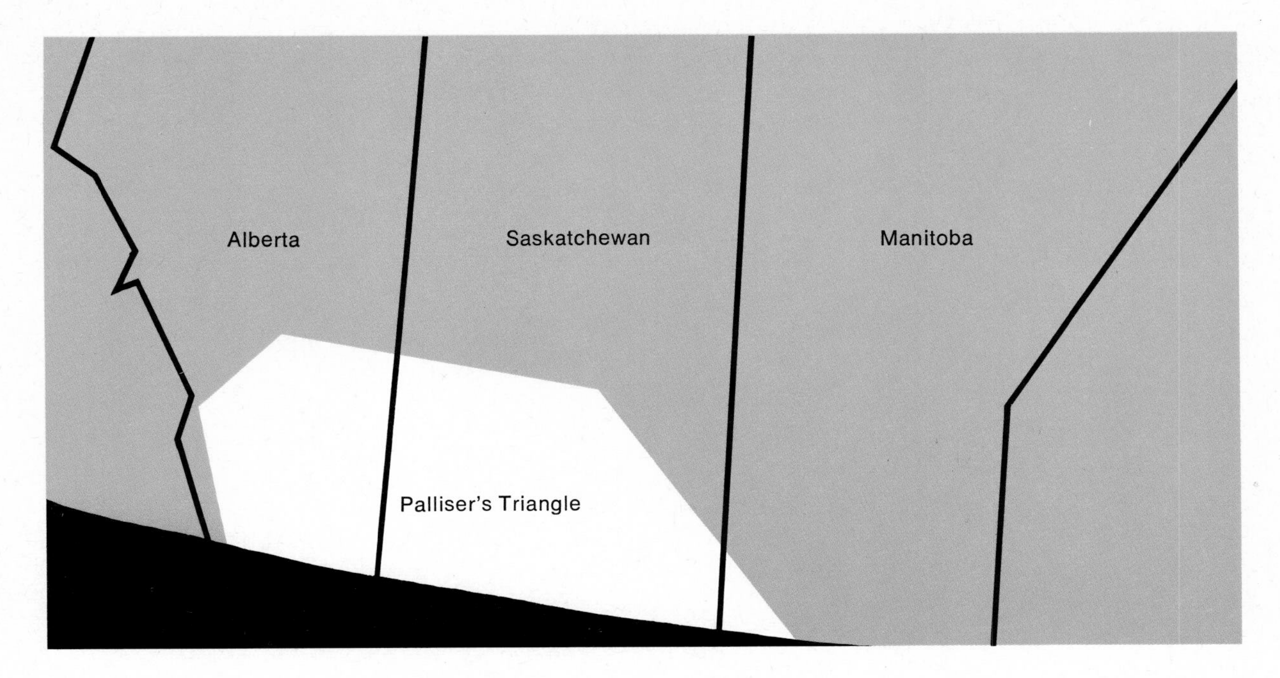

PALLISER'S TRIANGLE
The five-sided area commonly known as Palliser's triangle corresponds roughly with the dry short-grass and the mixed-grass prairies that were condemned as unsuitable for farming by the Palliser expedition of 1857. The aspen-grove prairie enclosing this semi-arid region of about 850,000 square miles was called the Fertile Belt. Improved methods of agriculture and water preservation have made Palliser's Triangle one of the world's most profitable wheat-producing areas.

life is found, and the main subject of this book. The prairie itself can conveniently be divided into three sections – the short grass, the mixed grass, and the aspen grove prairie.

The short grass prairie has the least rainfall, the poorest soil and consequently the least trees of the three prairie regions. It is where the antelope play – deer rarely play with them, being more partial to the bush – and the cowboys ride the range. There are fewer sloughs and more man-made dugouts. All the short grass country is in an area often called Palliser's Triangle, named after John Palliser, who in 1857 led a scientific party into the region and reported to the Imperial government that it would never be of much use.

He was right about some localities. The Great Sand Hills and the Middle Sand Hills in the centre of the region are mostly rolling sand dunes, with barely enough vegetation even for beef cattle. The Cypress Hills, higher in altitude, 4,700 feet above sea level, receive more rainfall than the surrounding country, and are a physical anachronism. Here, in the midst of this semi-desert, are lakes, streams and forests of aspen, birch and pine.

In other places, principally in the valleys of the Red Deer, Milk, Frenchman and Big Muddy Rivers, are the badlands – without vegetation of any kind. Wind and water have eroded the soft river-bed formations into grotesque gullies and mesas known appropriately as "hoodoos." Here there is no sound save the ever-pressing wind, the howl of a lonely coyote far off, and that of the swirling rivers. Fossil skeletons of dinosaurs, dead more than sixty-three million years, are bared to the eyes.

On the western rim of the region however, man has taken a hand to improve the situation. Dams on the St. Mary, Oldman, Belly, Bow and Red Deer rivers provide huge reservoirs from which the surrounding land is irrigated. Here sugar beet, forage crops, and vegetables thrive in the watered land. But the short grass country is the least hospitable to man and its 51,000 square miles are the most sparsely settled of all the plains regions. The towns are small and widely scattered; the only city of any size, Medicine Hat, Alberta, has barely twenty-five thousand people.

The mixed grass region stretches in a crescent surrounding the short grass region. Palliser classed much of this area with the short grass country, but there were subtle differences that he was not likely to notice. First, the soil is much superior to that of the short grass area; instead of the light brown and sandy soils of the ranching country, there are dark brown and black soils. Since the introduction of power machinery, a circumstance that Palliser could not have foreseen, these heavier clay soils have been recognized as the best for growing grain.

As the quality of soils is the most important single factor in determining life on the plains, it's important to understand something about them. All soils originate from the weathering of rock, and contain the minerals found in that rock. Added to this is organic matter from decaying plants and elements drawn from air and water, as well as the bacteria and other forms of life found in the soil.

Good soil contains sixteen elements essential to plant growth and they must be present in forms that the plant can absorb. Three of these, carbon, hydrogen, and oxygen, the plant obtains from water and air. Nitrogen, potassium, phosphorus, calcium, magnesium and sulphur are sometimes lacking in soils and must be replaced by fertilizers in the required proportions. The other elements, classed as trace elements, required only in minute quantities, include: boron, manganese, copper, iron, zinc, molybdenum and chlorine.

When some of these elements are lacking in soil they can be supplemented by commercial fertilizers, but there is another characteristic of soil just as important as its plant-nutrient content – the soil's ability to hold moisture. Not all the moisture in the soil is available for plant use. When moisture content drops to a certain level, plants begin to wilt and this is called the "wilting point." The total amount of moisture that the soil can hold is called its "field capacity." Thus the amount of moisture available for plant growth is the difference between the wilting point and the field capacity.

A comparison of soils will indicate why the dark brown and black soils are the best for wheat growing, considering that up to a ton of water is needed to produce one pound of wheat. Sandy loam soils can hold 1.1 inch of available water per foot of soil depth, while heavy clay soil can hold 2.2 inches, exactly twice as much. Also, the best soils of the plains have an "expanding lattice." This means that the clay minerals of the soil are arranged in layers or "plates" between which water can be held for a long time.

Perhaps even more important, the clay particles in the expanding lattice carry a negative charge which attracts and holds the positively-charged plant nutrients, and helps to prevent them from leaching out with the downward movement of soil moisture. So great is the water-retaining quality and fertility of this soil, that a scientist at the University of Saskatchewan estimated, early in August of 1967, that in the Gull Lake area where there had been no rain since May 15th, they could expect a crop of twenty bushels to the acre.

The mixed grass region includes the Red River and Souris River plains in southern Manitoba, the Regina plain, the great wheat growing plains of Rosetown and Kindersley, and the central part of Alberta, including the region around Calgary. Very gradually the mixed grass prairie blends with the aspen grove prairie to the north. Again the lines of demarcation are indefinite and uneven and there are patches of aspen prairie in both the short grass and mixed grass regions. Of all the settled regions of the plains, the aspen grove prairie is the largest and the one receiving the most moisture and having the highest proportion of black soil – consequently it is the most productive.

In the mixed farming country, Edmonton, for example, farmers boast that since the area was first developed, about the turn of the century, they have never had a crop failure. The great wheat-growing areas of Portage la Prairie, Yorkton, Humboldt, Melfort, Saskatoon, North Battleford, Lloydminster, and of course Edmonton, are all in the aspen prairie region.

The aspen prairie is often called the aspen parkland, but this name is misleading. Although there are more groves of quivering aspen here than farther south, the terrain is still very much grassland. Sloughs are a bit more common than they are farther south, but rivers and lakes are not. In recent years the trend has been for the aspen prairie to extend farther south. There are a number of reasons for this. In the first place, the aspen is the hardiest and commonest tree in Canada. Wherever a forest is destroyed, the aspen is the first tree to fill the gap.

On the plains the aspen takes over from the grasses wherever possible. The progression is always the same. There is a break in the grassland caused by a gopher or badger digging a hole and piling up the earth beside it. Along comes a prairie chicken or sharp-tailed grouse to have a dust bath in the loose earth. Inevitably it leaves some droppings that contain seeds of the lowly snowberry, a hardy, quick-growing shrub that thrives in the rich earth. This is followed by rose bushes, whose seeds are also carried by birds, and low-growing willows. All of these provide shelter for coyotes and foxes who cultivate the

The fertile land, near Cowley, Alberta, is strip-farmed to the last yard as it butts against the Rockies foothills.

land and further prepare it for the wind-blown aspen seeds.

In the past this process was continually interrupted by buffalo herds that trampled the young trees and rubbed against the big ones, and by deer and elk who often destroyed groves by over-browsing. Besides, the open plains were often devastated by prairie fires, sometimes lit by the Indians to drive buffalo; while not hindering the grass, fire destroyed the trees.

When the white farmers came to the plains, they helped to destroy the aspens by feverishly cutting down the trees and planting the land to grain – with disastrous results. Today the buffalo and elk have disappeared from the farming country, while grouse, gophers, coyotes and foxes are still plentiful. Farmers, after some years of soil-destroying dust storms, have come to realize that the aspen groves are more valuable than the farmland they occupy. Aspens are thriving again and gradually enlarging their range over the plains.

5 THE BOUNDLESS BUSH

North of the prairie, with the exception of the Peace River country comprising fifty million acres of typical aspen prairie, the plains region is extensively covered with bush. In some places the stands are as dense as any in eastern Canada, but in others there are patches of grassland and muskeg, the name given to low, wet areas filled with organic matter into which a bulldozer or truck can sink, never to be seen again.

The trees are typical of the taiga – aspen and other poplars, willow, birch, tamarack, spruce and jack pine grow there. It is a land without cities and few towns, a land where a handful of Indian trappers and the animals they live on still have all the space they would ever want; land where the geologist, mining engineer and oil worker dwell in homes that have all the conveniences of homes in Edmonton; land that although twice the size of the settled part of the plains has a total population less than that of Prince Albert. It is Canada's great unknown.

To visit this region, board a plane at Edmonton's commercial airport, one of the busiest on the continent, and fly north. Once airborne you are struck by the vastness and flatness of the land. Further north huge bumps rise out of the plains – the Birch Mountains, Caribou Mountains and Cameron Hills – misplaced projections heaved up by the same forces that raised the Rockies far to the west.

In between the humps there are huge marshes, like those in Wood Buffalo Park, drained by streams emptying into the Mackenzie system, then hundreds of lakes and more marshes again. The plain narrows farther north, with the Canadian Shield on the right and the Cordillera on the left hardly more than two hundred miles apart. The low-lying land gives the impression, that were it depressed even slightly, it would be under water, as it was many times in the geological past.

Now follow the main stream of the mighty Mackenzie with the McConnell mountain range on the right and tiny settlements hugging the bank – Wrigley, Fort Norman and Norman Wells. Coming through a pass in the mountains the cluster of buildings that is Fort Good Hope comes into sight. From there on the river runs through lowlands to the delta – miles and miles of marsh and wandering streams – with the towns of Inuvik and Aklavik on either side. At Kittigazuit and Tuktoyaktuk the land ends with the Arctic Ocean stretching ahead.

Alternatively go by train to Peace River and then by road north to Hay River, on Great Slave Lake. Another road leads west to Dawson Creek, and then north by the Alaska Highway to Fort Nelson. But here the road cuts west into the mountains of the Cordillera leaving the plains. Whichever route is chosen you will see few people; except for the oil and gas beneath the ground, there is little to support them. The grey wooded soils of the forest will not grow much that is useful to man. The climate is colder than that of the southern plains, and no wetter. Wood products are hardly worth the effort of transporting them.

Although inhospitable to man, the environment is perfect for wildlife. Wading and swimming birds, that have been dispersed by man from the southern plains, have found brief refuge here in the North. There are eagles and pelicans, moose, bear, otter and wolverine and perhaps some woodland caribou – even buffalo in Wood Buffalo Park. At Reindeer Depot great herds of barren-ground caribou graze in pastures. The rivers and streams are full of northern fish. The mouth of the Mackenzie River is more than seventeen hundred miles, as the crow flies, from the point east of Winnipeg, which is the beginning of the great western plain.

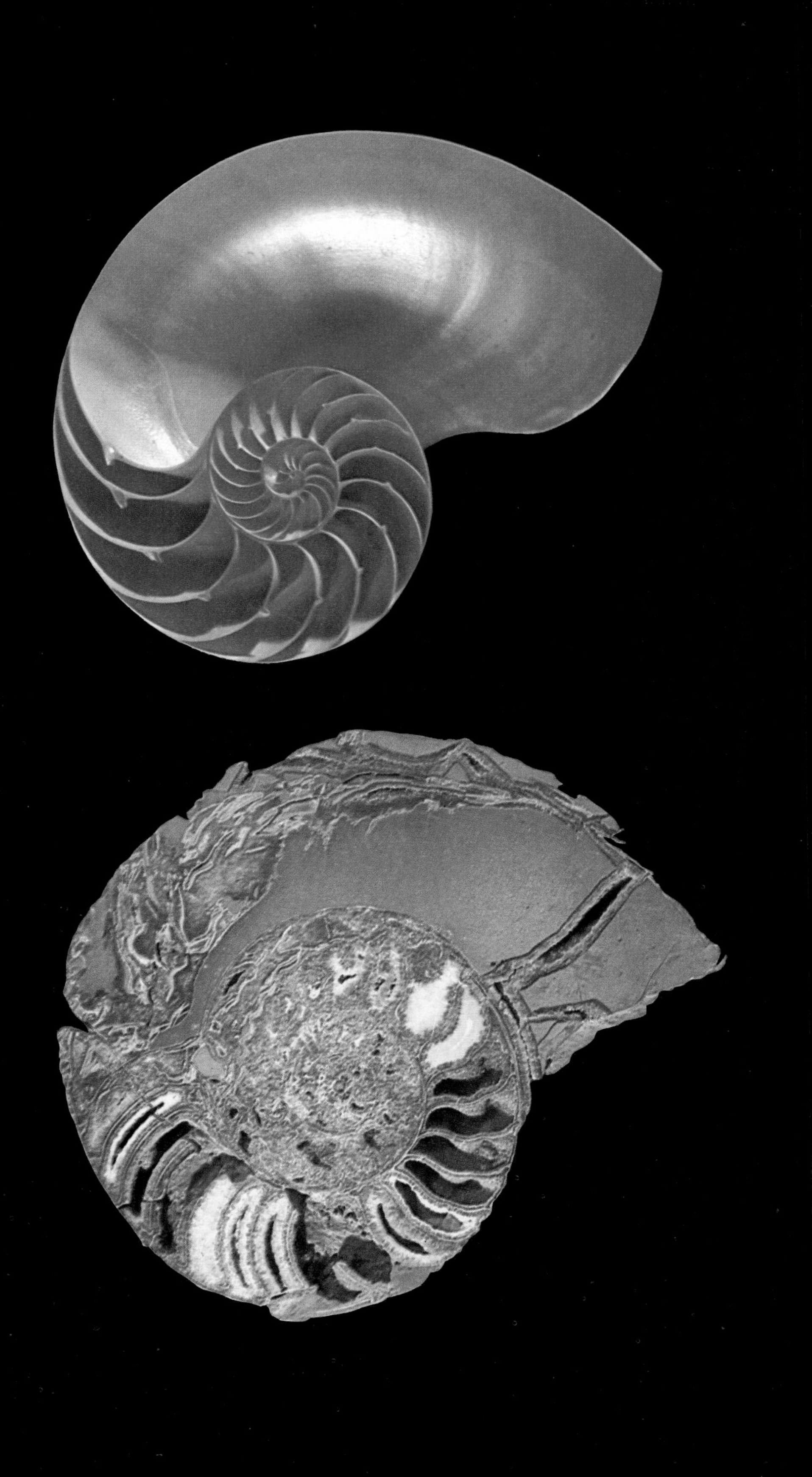

TREASURES OF THE PRAIRIES

Until explorers and pioneers stumbled upon fossils and examined oil seeping through the ground, the 400-million year "record of life" and its gift to man lay undisturbed. The minerals deposited by the huge dried-up seas of the past, and the residues of eons, have left below the soil a heritage as rich as the golden grain harvest on the surface.

The pearly nautilus of today (top) is a link with the 100-million year old ammonite fossils (left) and minerals contributed by them.

Prehistoric seas . . .

A succession of vast seas flooded the shallow trough of the continental interior over a period of thirty million years during Cretaceous times, often submerging the plains and at times reaching the Arctic. Sediments eroded from the Coast and Interior mountains of British Columbia, then rising in the east, built up sandbars and deltas that eventually replaced the seas with deep layers of sandstone interspersed by marine shales containing fossils.

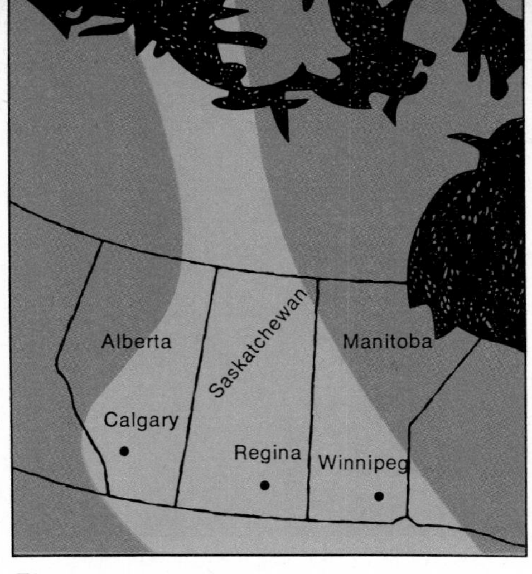

The Dunvegan Sea was indented by sediments from the northwest.

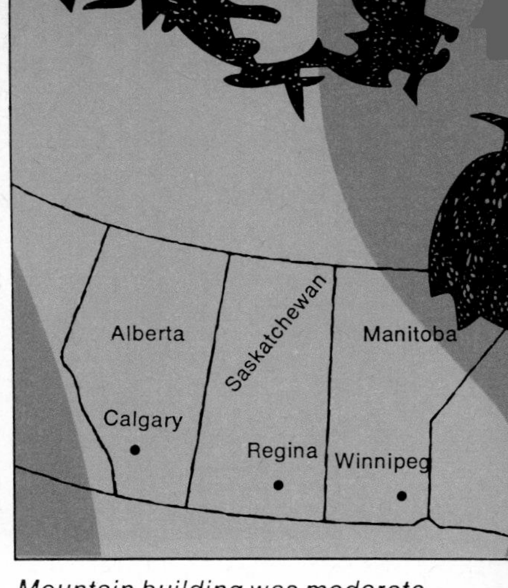

Mountain building was moderate during the Wapiabi Sea stage.

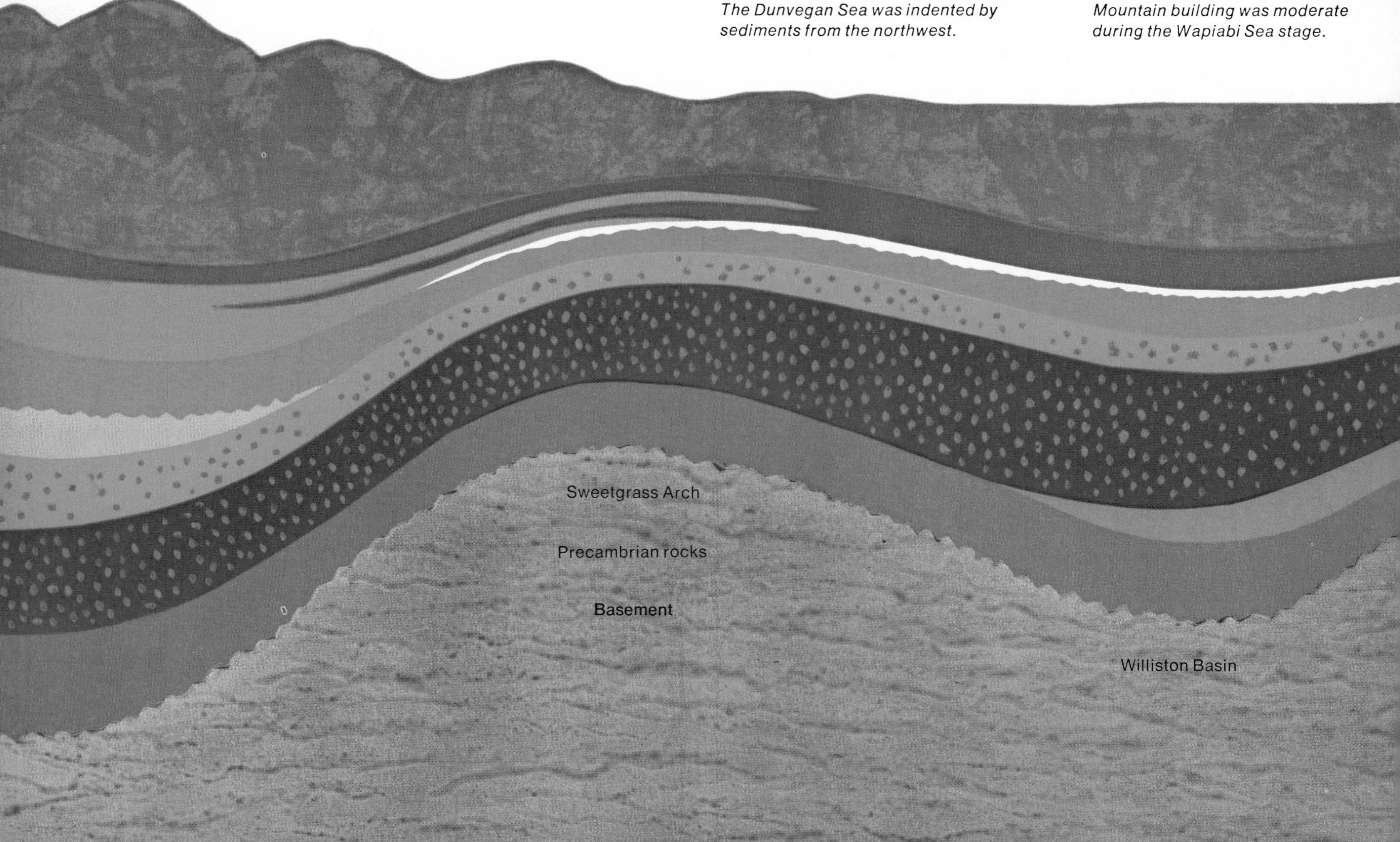

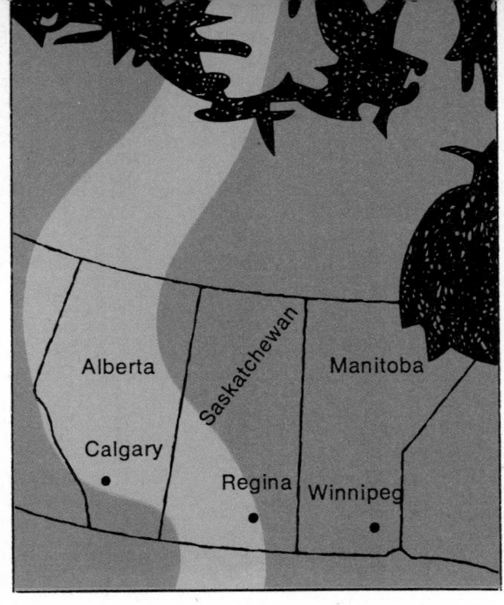

The Milk River Sea was curbed by uplift in the southwest.

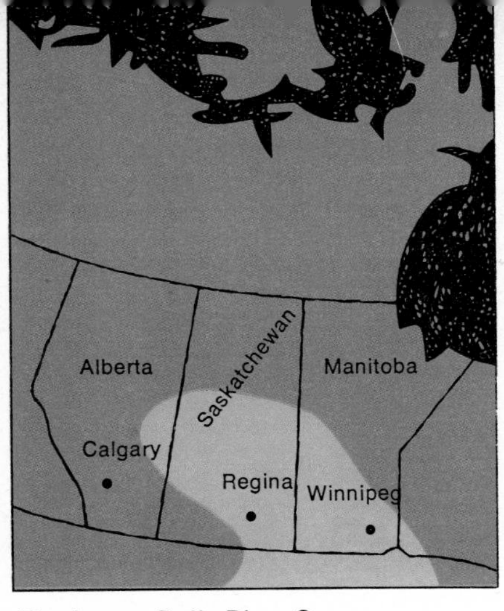

The Lower Belly River Sea was hemmed in by massive sediments.

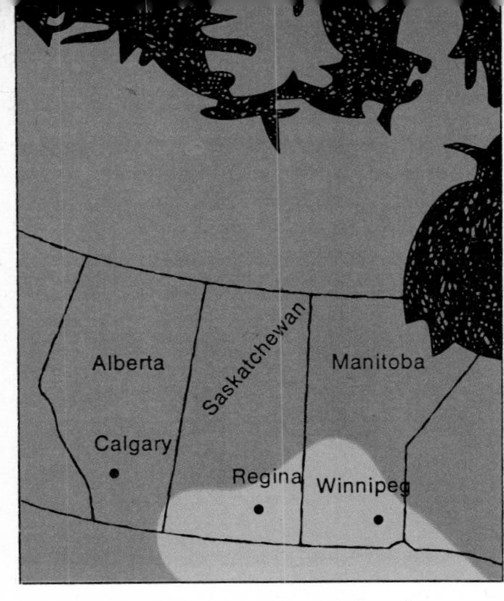

Mountain erosion shaped the shores of the Upper Belly River Sea.

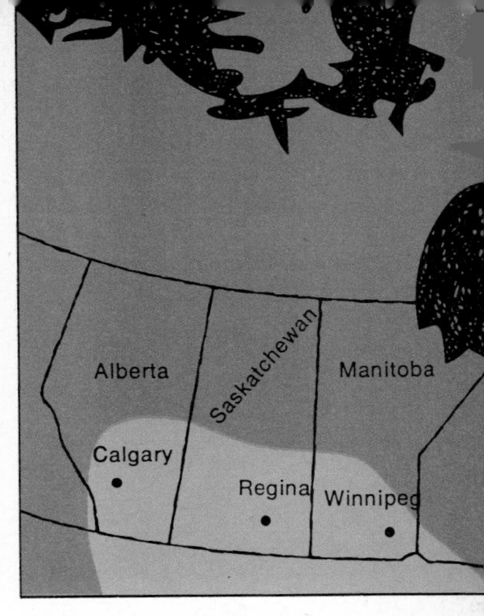

The Bearspaw Sea was the last one to flood the prairie region.

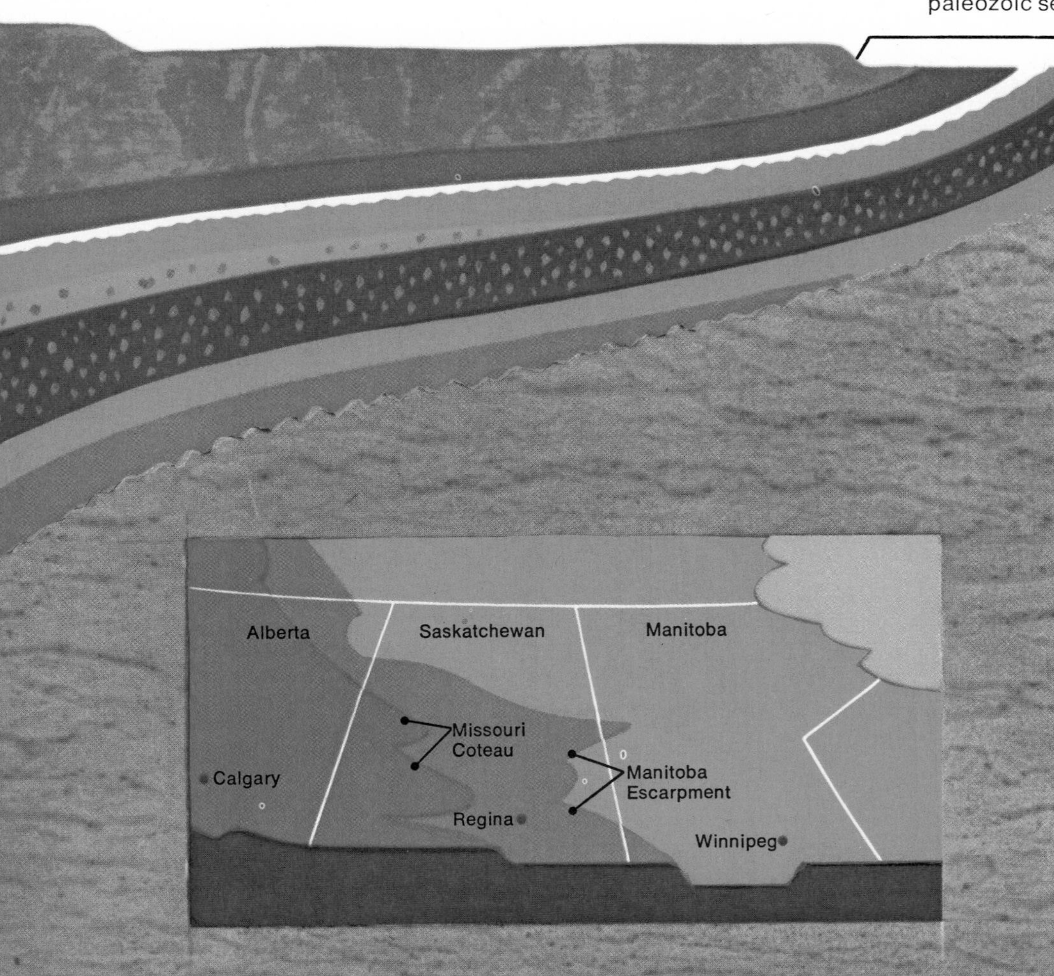

...recorded in rock

Under the prairies a layer of sedimentary rocks 10,000 feet deep are cradled by the basin of igneous rocks which are a direct extension of the Canadian Shield. These rocks have remained undisturbed for over 600 million years. The bottom sediments of Cambrian rock-fragments, (which are exposed between Lakes Winnipeg and Winnipegosis), are covered by sandstones and shales of the Ordovician and Silurian periods. The Devonian sediments are rich in oil, gas and potash. Marine deposits provided an almost continuous record of life until they were overlain by deep Cretaceous deltas that spread from the mountains which sloped gently from 4,000 feet in the foothills of Alberta down to 500 feet above sea-level at Winnipeg. The surface of the prairies has been carved into three levels: the hills of the Manitoba Escarpment, the Missouri Coteau, and the foothills (see inset map on the left).

Ancient sea creatures

The arthrodire was the supreme submarine ruler of the Devonian period for fifty million years. *Gemuendia* was a smaller skate-like member of this armourplated family of fishes that died out about 350 million years ago. *Cladoselache*, a relative of the shark, only attained four feet in length. Some of the fierce eurypterids, "water scorpions," grew to the size of a man, and many of the squid-like cephalopods grew even larger. The bottom of the shallow sea teemed with lamp shells, trilobites, corals, sea anemones, glass sponges and delicately branched bryozoans.

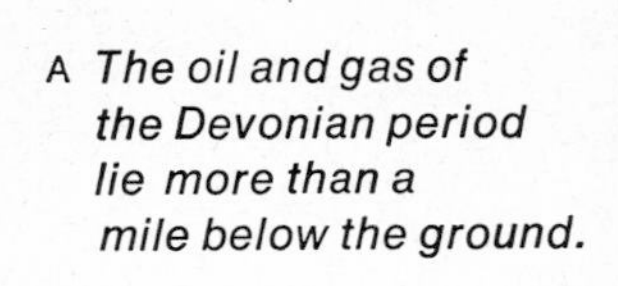

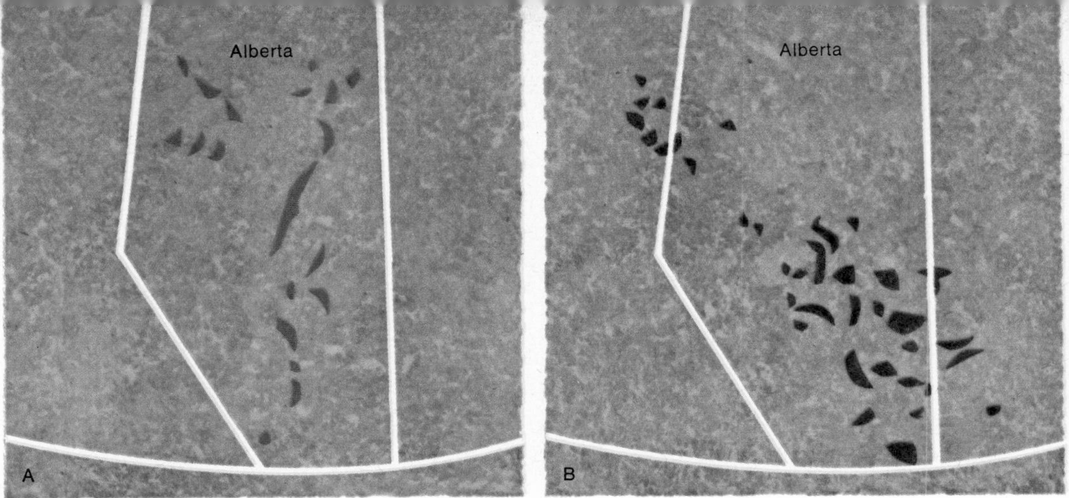

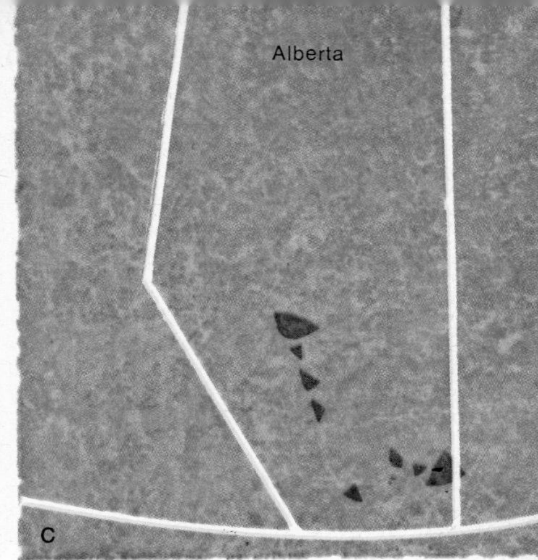

A *The oil and gas of the Devonian period lie more than a mile below the ground.*

B *The Lower Cretaceous oil and gas have permeated porous sandstone formations.*

C *Upper Cretaceous oil is found close to Pembina-gas in Medicine Hat sandstone.*

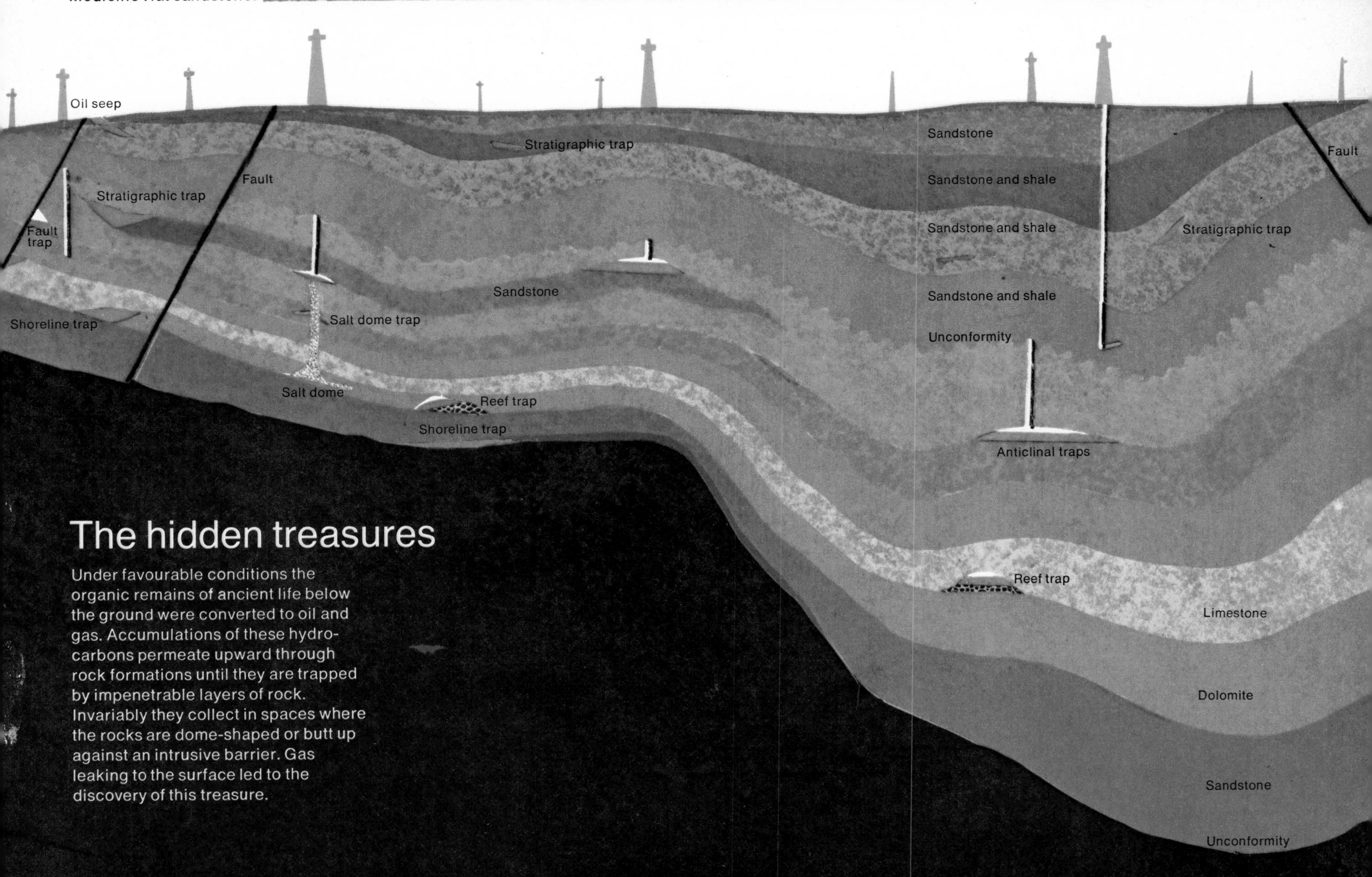

The hidden treasures

Under favourable conditions the organic remains of ancient life below the ground were converted to oil and gas. Accumulations of these hydrocarbons permeate upward through rock formations until they are trapped by impenetrable layers of rock. Invariably they collect in spaces where the rocks are dome-shaped or butt up against an intrusive barrier. Gas leaking to the surface led to the discovery of this treasure.

Gorgosaurus
Parassurolophus
Hesperornis
Trachodon
Paleocincus
Turtle
Chasmosaurus

Giant reptiles invade the plains

Grotesque reptiles dominated the swamps of the Cretaceous plains. Gorgosaurus, the ferocious carnivore, grew thirty feet long and weighed eight tons. Most dinosaurs were plant eaters; those living on land were well protected by bony plates and horns. Duck-billed variants lived and fed mainly in shallow water. Some developed wings with a 25 feet span. The first flowering plants made their appearance, but despite this new source of food none of the dinosaurs survived. Diadectes resembled the existing tejgu, and turtles have changed little. True birds like the Hesperornis had developed. Fossils of the dinosaurs illustrated here have been found in the southern region of the plains.

Oligocene times

see picture on next page

By Oligocene times, about thirty million years ago, mammals on the plains were assuming recognizable shapes. Titanotheres stood eight feet high at the shoulders, but despite their size and aggressive appearance, they had poor teeth and relied on soft vegetation. Their brains were small and they were doomed to extinction along with the carnivorous Hyaenodons. Other contemporaries developed into modern species. They include Mesohippus, the three-toed ancestor of the modern horse; Hyracodon, a small fleet-footed rhinoceros; Archaeotherium, a distant relative of the pig, with strong teeth and sharp hooves; Poebrotherium, a diminutive camel, and a small antelope, the Leptomeryx. The Palaeolagus, an early rabbit, nibbled the plants that were beginning to resemble present day vegetation.

Hyracodon
Hyaenodon
Poebrotherium
Leptomeryx

Titanothere
Mesohippus
Palaeolagus
Stylemys turtle
Archaeotherium

How glaciers made the plains fertile

15,000 years ago the entire region was covered by ice, 4,000 feet thick, which changed the look and life of the plains. The greatest single benefit was the well mixed debris spread over the land by the Wisconsin glacier which forms the basis of today's soil. Lake Agassiz, larger than all the Great Lakes combined, twice covered southern Manitoba and about 8,000 years ago finally drained into Hudson Bay. The shore of this lake can be traced along the Manitoba Escarpment. The moraines abandoned by the ice extend to the foothills of the Rockies. Athabasca, Great Slave and Great Bear lakes, which were once much larger, were also formed during the melting period. Many fertile clay plains were once bottoms of shallow lakes.

Alberta
Saskatchewan
Manitoba
Grey wooded soil
Black soil
Dark brown soil
Brown soil

Like a giant sickle, the rich black soil of the prairies encloses the dark brown and brown soil regions of the grassland, and marks the boundary with north woods.

Rich black soil

The plains were barren when the ice left 10,000 years ago. The mineral particles strewn about by the glaciers weathered, gradually changed their chemical composition, breathed, absorbed the rain, were invaded by micro-organisms to fix nitrogen from the air and became host to the grass that anchored the soil with its roots, producing humus on which new generations thrived. Climate and vegetation are the conspicuous factors affecting fertility. On the prairies man has learned to respect the soil, by replacing vital chemicals, preventing erosion by proper cultivation, adjusting to the short growing season, and preserving moisture vital to growth.

B
C

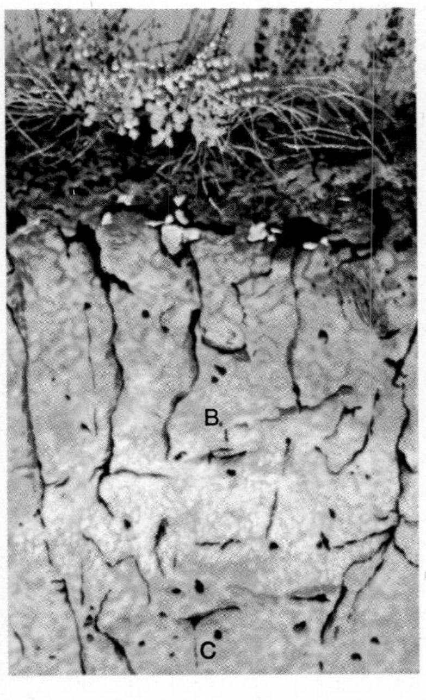

Soils are classified by their colour at the surface. The soil "profile" is divided into three levels. A, the top soil; B, the sub-soil; and C, weathered bed-rock. The chernozemic (Russian for black earth) soils illustrated are from Saskatchewan.

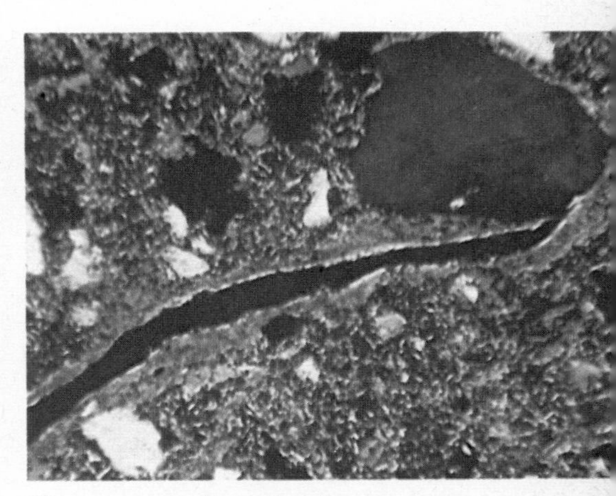

This cross-section of a clay accumulation taken from the B horizon of a grey wooded soil has been magnified seventy times. The dark line running across from bottom left is a void bordered by dense clay skins which enclose the soil matrix consisting of graded mineral grains. Shape and size of the matrix particles determine structure.

When the snow melts each year, millions of prairie sloughs hold reserves of vital water for the parched summer soil.

PART TWO / **GEOLOGY**

6 A BASINFUL OF ROCKS

Everything in existence, living or dead, is the result of changing forces that have affected it, or its forebears, since the world began. Thus, the plains of western Canada are the result of tremendous forces working for hundreds of millions of years, heaving up the land, depressing it below the level of the ocean so that for millions of years at a time it was drowned, changing the climate from tropical to a condition so cold that ice two miles thick covered the land. And the change is still going on, surely and relentlessly, ignoring the influences of man.

Most of the evidence of great forces that moulded the plains lies beneath the surface, in some places many miles down. Although the topography of the region may tend towards sameness, the rock below the surface is varied and contains more fossils than that of any other part of Canada. Only in recent times has the extent of their great variety been understood.

Envisage the bedrock of the plains as a great bowl with its edges at the Canadian Shield on the east and the Cordillera on the west. The bowl is much deeper in the west than in the east and is filled with layers of sedimentary rock laid down during succeeding geological periods. Between some of these layers of rock are pools of oil and natural gas, and layers of coal. Others enclose layers of pure salt, mostly sodium chloride and potassium chloride, now being brought to the surface to help enrich the soil. There is even sea water deep down that in places is working its way towards the surface, and fossils which, like the illustrations in a book, tell the story of what happened during the eons of time when there were none to observe – truly a bowlful of surprises.

The story begins about six hundred million years ago, when the earth was already three or four billion years old. What happened before that to the crust of the earth is still a secret buried deep in the basement rock of that crust. It is difficult enough to get a conception of six hundred million years, especially for beings accustomed to worrying about what's happening this day or this week or, at the most, this half-century. But even in one day, when a strong wind is blowing, it is possible to see the ridges of sand washed up on the beach of a lake. Imagine the result if the same wind blew daily for a year, a hundred years, a thousand years. A twig or leaf or remains of a fish partially buried in one day could be many feet deep by then, with many others piled upon it, and others upon them.

Or consider how in one sudden rainstorm deep gullies are gouged out of the shoulder of a new highway, and the silt is washed down into the ditch. Over a million years water running like that, with frost and ice to help it, can wear down a mountain and wash it into a plain. In six hundred million years this can happen many times. Seas can come and go, covering half a continent. Life forms can develop from one-celled organisms to highly specialized animals. A tiny reptile can develop into a dinosaur as big as a locomotive and become extinct. All this happened many millions of years before man, or anything like him, ever appeared on the earth.

The main rock of the earth's crust is igneous. Igneous, meaning "born of fire," is the molten stuff of the earth hardened into different rock types, according to its chemical composition and the history of cooling. They are the granites, basalts, porphyries, gabbros and others, often called "hard rock." But rock, as soon as it is exposed, begins to be broken down by air, water, frost, heat and chemical action into small grains of sand and clay that are then washed into low places where they settle out. These sediments, in turn, over long periods of time, pile up, are packed tightly together, and cemented into sandstone and shale.

Limestone, another sedimentary rock, is composed largely of calcium carbonate (calcite), which was either chemically precipitated from sea water, or assimilated by living organisms whose shells later sank to the bottom and became part of the rock. When igneous and sedimentary rocks are submitted to great pressure and heat, they re-crystallize into metamorphic rock – slate, schist, gneiss, quartzite or marble. Igneous and metamorphic rocks are found on the surface of the Canadian Shield, but on the plains they lie buried hundreds or even thousands of feet beneath sedimentary rock.

The first major event during the Phanerozoic eon (the geological term for the past 600 million years) caused a portion of the North American continent to sink very gradually and let the sea flow in. This Cambrian sea, as it has been named, inundated large sections of what is now the United States, and extended in a long channel north to the Arctic Ocean, flooding eastern British Columbia and western Alberta.

The Cambrian sea covered the western section of the plains region for approximately one hundred million years. During this long time no great events occurred on the low-lying land surrounding the sea. There were few animals and plants, and no soil. Some mosses and primitive lichens clung to the rocks, the wind blew incessantly over the barren landscape and the rains fell. In a hundred million years constant running water can turn even the hardest rocks into sediments. These were washed by the rivers into the shallow sea, forming sandbars and deltas that later hardened into layers of sedimentary rock.

Although the land was barren the warm shallow seas teemed with life. Sometime during the later part of the preceding eon – called Cryptozoic from the Greek, meaning "hidden life" – life had begun in the seas. The remains of millions of tiny invertebrates of a great variety of shapes and sizes are found in the Cambrian rock. The most prominent of all these creatures was the trilobite. It looked something like a huge water beetle and was distantly related to present-day lobsters. Trilobites ranged in size from a few inches to eighteen inches in length and were the most perfectly adapted creatures yet evolved. They could swim and crawl on the bottom with their many legs, while their segmented body permitted some to curl up into a tight ball for defence. They persisted on this earth for about 325 million years. The layers of rock that developed from the Cambrian sediments are mostly hard shales and limestones. In the mountains of western Alberta they are exposed, but under Calgary they lie about three miles below the surface.

Following the Cambrian period the land was again flooded. The Ordovician sea covered a much larger area than its predecessor. In its shallow waters billions of trilobites continued to thrive along with countless other invertebrates. By then other creatures had appeared. There were molluscs related to modern squids, and the largest of them was a spectacular cephalopod that looked like an oversized horn of plenty and grew to a length of fifteen feet. In this sea also appeared man's earliest ancestor, the first of the chordates, the name given to the phylum of animals that have backbones and related internal supporting structures. It was a fish with a backbone, but no jawbone, related to the nefarious lampreys that infest the Great Lakes and live as parasites by sucking the life from commercial fish.

The fossils of these creatures are found in Ordovician sedimentary rock. During the seventy-five million years that the Ordovician sea covered about seventy per cent of North America, the process of weathering continued. More and more sediments were washed into the sea, sank to the bottom, and over long periods of time were cemented into rocks. Since in other areas of the plains they are covered by later formations, the most extensive outcroppings of Ordovician rock are found in eastern Manitoba. Geologists name them after the regions where they are found.

There is the Winnipeg formation, consisting of sandstone, siltstone and greenish shale, resting on the eroded surface of Precambrian or Cambrian rock. The Red River formation is mostly dolomite, a hard variety of limestone containing magnesium, which is often used as building stone. Between Garson and Tyndall, Manitoba, this dolomite is close enough to the surface to be extensively quarried. Under the name of Tyndall it is shipped to many parts of the country. It can be seen in the legislative buildings in Winnipeg, and part of the parliament buildings in Ottawa.

Many millions of years after the seas of the Ordovician period had left the land dry, and the constant winds and running water had done their work of erosion, the region of the plains was again submerged. Since this occurred during the Silurian period, which began about 425 million years ago and lasted twenty million years (a short time in geological history), it is called the Silurian sea. The sedimentary rocks it left are mostly hard dolomites, and the fossils show that many of the creatures of the Ordovician seas were still there – notably the trilobites in a modified form, corals and a nine-foot water scorpion. A much smaller scorpion of this sea may have been the first creature to crawl out onto the dry land. Whether it stayed there or returned to the water, palaeontologists have not yet determined. Gypsum occurs in the Silurian formations, and is mined near Gypsumville, Manitoba, and near Great Slave Lake.

The word "Devonian" is important to the western plains, because during the Devonian period, 405 to 345 million years ago, much of the vast wealth that lies beneath the surface originated. The inland seas that periodically inundated much of the continent during those sixty million years covered the

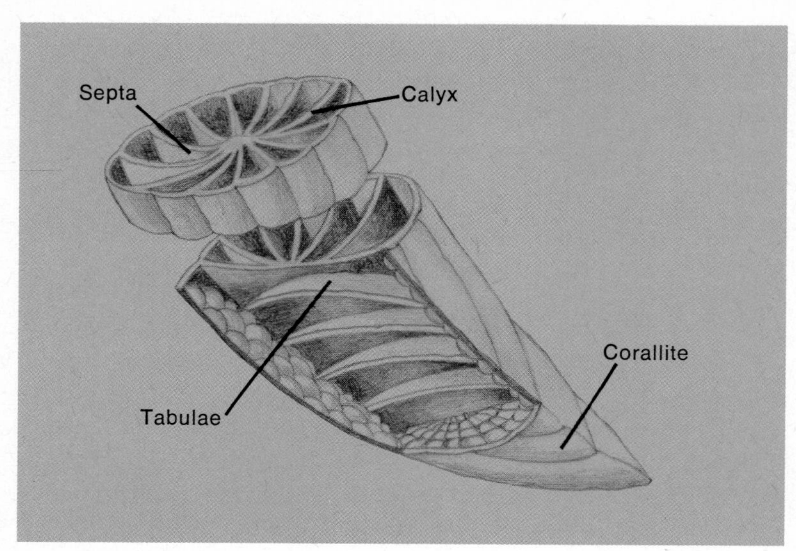

The individual polyp, greatly enlarged above, combined by the billions to build reefs that are now thousands of feet below the surface.

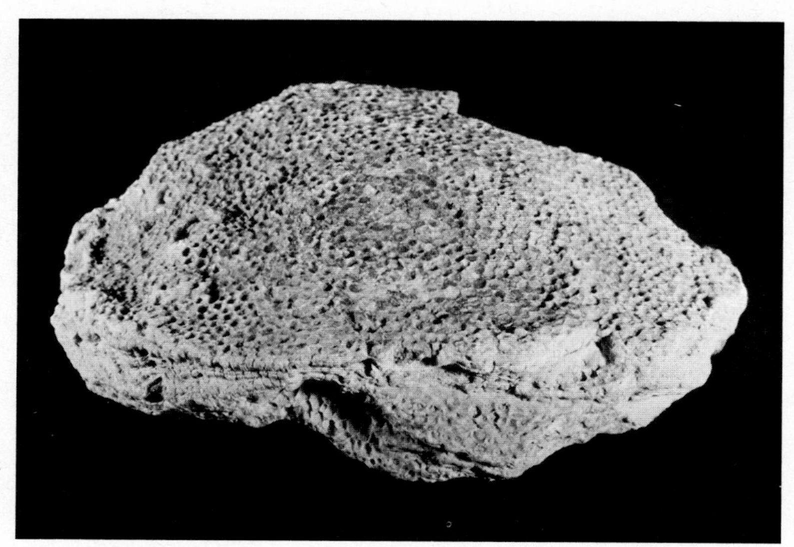

This typical piece of oil-bearing limestone consists of fossilized skeletons of Favosites *corals that lived in the warm Devonian sea.*

entire plains region as we know it today, as well as sections of the Canadian Shield and the Great Lakes region. The seas were warm, shallow, and teemed with life.

In these shallow seas billions upon billions of tiny invertebrates and plants constituting the plankton died, sank to the bottom and were quickly covered by sand and silt brought there by the rivers. The most accepted theory of petroleum formation explains that this quick covering prevented decay. Then, during the course of millions of years the hydrocarbons in these marine carcasses, by chemical processes not thoroughly understood, changed to petroleum and natural gas.

At the same time, because the seas were tropical, great reefs, built by coral-like animals called *stromatoporoids,* developed. Being porous, the reefs permitted the oil to accumulate within them. A pool of oil is often topped by a quantity of natural gas that may serve to keep the oil under pressure. But some of the oil and gas is never trapped underground and finds its way to the surface, a circumstance that disclosed the presence of oil to man and led him to drill for it.

The first oil discoveries on the plains (oil from Devonian rock was found in Lambton County, Ontario, as early as 1855) were made in Turner Valley, Alberta, in 1903. It happened quite by accident, when a farmer named Bill Herron found seeping gas on his land about seven miles west of Okotoks. He collected some of the gas by upending a barrel over the seepage, and had it tested – it was petroleum gas. For ten years Herron astutely bought up as much of the surrounding countryside as he could, and set out to get backing for his oil enterprise. Nobody was interested at first, but he finally managed to persuade two experienced oilmen to visit the site. He convinced them by lighting the gas, as it came out of the ground, and frying eggs for their breakfast on the flame.

The Calgary Petroleum Products Company was organized in January 1913, and after considerable digging, they sank a well. The next spring at a depth of 2,700 feet the drillers hit a gusher that shot a stream of "sweet, wet gas" (natural gas saturated with naphtha) high into the sky. When the news reached Calgary the rush was on, with everyone who could get there by foot, bicycle, horse and buggy, or new-fangled automobile rushing to the site. Some of the raw product from the well was put directly into the gas tank of a car, which drove off to the cheers of the crowd.

From then on Turner Valley was the leading oil producer in Alberta, but the growing need for petroleum products led oil companies to spend millions of dollars trying to find more. Then, in February of 1947, drillers penetrated the Devonian

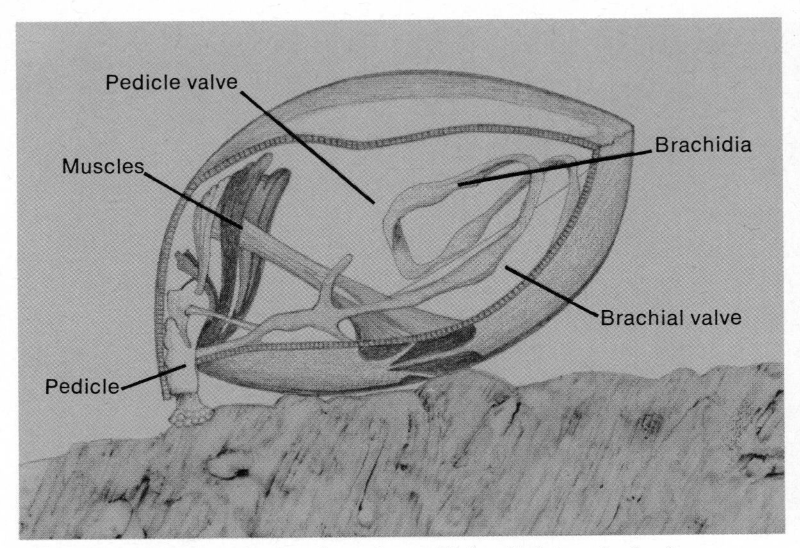

The lamp shell family developed a stalk (pedicle) to find a foothold in shallows, and strong muscles to articulate hinged valves.

There are over 30,000 varieties of the common lamp shell fossil found on the plains. This one is over 350 million years old.

formations near Leduc, south of the city of Edmonton. It was oil that occurred in formations millions of years older than the oil horizons of the Turner Valley. After the Leduc find, oil explorations throughout the plains led to the development of many other fields, making this area one of the world's largest sources of petroleum products.

That the Devonian period rock is only beginning to yield its treasure, is indicated by the recently discovered Rainbow oil and gas field, 180 miles north-northwest of Peace River, Alberta. More than a mile beneath the surface in the middle-Devonian rock lies a pinnacle reef that cuts through the Keg River and Muskeg formation, and has been called the Rainbow Member. This consists of a great fossil-filled reef of limestone with an intrusive evaporite plug in which have been trapped great quantities of oil and gas. Since the first oil was brought to the surface in March, 1965, the region has seen the greatest oil rush since Leduc.

Something else had happened during the Devonian period that also left a great store of wealth beneath the plains. As the supply of water to the shallow sea that covered much of what is now southern Saskatchewan was cut off, the waters very slowly evaporated. Like all sea waters, these were heavy with salt, and left behind a ten-foot thick layer of potassium chloride mixed with sodium chloride.

During early oil explorations, drill cores brought up samples of the white salt. Geologists were interested but for some time industrialists were not impressed. Then, in 1955, an exploration programme showed that the potash beds in Saskatchewan were 450 miles long and fifty miles wide, and that they extended into Manitoba. Having nothing but common salt mixed with it, the ore was of exceptionally high grade, making this the world's richest potash deposit yet discovered. Now, tourists on the plains may be surprised to see, in the midst of a field of grain, the headframe of a mine beside a huge refinery from which pipes lead to a number of squat, cone-shaped storage bins. Nearby a big white pile of table salt, for which there is no market, grows steadily larger.

If tourists stop and make arrangements with an accommodating public relations man, they may descend, together with a cage-full of farm boys turned miners, 3,140 feet straight down to the potash bed. Here is a strange, grey-walled, salty cavern. On the back of a truck they may travel for a mile or more, past branching tunnels all seven and a half feet high and thirteen feet wide, to a great 52-ton monster, chewing the chunks of salt from the mine face. This "continuous miner," as it is called, rips out salt at the rate of more than five tons a minute, and it never stops. There are half a dozen of these mines in operation at the present, each producing more than a million tons of potash a year. The market for potash, the principal ingredient in many fertilizers, is considered to have an almost limitless potential, especially when the great Asian nations develop much-needed, extensive fertilizing programmes.

In the Devonian seas, along with great numbers and varieties of invertebrates, fishes were abundant. In the saltwater seas and freshwater ponds, numerous classes of fish developed, some of which became extinct during the same period or later, and some of which have survived to the present day. Among them was the adaptable lungfish which, when its pond dried up, could crawl through the mud to find other water. One group of air-breathing fishes evolved into the amphibia.

During the Devonian period also, water plants that had early begun an uneasy growth on land made tremendous progress. There were no trees as we know them today, or flowers or grasses, but there were green plants nonetheless, forerunners of the monstrous ferns that were to follow. Millipedes, scorpions and spiders had also developed the ability to live out of water. By the end of the period many kinds of insects had appeared, including dragonflies with a two-foot wing span.

The Carboniferous period, which followed the Devonian, lasted for another sixty-five million years and is divided into two sub-periods, the Mississippian and the Pennsylvanian. During part of this period a vast inland sea covered much of what is now western United States, and a large part extended north into the Canadian plains region. In this sea the petroleum-forming processes continued, resulting in the oil and gas fields of Turner Valley, Pincher Creek, and Jumping Pound in the southwest corner of Alberta.

Following the Carboniferous period, a long season of erosion persisted through the Permian (280-230 million years ago), the Triassic (230-181 million years ago), and into the beginning of the Jurassic period (181-135 million years ago). The seas that returned later during this period left massive sediments on their floors – up to 1,500 feet thick in parts of the southern plains. The animal remains in these deposits yielded oil and gas accumulations found in the Jurassic formations south of Lethbridge, near Wapella in southeastern Saskatchewan, and at Shaunavon in southwestern Saskatchewan.

7 THE AGE OF DINOSAURS

The Cretaceous period, 135 to 63 million years ago, was the most important of all to the western plains. Not only did it leave the greatest thickness of bedrock over most of the area, but within these rocks are found oil, gas, great quantities of coal and dinosaur remains.

Much of this is due to the last great sea to cover part of the North American continent. It extended from the Arctic Ocean to the Gulf of Mexico, inundating almost the exact area of the present plains, in Canada. During millions of years thick mud and sand deltas were formed by the rivers running into the sea from the west. Great deltas and sandbars built up and were buried beneath tons of rock. The Cretaceous sediments are the ones most commonly found on the surface of the plains where erosion has disposed of the surface soil. The famous badlands along the Red Deer and other rivers are good examples.

The sediments caused by sandbars and deltas overlaying older formations have formed numerous stratigraphic traps filled with oil and natural gas. The wells in the extensive Pembina oil field are in Cretaceous rock, as are those of Lloydminster, Joarcam, Joffre and Smiley-Coleville, to mention but a few. Volcanic action south of the U.S. border filled the air with ash, which, when it settled and decomposed formed bentonite. This, mixed with other clays has formed a soil with the ability to absorb large quantities of water, called "gumbo" by plainsmen.

Probably the most valuable of all petroleum deposits are contained in the bituminous sands found near the surface along the Athabasca River. For years engineers knew the extent of these sands – about 100 miles long, 250 feet thick – and their potential oil production, but they couldn't perfect an economic method of separating oil from sand. Now they can, and as a result a town of 500 homes is being built near Fort McMurray, where huge ferris-wheel-like diggers are scooping up the sands by bucket-loads. The sand is removed from the mixture by washing with water, and the other impurities (mostly carbon and sulphur) by running it through a chemical bath. The resulting oil is pumped into a 260-mile pipeline that carries it to

Edmonton, where it is fed into the interprovincial pipeline.

The Cretaceous sea teemed with a great variety of fish and feeding upon them were dragon-like reptiles; some of their bones have been found embedded in Cretaceous shale along the banks of the South Saskatchewan River, in the Pembina formation near Morden, Manitoba, and at a place near Nobleford called Scabby Butte. One of these was a fierce-looking, air-breathing creature with a long body and scaly skin called a mosasaur. This voracious creature looked like nothing that crawls or swims today. Reaching lengths of thirty feet, it had a body something like a crocodile, but with short, flat flippers in place of legs. A spiny keel ran along the back and tail, giving it balance while swimming. The head looked something like a monitor lizard's, but had rows of pointed teeth.

In feeding habits the mosasaur was much like a seal, diving for its prey and swallowing the fish whole. Smaller skeletons mixed with the larger ones in Saskatchewan Cretaceous rock indicate that the big mosasaurs often gobbled up their smaller relatives. Perhaps most important of all, the mosasaur is believed to have borne its young alive, much as seals do, rather than squirm up onto the shore to lay eggs. It is likely, palaeontologists believe, that the mosasaur, a swimming lizard, descended from lizards that once lived on land.

Another grostesque reptile that once swam where the fields of grain now thrive was the plesiosaur. This animal looked like descriptions of Ogopogo, the dragon-like creature that some people claim they have seen in Okanagan Lake. It had a small head, often a long thin neck, a body like a turtle with huge flippers and hardly any tail. Some grew to be forty feet long. It is believed that the plesiosaur was a much slower swimmer than the mosasaur, and a surface feeder. But one of the strangest things about them are the stomach stones, called gastroliths, that are found with the monsters' bones. Nobody knows their purpose, but it is interesting to speculate that they may have helped in the grinding of food in the manner of stones in a bird's gizzard.

One sea monster of the Cretaceous deep, although it left little evidence on the plains, did leave descendents, the giant sea-turtle. This twelve-foot monster that swam ponderously a hundred million years ago, evidently looked very much like the sea turtles that inhabit modern tropical oceans.

Another characteristic of the Cretaceous period has made it the happy hunting grounds for palaeontologists from the days of Palliser to the present. As stated, the sea was shallow and warm. But it was also bounded on the west by a newly-formed elevation from which swift-running waters poured, bringing great quantities of sand and mud with them. Over millions upon millions of years these sediments built up extensive deltas and flood plains, in the region of southern Alberta and Saskatchewan, on which the tropical vegetation came to be dense.

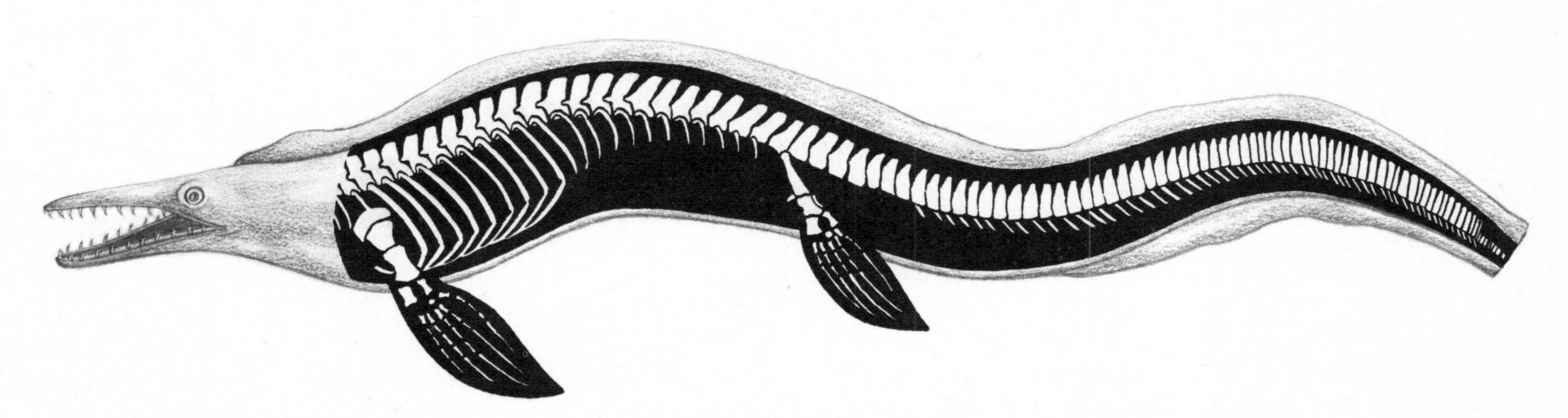

The Mosasaurs, aquatic lizards up to 30 feet in length, were powerful swimmers who used their flippers as rudders. They could expand their jaws like a snake to swallow large prey, sometimes their own progeny, which were born alive at sea.

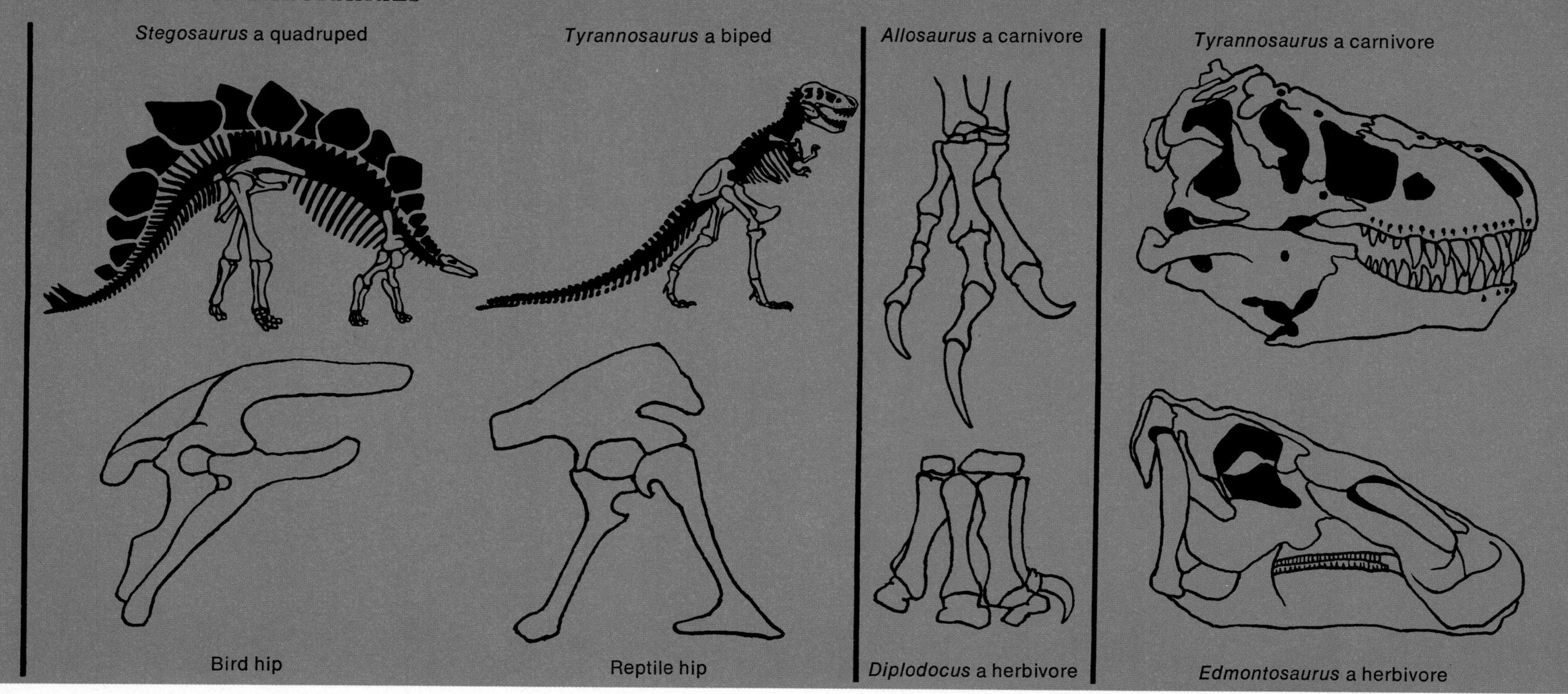

There were two kinds of dinosaurs: "bird hips" with a three-pronged pelvis, and "reptile hips" with a four-pronged one. Both these groups included four-legged plant eaters, but all carnivores were bipedal.

Anatomy of forelimbs shows adaptation to the feeding patterns.

The jagged teeth in the four-foot skull (top) *contrast sharply with the duck-billed dinosaur's flat molars.*

Thus on these lush coastal plains a family of reptiles that had been developing during Triassic times reached their full potential and came to the end of their line. These were the dinosaurs, and nowhere on earth are more of their fossilized remains to be found than in the badlands along the valleys of the Red Deer, the Oldman, Milk, Frenchman and South Saskatchewan Rivers.

The sandstone and soft shale of these areas has been eroded by wind and water since the ice age, laying bare the fossilized remnants of skulls, backbones, whole skeletons, eggs, and even skin. The famous Steveville-Deadlodge Canyon area, northeast of Brooks, Alberta, has produced and continues to produce remarkable specimens. Remains are found along four Cretaceous period shorelines, known as the Aquilan, Judithian, Edmontonian, and Lancian. Each is recognizable by the type of rock strata in the different locations.

The Aquilan, submerged about eighty million years ago and the oldest, has so far yielded no complete skeletons. However, teeth and bones have been found that, since they belong to groups found in later strata, prove dinosaurs were abundant. Also, although not yet found in Canada, remains of the fish-eating Pteranodon, a flying reptile with a wing span of twenty feet, have been found south of the Canadian border.

It is in the well-exposed Judithian formation that the most and best remains are found. The famous Centrosaurus, for instance, a horned dinosaur whose head bore a remarkable likeness to the modern rhinoceros, roamed peacefully through the swamps feeding incessantly to sustain his huge bulk. Its horns gave some protection, it is hoped, from the huge Gorgosaurus, a thirty-foot-long, flesh-eating monster who weighed up to seven and one half tons, walked on two legs, and had a gigantic head filled with immense teeth.

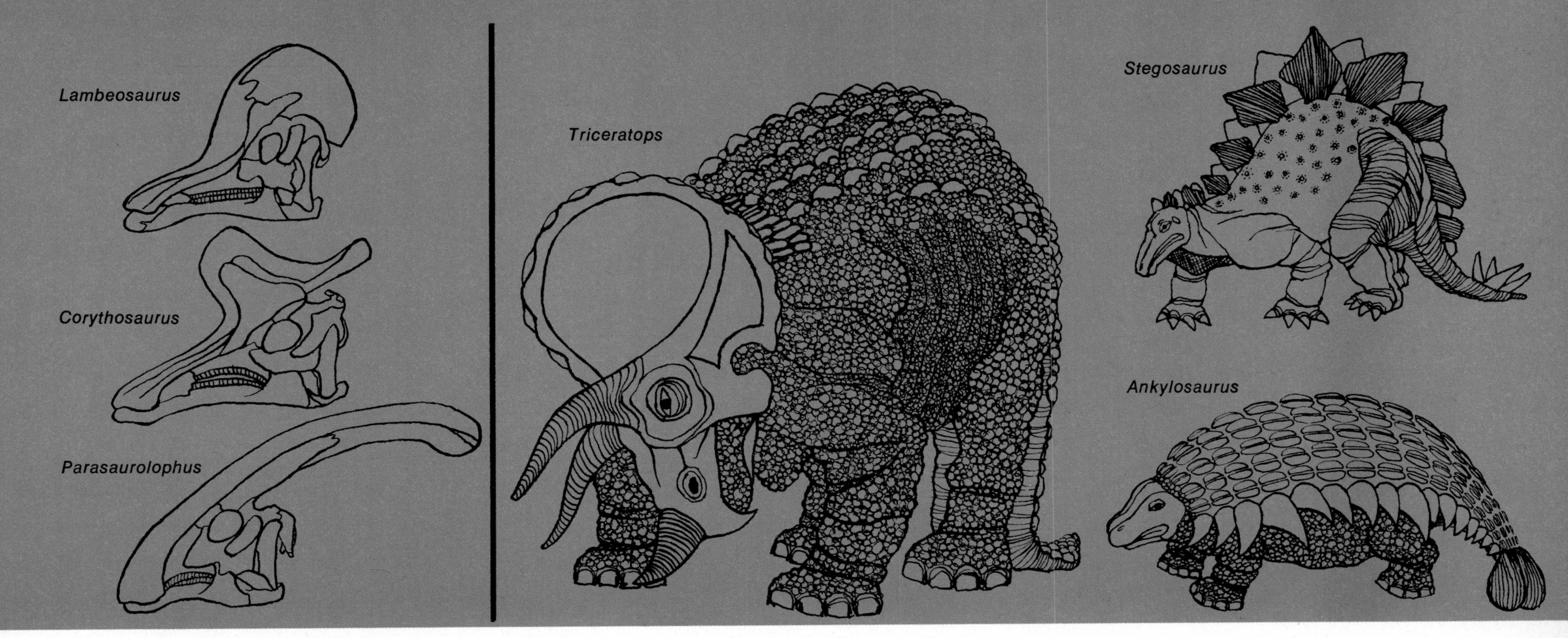

Duck-billed, plant-eating dinosaurs, about 30 ft. long, developed bizarre bony structures on their foreheads.

Early in dinosaur history the small-headed, mini-brained Stegosaurus *grew two rows of grotesque armour-plates, and long spikes on its tail. It was followed by the* Ankylosaurs *which have been termed "reptilian tanks." Horned dinosaurs,* Ceratopsians, *were last in line.*

There were enormous Ankylosaurs, whose bodies were covered with armour-plates for protection, and who could use their two-hundred pound knobby tails as clubs to bludgeon their attackers. Also in the Judithian are found the remains of the duck-billed Hadrosaurs, thirty-foot long plant eaters, which walked on two feet but were no match for the flesh-eaters. They spent most of their time wading or swimming in the shallow waters of the lagoons.

Smaller flesh-eaters, sometimes called the ostrich dinosaurs, Ornithomimids, which were about twelve feet long and ran on two legs, swallowed smaller lizards that crossed their path. They had small heads without teeth, and three finger-like appendages at the ends of their long forelimbs which they could use as we use a finger and thumb. The Edmontonian delta in the Central Alberta region, about sixty-seven million years ago abounded in much the same type of dinosaurs as did the Judithian but, as would be expected, they tended to be larger and more highly developed than those of a few million years before.

The last Cretaceous flood plain, the Lancian, supported numerous dinosaurs, larger than those of earlier times. The remains of the most ferocious flesh-eaters of them all, Tyrannosaurus, have been found in Saskatchewan. Perhaps they were altogether too big to survive. Whatever the reason, this flood plain was the last region on earth that saw dinosaurs. Sometime within the three million years that span the end of the Cretaceous period, sixty-three million years ago, dinosaurs disappeared completely from the face of the earth.

The great discovery of dinosaur remains on the western plains began with the Palliser expedition of 1857-60. A geologist by the name of Dr. James Hector spent most of his time digging in the eroded river beds and came up with a number of fossilized mollusc shells. Naturally he was intrigued by the

THE GEOLOGIC FREAK
Looking north across Medicine Lodge Coulee, the scarp of the Cypress Hills in southern Alberta now presents vistas of grassy knolls and stands of aspen, spruce and lodgepole pine. When the ice shelf rolled down, this area – the highest land (4,810 ft.) between Labrador and the Rockies – escaped the force that levelled the plains. The eighty square miles surrounding the "Head of the Mountain" formed a nunatak – the Eskimo term scientists have adopted to describe peaks that stand above glaciers. Yet 30 million years ago even this peak was submerged under rubble eroded from the Rockies, 150 miles away. Today the Cypress Hills get 25 per cent more rain and snow than the adjacent prairie; they are ten degrees cooler during the sweltering summer, and warmed by high Chinook winds in winter. When settlers began to move west, this region became one of the last refuges for the great plains grizzly, the "lobo" wolf and kit fox, which have disappeared since then together with the large flocks of trumpeter swans that once nested there. In July, 1859, Captain John Palliser, leading the first official exploration of the Cypress Hills, wrote in his diary: "These hills are a perfect oasis in the desert we have travelled." In 1886, a fire left the region in the photograph charred and bare – now it provides lush pastures.

find, but lack of equipment and time prevented him from digging up any of the fossilized bones.

Almost twenty years later geologist Dr. George Dawson was in the same area as a member of the North American Boundary Commission, engaged in drawing the line between Canada and the U.S. across the plains. Dawson was an indefatigable collector of everything available, including animals, plants and fossils. Late in the 1873 season the party had reached a point on Morgan Creek south of Wood Mountain, about six miles west of the present village of Killdeer, on Highway 2. Here, digging in the stratified shale, Dawson unearthed some fossilized bones which he added to his collection. Later they were identified as the bones of ancient turtles and a hadrosaurian dinosaur.

The following July, several hundred feet below Comrey sandstone, on the bank of the Milk River, Dawson discovered some bones that were far too big for any modern animal. They turned out to be parts of the sacrum and long bones of a dinosaur. Later, Dawson joined the Geological Survey of Canada, and in 1881, his assistant, Richard George McConnell, found more dinosaur remains in the Scabby Butte escarpment, about three miles east of Nobleford. These men were followed by a succession of dinosaur hunters who travelled on horseback, by wagon, and in river-scows to prospect the Cretaceous rocks of the badlands.

Most of the activity veered north to the badlands along the Red Deer River, which proved extremely fertile in dinosaur remains. Battling mosquitoes, storms, floods, and landslides, these men worked their way into remote areas. Finding the bones was only a small part of the job. For days they crouched on the hard ground, painstakingly removing fossils, bit by bit, from their beds of stone. Then came the job of transporting the crumbly remains out of the area, and getting them intact to a railway line, whence they could be shipped to a museum.

They developed a method whereby they covered the remains with gum arabic or shellac, bandaged the fossils and the rock surrounding them in plaster and burlap, and put them in stout wooden crates. Museums in many parts of the world – particularly in Ottawa, Toronto, New York and London – were soon displaying immense dinosaur skeletons that had reposed for upwards of one hundred million years in the shales of the western plains. Today the search goes on, both in the prairie region and in the northern section of the plains, particularly the Mackenzie Valley where it is believed new and important discoveries will be made. The seekers are well aware that fresh finds may disclose new facts that could change, at least in some details, the story of what happened on the plains during the Cretaceous period.

More important than the giant reptiles that inhabited the Cretaceous flood plains was the green foliage they ate. When the seas flooded the swamps and killed the vegetation — as a beaver pond does today — the foliage was removed from exposure to oxidation and thus prevented from decaying. Gradually the leaves, trunks and stems were buried deep beneath layers of hardening sediments. Biochemical changes, brought about by bacteria, broke down the vegetable matter and transformed it into another hydrocarbon — coal.

The western coal is almost two hundred million years younger than that of the Maritime provinces and is of a much softer variety – lignite, the lowest grade of true coal – but there is plenty of it. Almost all of southern Alberta is underlain with lignite and some low grade bituminous coal that comes out of the ground in huge chunks which break into fine lumps and coal dust when handled. Coal-fields near Drumheller, Edmonton, Lethbridge, and other locations, until recently provided most of the heat and power for the plains. Before its rival hydrocarbons, oil and natural gas, took over, coal heated the homes, cooked the meals, powered the railway locomotives and created steam to produce electricity.

Many of the coal beds of western Alberta are associated with an early Cretaceous formation known as the Blairmore Formation, deriving its name from the coal mining town of Blairmore, Alberta. In parts of Saskatchewan the Blairmore is a two-hundred-foot-thick, unconsolidated, water-saturated layer of sand and shale and muck under a pressure of seventy-five pounds per square inch.

When the potash miners were sinking their shafts they encountered this formation at 1,250 feet, and were in serious trouble. No matter how they tried, they could not prevent the water from flooding the shaft. Concrete cribbings were of no use, the water simply spurted out between the joints. Finally a new and unique method was adopted. First, the Blairmore formation was frozen solid by drilling sixty-two freeze holes into it and then circulating brine at sixty degrees below zero.

In this way the water in the formation was frozen solid and there was no danger from seepage. Then, using concrete-breaking jack hammers, the workmen began digging through this giant ice-cube. As they dug they fitted into place special steel tubes, bolted them together, and water-proofed them with steel sealing rings and hardwood wedges. It was a long, painfully slow, costly process, but it kept the water out of the shaft.

By the end of the Cretaceous period the bed rock of the plains contained the thickest layer of sedimentary rocks – shales, limestone, sandstone, and conglomerates – of any part of North America. It has remained comparatively stable with few breaks or upheavals. Directly to the west, however, due to great pressures within the earth, the crust was broken and heaved up to form a jagged ridge of mountains.

This brought about a tremendous change in the climate of the plains region. Now they were shut off from the warm, moist winds of the Pacific, and the climate changed from tropical to temperate, with cold winds from the north. It may have been this drastic change that finished the dinosaurs, or it may have been a combination of this and other causes, but whatever it was, the great reptiles disappeared forever from the face of the earth. They dominated their part of the world for a hundred million years (compared with man's one million to date), and they grew exceedingly large and prolific. But they left without really changing anything, and their total legacy is a few fossilized skeletons which are collected by palaeontologists and displayed in museums, providing conclusive evidence of prehistoric life.

When the Cretaceous period ended sixty-three million years ago, no more great seas flooded the plains. The work of weathering and erosion continued – winds blew incessantly, accompanied by dust storms that would make those of modern times look like breezes. Rains continued to fall and fill the rivers, carrying rock particles in the form of sand and clay from the high places to the low places, and burying them many hundreds of feet deep. Violent thunderstorms and tornadoes assisted in the never-ending work of changing the landscape.

Snow, ice and frost helped to split the rocks apart. It was a great time of wearing down the rock and distributing it according to nature's dictates. In the soil produced by the breaking down of rock, plants flourished; and the plants nourished the thousands of animals, from mice to woolly mammoths, that had developed on the earth. This was the age of mammals who roamed the plains by the millions.

The period following the Cretaceous is known as the Tertiary, and is divided into five epochs. During these epochs important things happened to the plains area. The relentless weathering of millions of years completely wore down the mountains to the west, and again the warm, moist winds transformed it into a subtropical area. Great trees flourished, died, and were buried to form more coal which, because of its recent origin (some twenty-five million years) is even softer than the sub-bituminous and lignite of the Cretaceous period. It is strip-mined near the surface in the Estevan area today, and burns well in the special forced-draft furnaces of thermal electricity plants. Thus natural energy derived from the sun twenty-five million years ago is used to make electric energy carried by wire to light the buildings, pump the water, and operate machinery on the farms and in the factories of the plains.

But conditions on the earth's surface never remain stable for long, geologically speaking, and sometime during the late Miocene epoch there was a drastic change in climate. For a variety of reasons, still subject to conjecture, the warm moisture-laden winds were replaced by cold dry ones. The specialized tropical plants disappeared and were replaced by the most vigorous, adaptable and useful plant family that has ever appeared on earth – grass.

As far as anyone knows, the grasses established themselves about fifteen million years ago and began modes of life that depend upon the growth of this inconspicuous, close-to-the-ground plant. Hundreds of species of grazing mammals live on grass and in turn are eaten by hundreds of species of carnivorous animals. Both types of animal, along with the cultivated grasses, provided sustenance for man, who, although he did not develop on the plains, ultimately made his home there.

But before man arrived on the scene other great changes took place on the plains that ultimately made the environment more hospitable to him. These events took place during the Pleistocene epoch (from one million years ago to the present) and, although nobody is quite certain why it happened, it has left plenty of evidence in all parts of Canada.

8 THE LEGACY OF THE ICE

The great glaciers of the Pleistocene epoch that covered almost all of Canada, as well as parts of the northern United States, had a tremendous effect upon the plains area. Naturally, the last glacial period – known as the Wisconsin – which began 60,000 to 100,000 years ago, is the one whose surface record is clearest. Advancing slowly from the northeast, it ploughed down over the Canadian Shield onto the plains and then, striking the obstacle of the raised prairie levels, changed direction and advanced in a southeasterly direction over what is now southeastern Saskatchewan and southern Manitoba.

As the ice moved, it picked up large quantities of rock, sand, clay, and organic matter and carried them along to drop them in odd places and shapes, when the ice began to melt. The most important action of the Pleistocene glaciers in the prairie region was the scraping of vast quantities of soil from the Canadian Shield, and its deposition on the plains. The material deposited by a glacier is called till, and the areas where it is deposited in relatively flat layers is called a till plain. At places where the mountain of advancing ice stood still for a number of years the glacial till collected in a ridge known as a moraine.

Other actions of the glacier deposited till in hills of various shapes and sizes, known as eskers, kames, and drumlins. The retreating glacier also left "outwashes," flat land washed by the water running away from the edge of the glacier; kettles, which are small low places or potholes; and large glacial lakes that after thousands of years dried up to leave lacustrine plains. In the plains area moraines, kettles and lacustrine plains are common but eskers, kames and outwashes are relatively rare.

Moraines, usually referred to as "rolling land," are found in most regions. A ridge extends from the Manitoba border, in the Moosomin region, northwest to near Saskatoon. The trans-Canada highway crosses another one between Regina and Moose Jaw. The most widespread effect of the Wisconsin glacier on the plains region occurred during the thousands of years

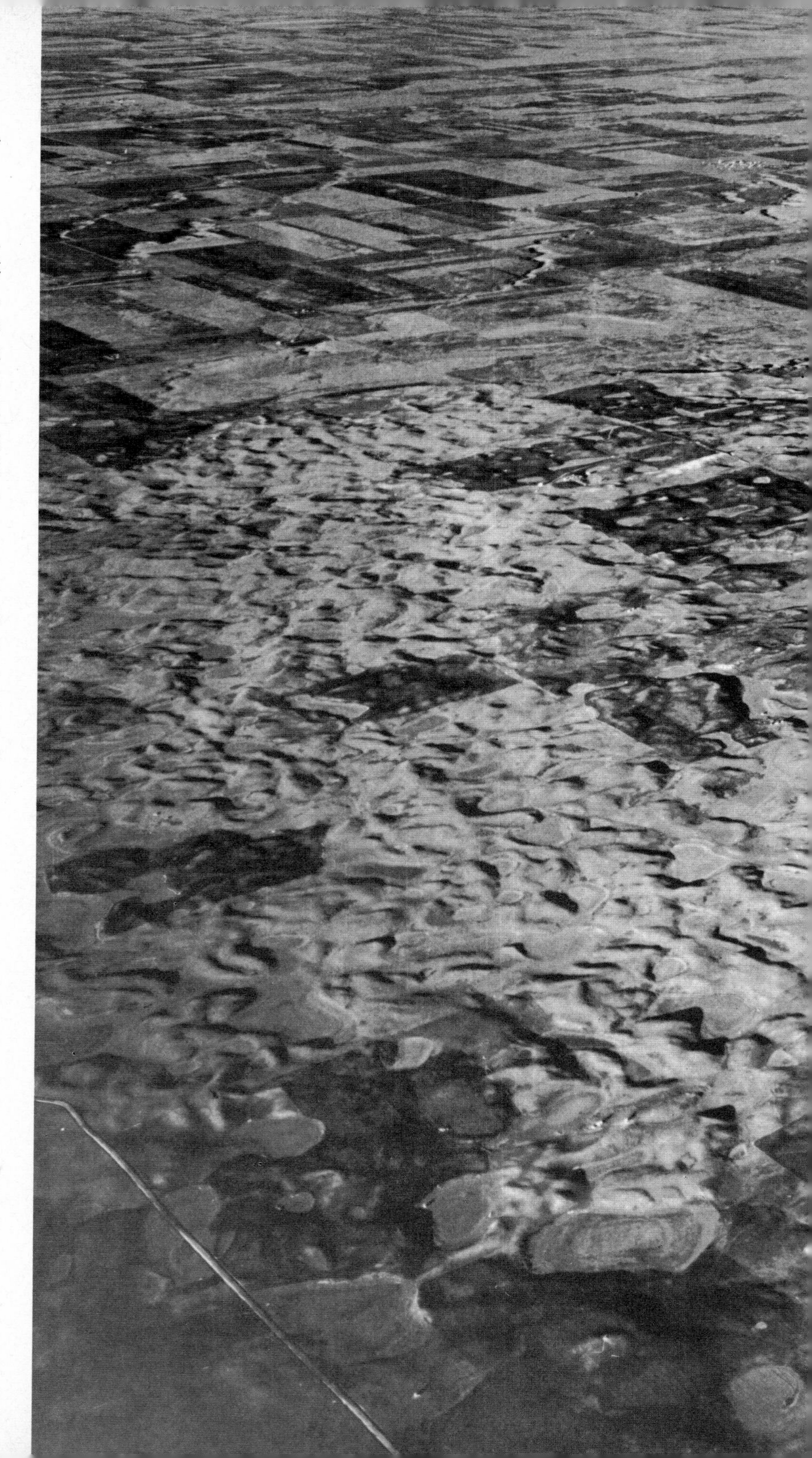

This perfect example of a "till plain" breaks the monotony of the landscape in southern Saskatchewan. Rubble dumped by glaciers 11,000 years ago lies scattered across the prairie.

that the great ice pack was melting – the formation of glacial lakes. It was not a steady process; at intervals the retreat of the glaciers was stopped by changes in weather and the ice, like a reluctant parting guest, would return. Since melting ice provides large quantities of water, numerous lakes developed on the prairies, and the Canadian Shield.

Whereas on the hard rock of the shield most of the lakes still remain, on the more porous land of the plains they have largely disappeared. But from the remaining deltaic, bottom and spillway deposits, geologists have been able to establish, with a fair degree of accuracy, the shorelines of these old lakes.

The largest and most important was glacial Lake Agassiz. For thousands of years it covered most of central and southern Manitoba and overlapped into Ontario and the United States. Agassiz began to form in the upper part of the Red River Valley, and as the great mountain of melting ice retreated northward the lake extended its boundaries; it drained southward into the Mississippi system. Lake Winnipeg, Lake Winnipegosis, Lake Manitoba and the smaller associated lakes are the remains of Lake Agassiz. The old beaches of the lake, often thirty feet deep and a mile wide, provide sand and gravel for construction, including new dams to hold back present-day waters.

Another lake to the southwest of Agassiz formed in much the same way and discharged into the Missouri system. It has been named Lake Souris. There were other smaller glacial lakes in Manitoba, including Lake Carrol and Lake Brandon. In Saskatchewan, practically the entire length of the Saskatchewan River was a chain of glacial lakes. It is sometimes called Lake Saskatoon and sometimes Lake Saskatchewan. Farther south glacial Lake Regina stretched from the town of Weyburn, northwest towards Elbow, where it drained eastward through the Qu'Appelle system into Lake Agassiz.

In southern Alberta there were a series of smaller lakes in the valleys of the Oldman and Red Deer rivers and in front of ice margins along the foothills. Farther north a glacial lake extended over much of the Peace River country, and a long arm of Lake Athabasca, bigger than the present lake, extended westward along the valley of the Peace. Also, Great Slave and Great Bear lakes were much larger than they are now.

It was these glacial lakes that made the plains what they are today. Over the thousands of years they existed, water draining into them from the surrounding areas carried a great deal of silt that was deposited on the bottom. Much of this silt is fine-grained buff and brown clay, the kind of clay that cannot be equalled for its water-retaining capacity and fertility. So it was water that had the most lasting effect on this driest of all Canada's settled areas.

After all the ice had gone from the face of the plains (Lake Agassiz drained into Hudson Bay seven thousand five hundred years ago), there was no vegetation and the land was vulnerable to the searing winds – and they blew as no man has seen them blow since. They picked up the sand from the old glacial-lake beaches and filled the air with it, depositing it in deep ridges known as dunes. There are pockets of those dunes all over the plains; examples are the great Sand Hills, north of the Cypress Hills; sandhills along the Saskatchewan south of Saskatoon, good for a golf course; and those west of Prince Albert.

And the clay blew, too – fine dust filled the air for days at a time and drifted against obstacles to form clay deposits, known as loess. Loess soil is by nature more fertile than dune soil, but it occurs in the driest parts of the region. Thus it is the type of land that benefits most from irrigation.

The dunes and the loess, along with moraines and other formations left by the ice, contribute to the hilly and rolling land of the plains. Much of the sandy soil is being reforested to prevent further soil drifting, but when the rains don't fall over a long period and the ground dries out, fine sand and dust begin to fill the air.

Gradually, despite the drifting soil after the glacier had left, the grasses crept back over the plains again, from seeds that had either remained dormant through the ice age, or those blown or carried northward from the grasslands in the south. The tallest grasses naturally grew on the best soils, and decaying generations left humus on the surface, to make the soil fertile.

Thus the way was prepared for the development on the plains of a great variety of grasses, cacti, shrubs, flowers, and trees, followed by many species of animals that fed on them, followed in turn by the predators of land and air, that fed upon the grass-eaters. And whatever developed, plant or animal, had to adapt itself to the terrain, the soil, the climate, and the other life forms of the plains. This ecology of plant and animal life shall be the subject of the following sections.

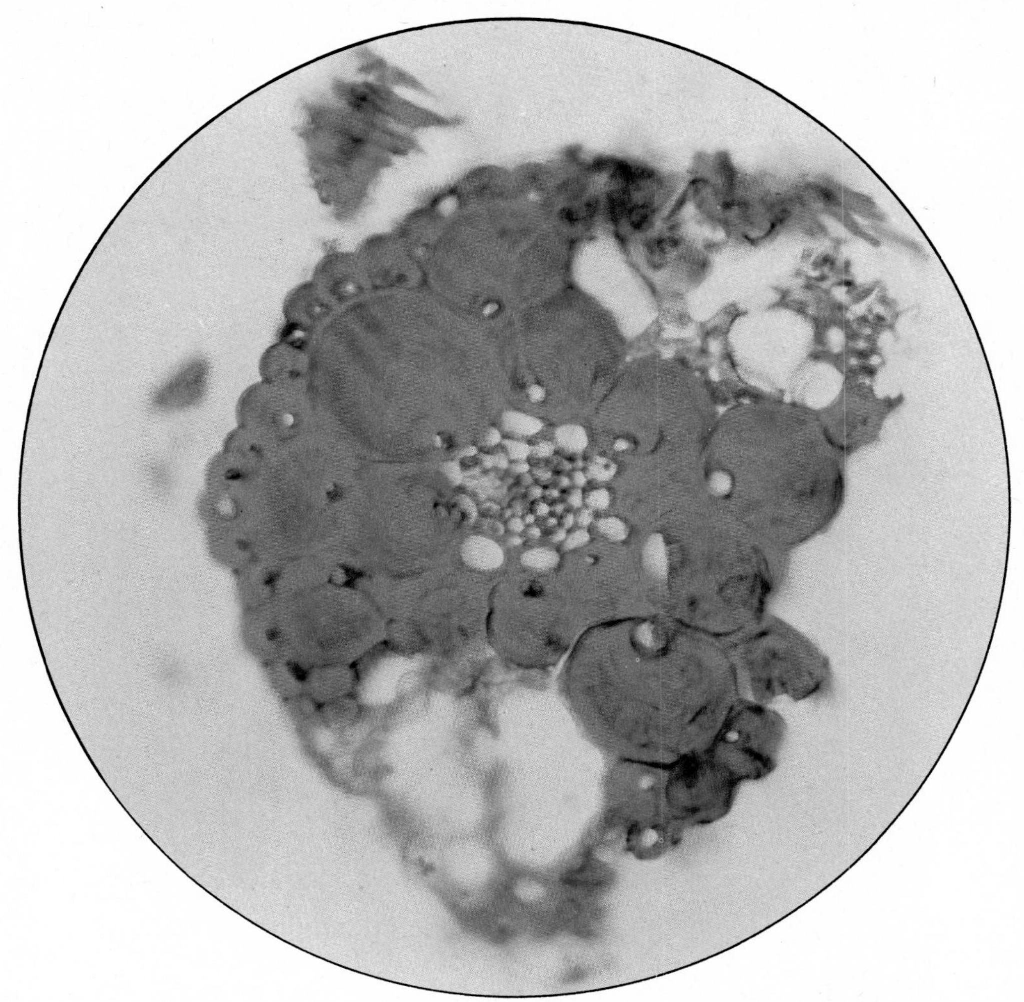

Not a pop-art pattern, but a cross-section of the tip of a grass seed much enlarged.

A SEA OF GRASS

The destiny of the prairies is linked with its vegetation–mainly grasses of nearly 200 species. An examination of this sturdy plant in all facets, wild and cultivated, reveals a highly specialized family. A bewildering variety of flower clusters, the delicate haze on a carpet of green, or a sea of golden corn–these are tokens of nature's gift to man, the plentiful harvest of the western plains.

Wild prairie grasses

Hundreds of wild grasses make up the pattern of growth on the prairies. Bluebunch fescue grows well in the shadow of the Rockies where the rainfall is lightest. The highly nutritious blue grama is found throughout the shortgrass prairie and the densely tufted alpine timothy does well in the Cypress Hills region. Nodding wild rye and alkaline cordgrass like sandy soil near a stream. Tall manna is common around sloughs and marshes in all areas. Big bluestem grows to a height of more than six feet on the tall grass prairies in the eastern part of the plains. Grasses are generally identified by their seeds and inflorescence, but other characteristics, like colour, leaf shapes and habitats soon become apparent.

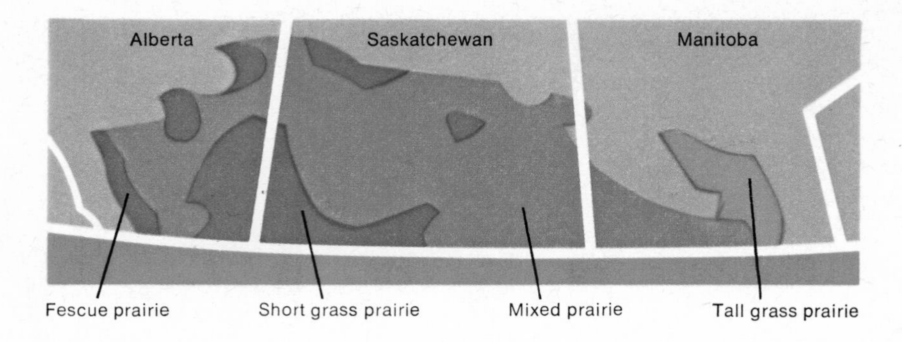

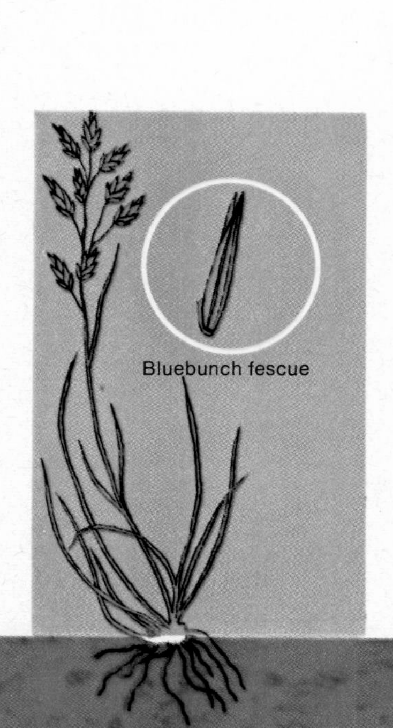

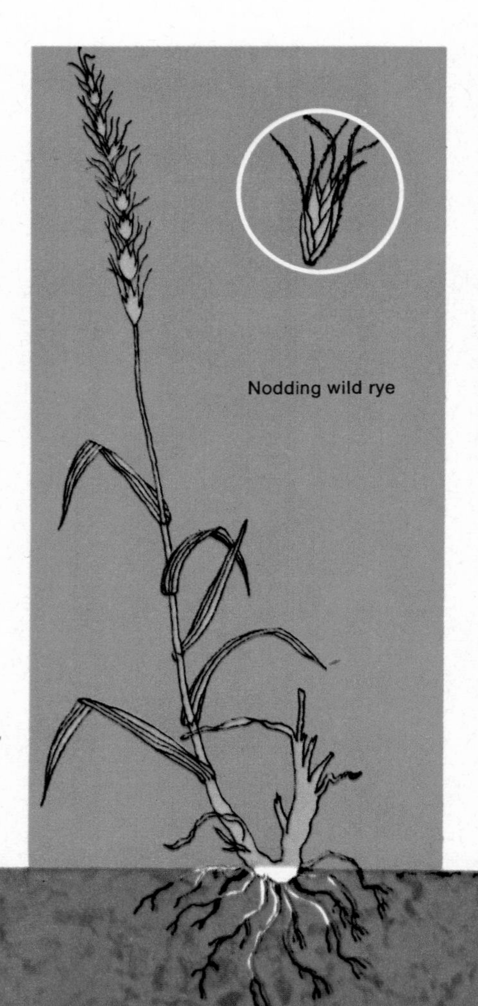

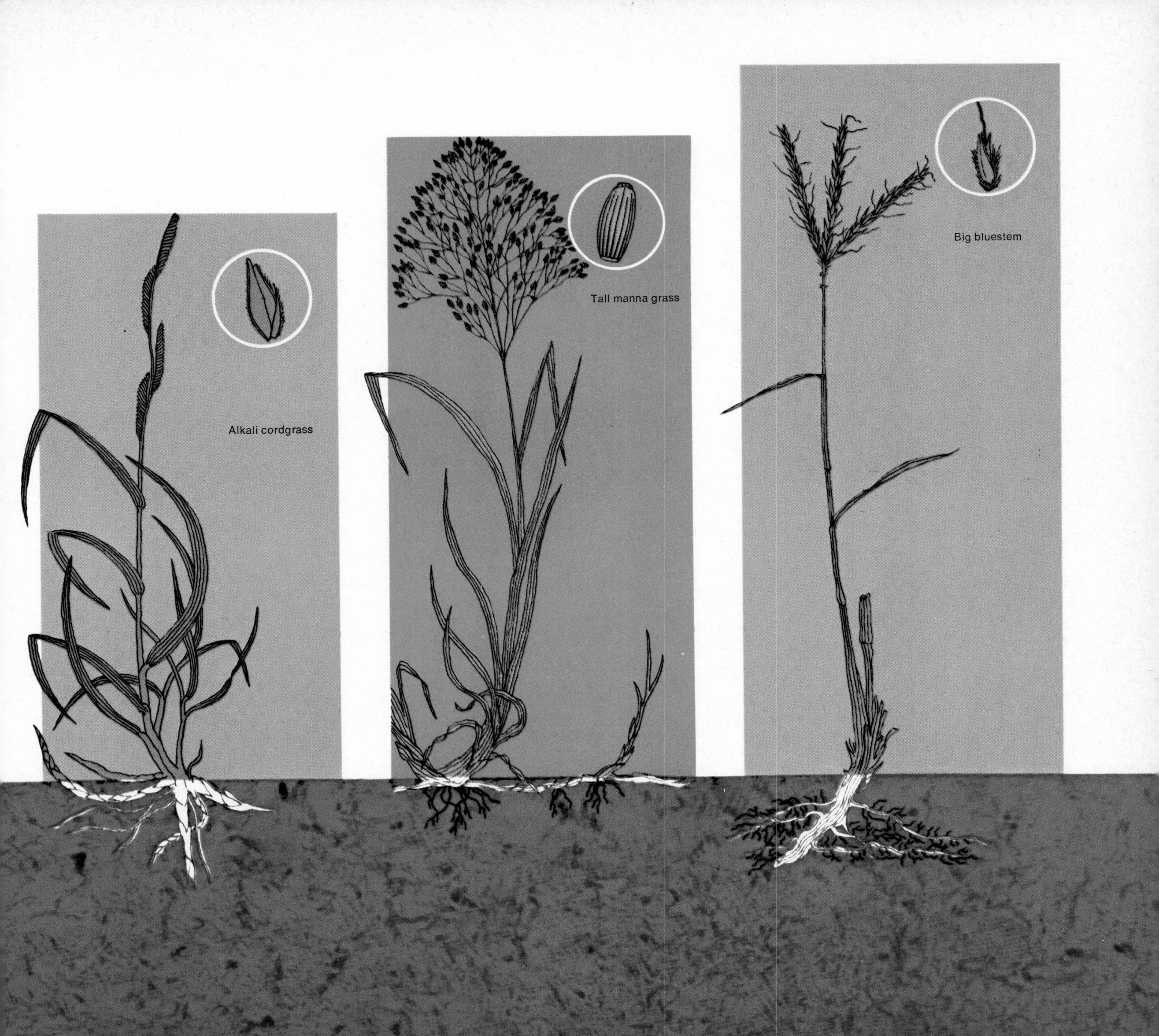
Alkali cordgrass
Tall manna grass
Big bluestem

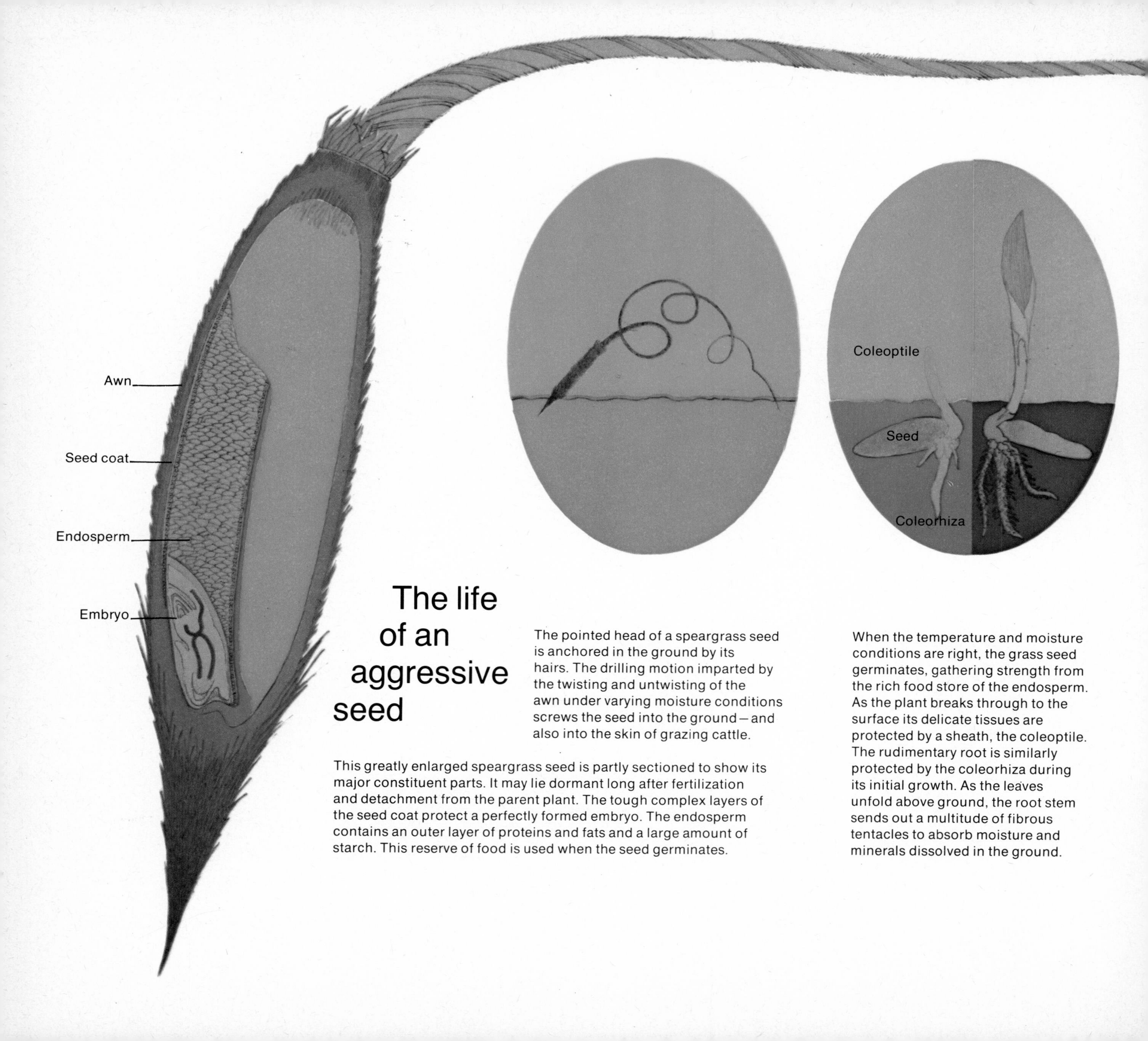

The life of an aggressive seed

The pointed head of a speargrass seed is anchored in the ground by its hairs. The drilling motion imparted by the twisting and untwisting of the awn under varying moisture conditions screws the seed into the ground – and also into the skin of grazing cattle.

This greatly enlarged speargrass seed is partly sectioned to show its major constituent parts. It may lie dormant long after fertilization and detachment from the parent plant. The tough complex layers of the seed coat protect a perfectly formed embryo. The endosperm contains an outer layer of proteins and fats and a large amount of starch. This reserve of food is used when the seed germinates.

When the temperature and moisture conditions are right, the grass seed germinates, gathering strength from the rich food store of the endosperm. As the plant breaks through to the surface its delicate tissues are protected by a sheath, the coleoptile. The rudimentary root is similarly protected by the coleorhiza during its initial growth. As the leaves unfold above ground, the root stem sends out a multitude of fibrous tentacles to absorb moisture and minerals dissolved in the ground.

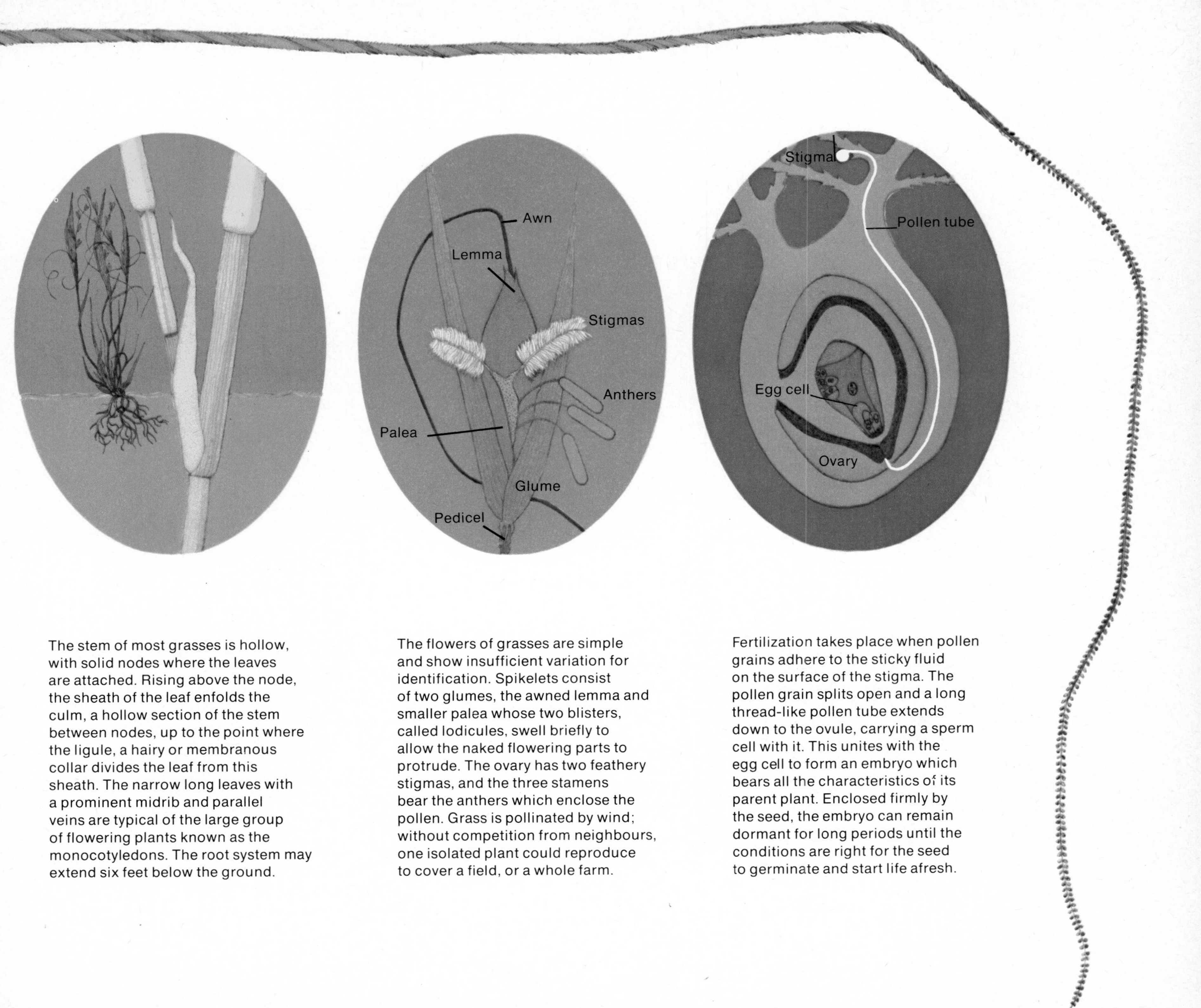

The stem of most grasses is hollow, with solid nodes where the leaves are attached. Rising above the node, the sheath of the leaf enfolds the culm, a hollow section of the stem between nodes, up to the point where the ligule, a hairy or membranous collar divides the leaf from this sheath. The narrow long leaves with a prominent midrib and parallel veins are typical of the large group of flowering plants known as the monocotyledons. The root system may extend six feet below the ground.

The flowers of grasses are simple and show insufficient variation for identification. Spikelets consist of two glumes, the awned lemma and smaller palea whose two blisters, called lodicules, swell briefly to allow the naked flowering parts to protrude. The ovary has two feathery stigmas, and the three stamens bear the anthers which enclose the pollen. Grass is pollinated by wind; without competition from neighbours, one isolated plant could reproduce to cover a field, or a whole farm.

Fertilization takes place when pollen grains adhere to the sticky fluid on the surface of the stigma. The pollen grain splits open and a long thread-like pollen tube extends down to the ovule, carrying a sperm cell with it. This unites with the egg cell to form an embryo which bears all the characteristics of its parent plant. Enclosed firmly by the seed, the embryo can remain dormant for long periods until the conditions are right for the seed to germinate and start life afresh.

Keeping the crops healthy

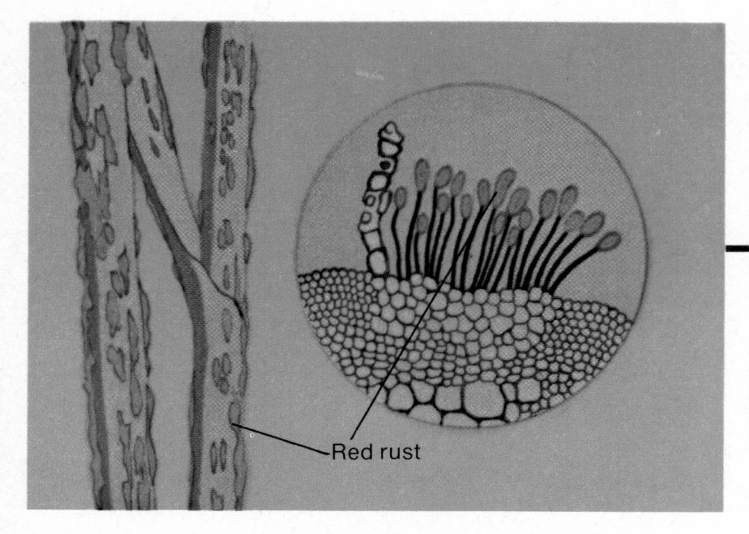

Spores of the rust fungus, carried by the wind, settle on wheat plants, feeding on the green tissues and multiplying alarmingly to sap energy from the crop.

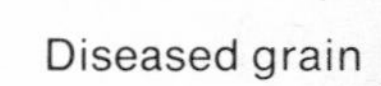

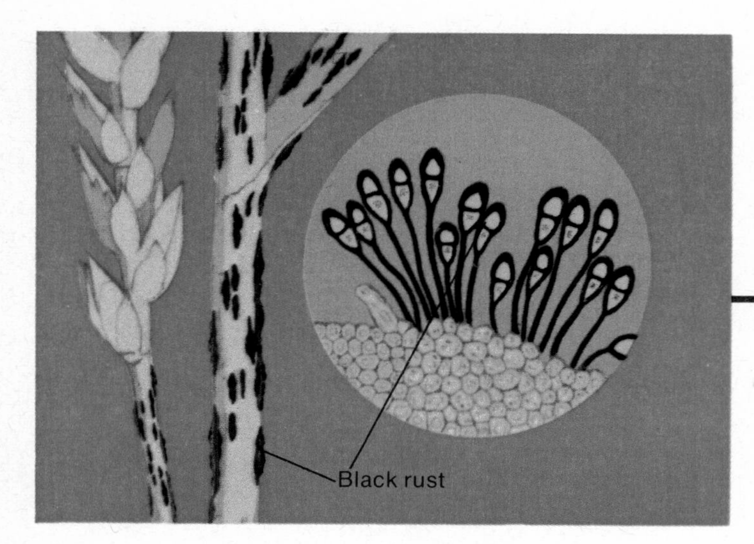

Black rust, a further stage in the development of this parasite, survives the winter and does most damage in spring if the weather is cool and wet.

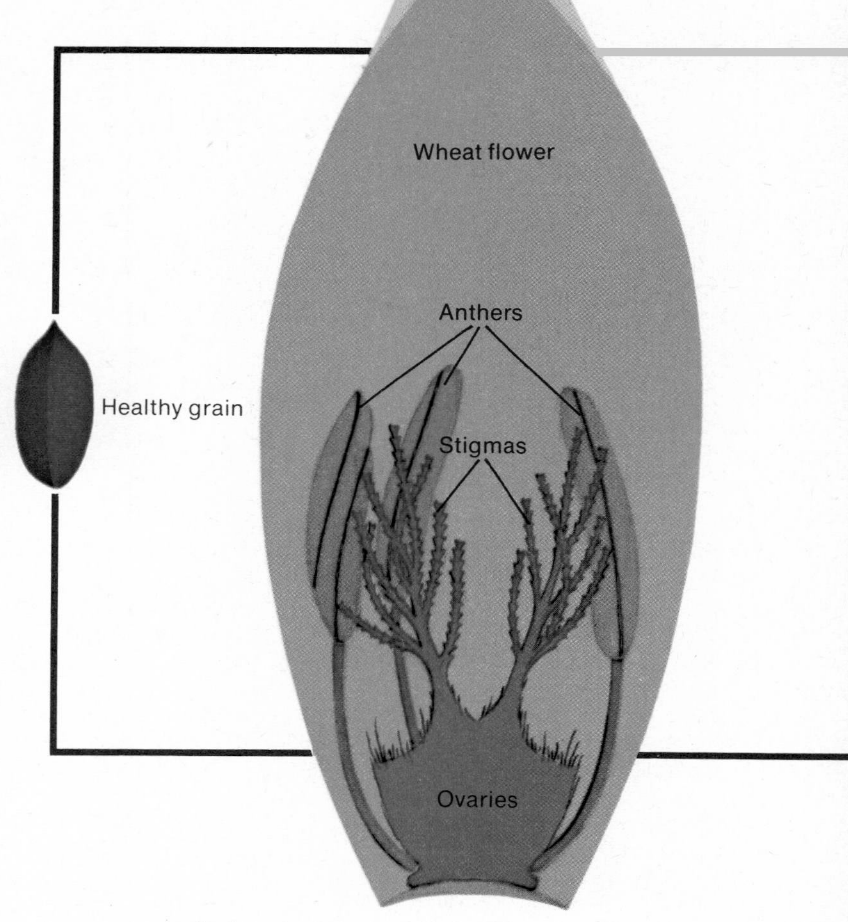

Agricultural scientists intervene in the natural process of fertilization using stringently controlled methods of cross-breeding to produce new hybrids of wheat and other cultivated grasses that take a decade to reach perfection. *Above:* Flower arrangement of the bi-sexual wheat spikelet.

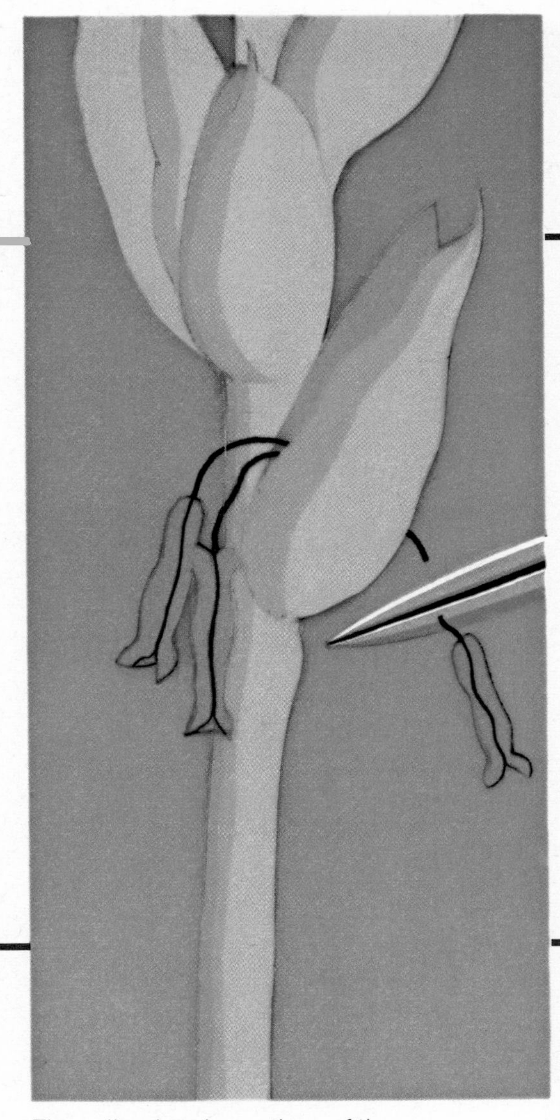

The pollen-bearing anthers of the female parent plant that will give birth to a new hybrid are removed. The wheat head is covered to stop accidental fertilization by stray pollen carried by the wind.

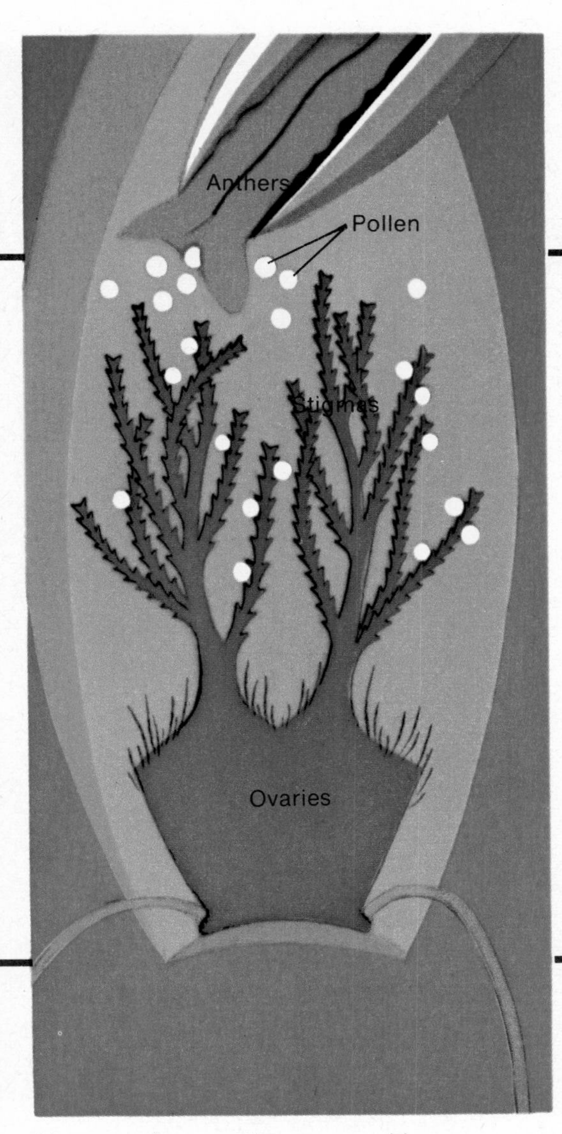

Mature anthers are then removed from the male parent plant with forceps and the pollen is scattered onto the seed flower. The cover is then replaced until the cross-fertilized grain matures about a month later.

Attaining consistent results in the baking of wholesome white bread is the ultimate aim of the cross-breeding experiments. Only eight per cent of new second generation hybrids are selected for further breeding to meet the highest internationally approved standards of bushel weight, protein content, colour and flour yield. The final tests determine baking quality.

Owl
Coyote
Jack rabbits

Fire — the ancient foe

Before the white man settled the plains, grass fires started by lightning swept all life before them as they roared unchecked through the parched vegetation during the hot dry summer. Grazers and predators alike joined in this frenzied stampede, ignoring each other as they tried to escape the roaring sheet of flame. With their roots intact, the perennial grasses recovered within a year, but trees and shrubs were destroyed. Prairie fires have now almost been eliminated from settled areas and the taller plants are making inroads on the flat horizon.

How the snowberry spreads

The western snowberry plays a vital role in the ecology of the plains. Common throughout the region, the white fruits of this shrub are an important bird food in winter. The seeds often pass unscathed through the alimentary canal of partridge, and other birds. Juices in the digestive tract may even end the dormancy of these tough seeds before they reach the ground. The wide distribution of the snowberry is the result of bird vagrancy.

Now the aspen takes over

Whenever a rodent digs a burrow in the lush grass, the exposed soil offers an opportunity for other plants to take root. A variety of shrubs usually takes over. They provide shelter and shade for foxes, birds, and eventually coyotes. In time the wind-blown seeds of aspens—tree-sized members of the willow family—take over and are propagated by root-runners, to turn into aspen groves. Early settlers chopped down all the trees within sight before their value as a windbreak against erosion was appreciated. The aspen's natural enemies, buffalo herds and fires, have been eliminated, to secure the habitat for doves and warblers, strawberries, violets, cottontails and browsing deer.

This dense tough grass has been selected by Canadian scientists to play a vital role in reclaiming eroded soil or over-grazed land.

PART THREE / **PLANT LIFE**

9 THE PLAINS TURN GREEN

It requires a lengthy narrative to convey a true impression of the large number and variety of wild plants growing on the plains – more than one thousand five hundred native species. Like the animals and settlers, they also had to adapt themselves to the soil and the capricious climate. As related in the previous section, life returned to the plains, left barren by the glaciers, only a few thousand years ago.

The wild vegetation that re-entered the plains then is barely distinguishable from that of the present day, compared with the very earliest plants. About two billion years ago, minerals dissolved in the sea triggered the spark of life and minute elementary organisms evolved. They developed into the algae and fungi that have survived as the most primitive form of plant life.

Millions of years of trial and error – natural selection – passed before plants started to cling to the rocks and learned to survive there. The lichens and mosses were among the first. They had no proper roots, stems or flowers, but clung to the bare rocks, taking their sustenance mainly from the air and water. And they started something else that was of immense importance: they helped to break down the rock into particles which, along with the decaying plants, helped to provide soil for those to follow.

To be successful on land, plants had to develop a complicated system of drawing nutrients and water from the soil, and carbon dioxide from the air. These substances, in conjunction with the green chlorophyll, enable plants to manufacture sugar which it stored in the form of starch. In the process the green plants give off oxygen, which is essential to animal growth.

Sometime in late Silurian and early Devonian times, according to the record in the rocks, this miracle took place; seed ferns developed and grew to the surprising size and profusion that produced the coal of the Carboniferous period. After that many other plants developed, and nurtured by the warm, moist climate of the plains, flourished on the shores, deltas and islands of the inland seas. Some, like the cycads, predominated for nearly 100 million years, and then became almost extinct. The conifers, on the other hand, have carried their abundance into modern times to become the main source of timber.

Flowering plants, the most important of all, developed about the beginning of the Cretaceous period. Besides the flowers, vegetables, shrubs and trees, they include the great family of grasses, the most abundant and useful of all plants.

It is probable, that grasses became fully developed between twenty and fifteen million years ago. Thus, as the climate of the plains area changed due to the rise of the Rocky Mountains, they gradually took over from the tropical growth that could not stand severe cold and lack of moisture. Probably at first they grew in isolated patches, but as the cold winds blew across the plains year after year, they gradually established themselves. Grass can withstand wind better than any plant. Its hollow stem, strengthened by solid nodes, will not break even if trampled flat against the ground. The flowers, seeds, leaves, and roots of the grassplant all combine to make a complex and competent mechanism that can survive very inclement conditions.

10 GRASS: THE SHEET ANCHOR

When a prairie dweller thinks of home he thinks of grass — looking with eager anticipation for the first signs of grass in bare places between the banks of melting snow; playing catch on the new grass; lolling on a grassy bank, lazily pulling out the stems and eating the tender tips; watching fields of grass undulating in the wind; playing in the long grass, finding mouse runs and rabbit paths; watching a dog jump through the grass in search of prairie chicken; inhaling the smell of new-mown hay.

His memory may go back much further, to sitting on a wagon piled with window frames and boards, urging a team of horses along a trail through the grass; of tethering his team in the grass for the night; of gathering grass to make a softer bed for his wife and children; and finally, when he got to his homestead site, of ploughing up the sod in straight rows and piling it like bricks to make four walls, and placing those window and door frames in the walls to make his first sod house. Some are still living who remember these things.

Before the settlers came the southern plains were almost

completely under grass, more than one hundred and forty different species; some tall, some short; some growing in bunches, others in solid patches; shooting up green in the spring, flowering and producing seed to be scattered abroad by wind and animals; dying and rotting away to provide the basis for the humus-rich brown and black topsoils of the prairies.

The grass was doing a lot more than feed the buffalo, antelope and other grazers. Grass, with its great mat of fibrous roots, was keeping the prairie soil from blowing away. Many a settler learned this to his sorrow years later after he had removed the grass cover and left the land naked to the winds. Only in recent years has he come to realize its importance, and put back much of the land to grass.

Although most of us walk on grass every day — even if it's just a two-by-four plot outside the apartment building – few stop to think of what a remarkable plant grass is. It will grow literally anywhere: half-submerged in the water, on the soggy shore; on the windswept desert, and on the highest mountain top; in the Arctic and on the equator. No place is too wet or dry, high or low, hot or cold for grass. It's almost impossible to kill grass. Trample on it, bury it, cut it to the ground, break it, burn it; it will rise again.

Why is grass so durable? Pull up a grass plant and look at it. Or better still, dig it up so that the roots can be seen. Of all plants grass has the best structure for survival. In the first place, most wild grasses are perennials. Like the trees, the plant grows year after year from the same root, at the same time spreading seeds to produce new plants. Many of the domestic grasses – wheat, oats, barley, rye, corn, for instance – are annuals, but they have the tender care of man to help them survive.

Let us assume the grass dug up is creeping red fescue, a favourite grass in the aspen prairies. It's an extremely hardy plant, growing in almost every part of Canada; it also flourishes in such diverse regions as North Africa, Eurasia, and Iceland. In fact, there are over a hundred different species of the fescue group of grasses growing in many parts of the world. The creeping red variety is the best known member native to the plains.

Look at the flowers of the plant. They are arranged in a rather loose-knit group known as an "open panicle"; other grasses have spikes, columns, sickles, spears, closed panicles, and feathery panicles that wave back and forth with the slightest breeze. Each of these flowers is wonderfully constructed for producing seeds. In the first place, pollenation is a simple matter, neither requiring the services of bees, nor other insects. The tiny pollen grains from the stamens of the grass flower find their way to the pistil of the same flower or one nearby, into the ovary, by contact or by being carried on the wind.

The seeds are encased in tough coverings called glumes (the chaff on wheat) which in many varieties are formed like wings to carry the seeds off on the wind. Others have little hooks on them for catching onto the hair of animals and thus hitchhiking a ride to a new location. Creeping red fescue seed, like all grass seeds, is oval-shaped and pointed. A tiny spear-like awn attached to the seed digs into the hides of animals or into the ground for germination. The spear, needle and porcupine grasses have long, tough awns that twist and turn with varying moisture conditions causing a corkscrew action that actually propels the seed into the ground.

The grass stem is hollow with few exceptions. Its job is to hold the flowers and seeds up above the ground so that they can germinate and be distributed – and they do this by one of the most ingenious mechanisms in nature. The hollow stem is separated into sections by solid nodes that not only give the stem strength, but perform another specialized job when the plant has been blown or trampled down. The turgescent tissue of the nodes contain cells capable of elongating under the influence of gravity. So, when the plant is in a horizontal or oblique position, the cells on the lower side of the node stretch and thereby bend the stem upwards to the light, the sun and the wind.

When the stems are broken or bitten off, new ones will immediately and rapidly grow from the crown at the base of the plant. This is also true of the leaf, which accounts for the fact that lawn grass has to be cut a couple of times a week during the growing season. The leaves of the grass plant are few and they are long and narrow. The limited surface area ensures that a minimum of water is lost through transpiration. At the same time, the leaves have the power of curling themselves closely around the stem in time of drought so as to cut down even more on water wastage.

But it is the incomparable grass root that plays the major

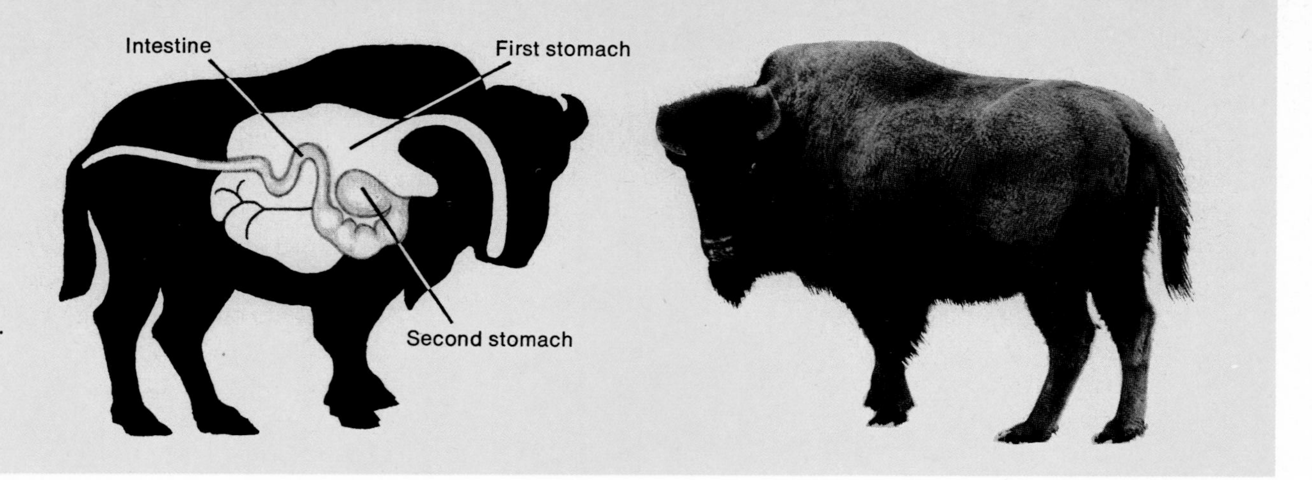

The cud-chewing buffalo thrives on prairie grasses. Like all ruminants, it regurgitates food before passing it to a second stomach.

role in the plant's ability to survive and spread. It is a fibrous root of unbelievable extent and flexibility, that may grow to depths of ten feet, and can spread out at least that far. The total lengths of a fully developed grass root, if it could be completely separated from the soil, would measure well over 350 miles. But such separation is impossible, because literally billions of root hairs, thinner than the thinnest thread, probe among the clay and sand particles to absorb the droplets of moisture that cling there. Thus, when there has been no rain for months, these hard-working fingers squirm their way deeper and wider into the subsoil, to take in water that may have been suspended there for many weeks.

Besides their remarkable water-gathering ability, the grass roots help propagate new grass plants. Underground rhizomes and stolons at ground level grow out from the main stock. Each is noded, and from each node there springs a new grass plant, capable of beginning the entire process over again. Attempts to eradicate quack grass from a plot of ground give sufficient frustrating evidence of this process. No matter how many of the scaly, yellow, underground stems are dug up, there are always others left in the ground to grow more quack grass.

This same plague of the lawns is a variety of wheat grass, *Agropyron repens,* much valued by stock raisers of the aspen prairie for its durability and beast-fattening quality. Besides its ability to survive anywhere under almost any conditions, grass constitutes a complete diet for grazing animals. Its high protein (up to 25 per cent) assures growth, while the starch it contains provides plenty of energy for galloping across the plains to avoid enemies. Grasshoppers, rabbits, ground squirrels, antelopes, buffalo – all live exceptionally well on a straight grass diet.

For those mammals, including man, whose stomachs can't handle the grass stems and leaves, there is the grass seed. Long before the white man came and used the land to cultivate grasses, Indians were grinding the plump seeds of Indian rice grass to make flour for bread.

Grasses are highly specialized plants. Some grow best on the heavy clay soils, others on the light, sandy soils; some like moderately wet weather, others like it dry; some like shade, others prefer bright sunlight; some even grow in sloughs. Thus each region and condition of the plains supports those grasses best suited to it.

When the first settlers came to the eastern part of the plains, either by York boat over Lake Winnipeg, or by Red River cart from the south, they found themselves neck-deep in grass. There was plenty of pasture for their cows and oxen and horses; more than enough to store as hay for the long, cold winter. It was grass unlike anything they had seen before, stretching from horizon to horizon, covering the heavy clay soil of the Red River Valley. They called it big bluestem, or blue-joint turkey stem, or simply beardgrass. Its proper name is *Andropogon gerardi.*

The word *Andropogon* comes from two Greek words, *andros* (man) and *pogon* (beard), because the head of the grass is bearded with long hairs, branching out from the bottom to resemble a turkey's foot. In a good wet year its pith-filled stems will grow to a height of six feet, and cover the ground so thickly that it is hardly possible to walk through it. But as the land that grew it was also the best for growing wheat, most of the big bluestem was ploughed under. Today only scattered stands are found along the Souris and Assiniboine river banks.

There were other grasses too, because in all parts of the plains grasses are mixed, with one or more varieties predominating. On the lighter, sandier land, as found in the Interlake district, grow dense stands of a smaller brother of the big bluestem, known appropriately as little bluestem. As a forage crop it does not compare with its larger relative. Only in the early spring are the leaves succulent and palatable to grazing animals, and when it matures, it drops drastically in both tastiness and protein content.

As the settlers moved farther west along the southern margin of the plains, they encountered progressively shorter grass that, instead of growing in thick patches, tended to grow in bunches. These are the grasses of the shortgrass region, and the most common of them all is blue grama (*grama* comes from a Spanish word for grass). This tough, short, sickle-headed grass provided good pasturage for cattle and other grazers during the early spring, but was not so popular during midsummer. Perhaps most important, it is a favourite with all grass eaters during the late fall and early winter when many other grasses can't be eaten. Blue grama can take a lot of trampling and grazing and still survive.

On the same cattle ranges, with blue grama are found june grass, *Koeleria cristata,* and spear grass, *Stipa comata,* often called needle-and-thread grass. June grass rarely grows in thick stands, but rather scattered among the other grasses, except in the mixed grass region between Kindersley and Kerrobert, where it is the dominant grass. Spear grass is the kind that irritates; the sharp-speared seeds stick to clothes and prick the skin, but it's one of the best forage grasses of the West. Even so, studies have shown that it takes about five thousand plants to feed one cow for one day.

Further north in the mixed grass and aspen grove regions are three more members of the needle grass family: porcupine grass, western porcupine grass and green needle grass. The latter is a great favourite with all wild and domesticated grazing animals. Besides that, it has a high protein content that is main-

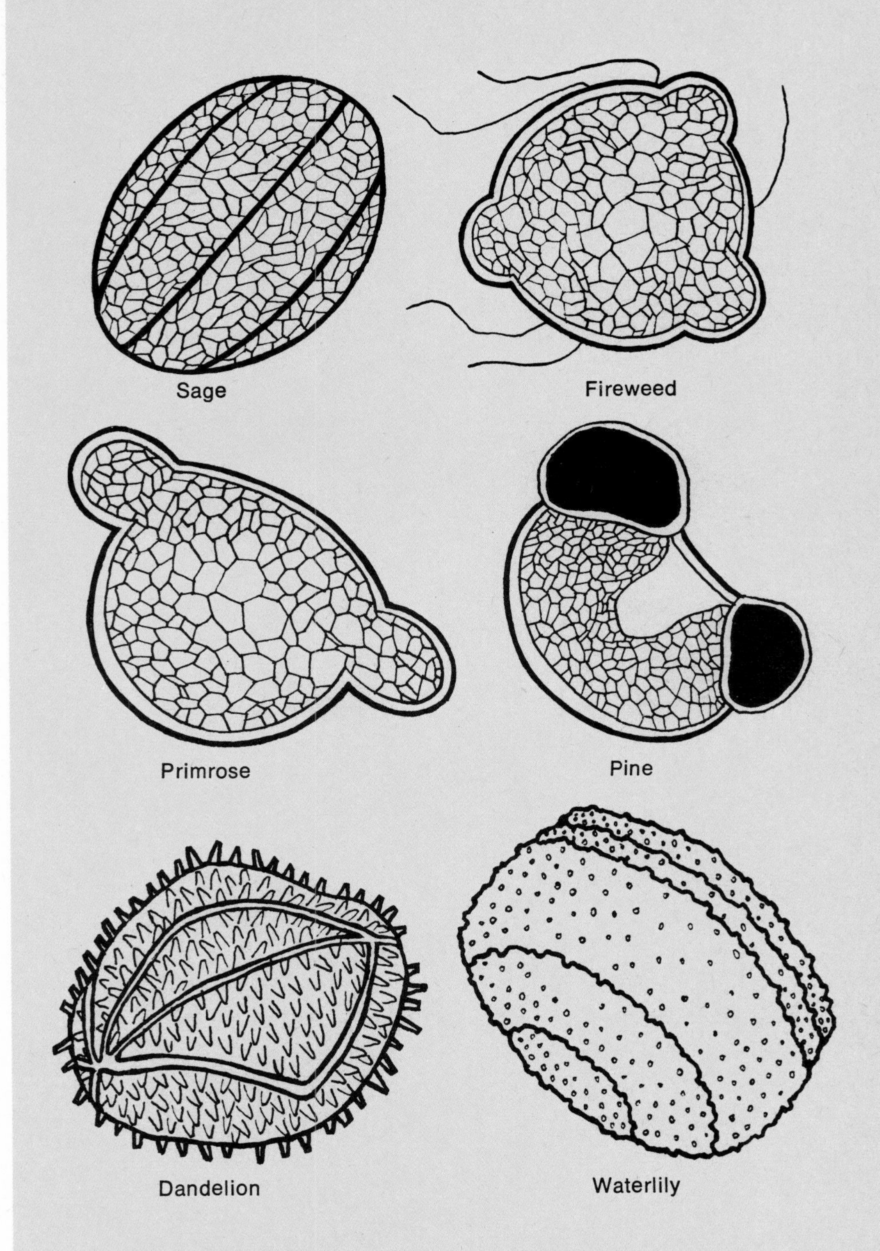

POLLEN: THE SPARK OF LIFE

Pollen grains carry the male cell (magnified about 1,000 times above) essential in the reproduction of plants. Provided with one of nature's toughest coatings, sporopollenin, and dispersed by untold billions, they only live for hours or days at the most. Distinctive shapes and surface textures enable palaeontologists to reconstruct the plant life of the past from specimens found deep in the ground.

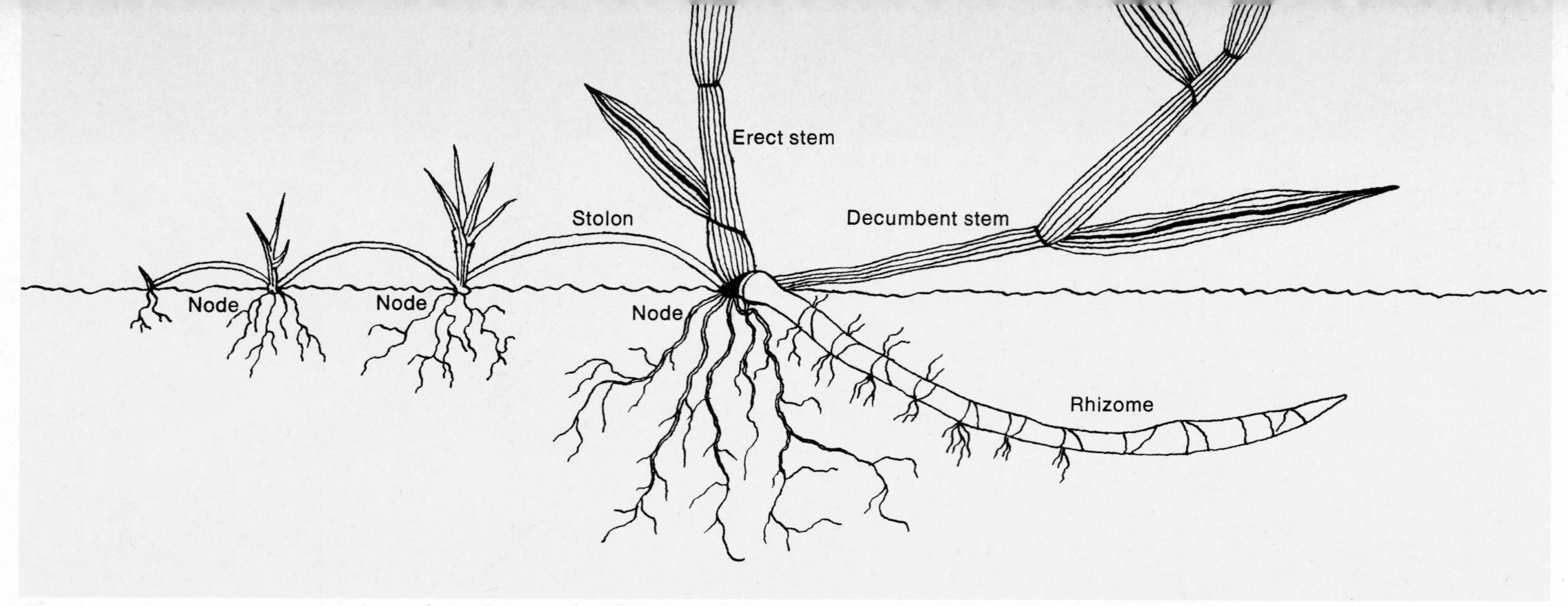

Grass stems can grow erect, or decumbent (bent at the joints), and can start new growths as stolons, or even underground as rhizomes.

tained after curing, and is satisfactorily resistant to severe changes in the weather, since its roots often penetrate to a depth of ten feet.

Another grass that likes the heavy clay soil of the aspen grove region is the indomitable wheat grass family. Four varieties are native and four have been introduced from Europe or Asia. Of the native varieties, western wheat grass, *Agropyron smithii,* is the most common. It has the advantage of a triple root system, one feeding near the surface, another delving five feet into the subsoil, and a third that creeps along just under the surface and propagates new plants. Thus it has survived many droughts. Northern wheat grass is almost identical with western wheat grass and will grow equally well in clay or sandy soils. Slender wheat grass and awned wheat grass are the other two native varieties, both of which provide pasturage, natural and cultivated, in the aspen grove prairies.

In the western portions of the aspen grove prairie the *Festuca* family of grasses is prevalent. Ranchers in the foothills and Cypress Hills like the bluebunch fescue because of all the grasses in the area the cattle eat it most readily. Besides, the plant has a deep root and spreads from tufts. Even in the short grass regions it is a good grass for irrigated areas. Its first cousin, creeping red fescue with its creeping roots, is also used to line irrigation ditches in Saskatchewan and Alberta. Many ranchers cultivate it both for summer feed and for hay.

Rough fescue requires an annual precipitation of at least eighteen inches and so is much better suited to the Cypress Hills, where there is more moisture than on the flat surrounding prairie. It grows well in association with the aspens and pines of the region, and its only drawback seems to be that in the spring the protein content is low. All of the fescues are susceptible to overgrazing. If the plants are kept cropped too low, weeds, other less desirable grasses, and sedges will take their place. It's a wise rancher who adheres to the carrying capacity of the land – 1 to 3.5 acres per cow-month.

These grasses, together with many others – The Canadian Department of Agriculture lists sixty-three varieties – covered the plains for millions of years before man appeared on the scene. Some, with their close relatives the sedges, grew in the wet, low places and adapted themselves to an abundance of water. Others fought it out in the dry sandy places, establishing their roots, consolidating land against the pressing winds. Wherever there was a patch of earth or swamp, some grasses grew.

Finally the white man arrived on the scene with his bags of cultivated grasses: wheat, oats, barley, rye. He tore up the millions of acres of native grasses and planted the foreign varieties, thus upsetting the natural growth pattern of the prairies. Today, after thousands of experiments, he is still trying to better adapt himself and his crops to the stubborn land.

Advancing across fields like a squad of automatons, Canada's harvesters thresh and clean about 500 million bushels of wheat annually.

11 THE WORLD'S WHEAT LARDER

The story of the search for a perfect wheat for the Canadian prairies reads like the search for the Golden Fleece. The demons that the scientific Jasons have had to fight are not centaurs and cyclops but early frost, drought, and a demon called rust. The fight has been difficult and long. It began when the first settlers reached the plains and tried to grow the wheat they had been growing in Ontario, the U.S., and elsewhere; and the fight is still going on in every experimental farm and university on the plains.

The story began in 1842, when a man in Glasgow sent some red-kernelled wheat to his friend David Fife in Peterborough, Ontario. David planted it, and it proved to be a good winter wheat, except for a few plants that turned out to be a spring-wheat variety with big, plump, red kernels. Fife saved these seeds, planted them again the next spring, and developed a strain of wheat which he called Red (after the colour) Fife (after himself).

Red Fife wheat went west with the first farmers and, thanks to its high yield and excellent milling qualities, became a favourite, except for one thing: it matured late and many farmers found their crops blackened by a September frost, before they could put a binder to it. The plains would never have become the bread-basket of the world on Red Fife.

The next name in the story is that of Dr. William Saunders of Ottawa; and a very good case could be made for nominating the Saunders family as the most important that ever lived in Canada. William was a druggist, and a farmer, who liked to fool around with new breeds of grain and fruit. He became so successful, that in 1886, he was appointed director of the Experimental Farms Branch of the Department of Agriculture. In this capacity he began collecting samples of wheat from many countries, and in 1888, obtained one from the Ladoga Lake region in Russia. He crossed it with Red Fife and produced a new wheat which he called Preston.

Preston eased some of the farmers' frustrations by maturing earlier than Red Fife, but its milling qualities were lower, and it was susceptible to stem rust, which was beginning to devastate the prairie crops.

Then, in 1892, a group of workers at the Experimental Farm tried another tack. This time they imported some wheat from India called Red Calcutta. They crossed it with Red Fife, and the result was a wheat that changed the whole story of the plains. After much more work, Dr. Charles E. Saunders, William's son, who had become Dominion Cerealist, sent samples to the prairies for field testing. He called it Marquis wheat.

Marquis was the perfect wheat. It ripened ten days before

The early "crocus" flower appears before the leaves.

Flowers of the prairie

The pincushion grows only 3 in. high, but 8 across.

When the melting snows surrender the prairie to the delicate blooms of the "crocus" spring has arrived. This much-loved member of the anemone family is Manitoba's provincial flower— but botanists regard its spread as a sign of overgrazing. The tiger lily with its showy flowers, emblem of Saskatchewan, is becoming increasingly rare. The prickly rose, Alberta's emblem, is a widely distributed shrub and a welcome addition to the diet of grazers. The seeds enclosed in the rose hip are extensively scattered by birds. Despite provincial prides, these flowers may be found anywhere on the prairies. The sweet and edible fruits of the yellow-flowered prickly pear and the pincushion cacti, are relished equally by pronghorns and man.

The prairie lily is one of 3600 species of lilies.

The evening primrose is often abundant in waste place.

The prickly rose blooms along woods, field and roads.

Red Fife, and those ten days often meant the difference between a bumper crop and a soggy, frost-ruined mess. The yield was heavy. The kernels milled into a creamy-white, protein-rich flour that was the best for bread-making ever devised. The prairie farmers adopted Marquis almost to a man. By 1928, ninety per cent of the wheat grown in western Canada was Marquis – and wheat was the keystone of Canada's economy.

But today it's hard to find a crop of Marquis wheat on the plains. Over the years, the fight has been against rust fungus. It's impossible to win, because as soon as the scientists develop a strain of wheat that is resistant to rust, it develops a new strain that will attack the plant. As each strain is bested, the new one, which up to then had been secondary, has an opportunity to grow and develop.

The great clay plains of the prairies also produce coarse grains – oats, barley, rye – which are used to feed livestock. Here the research is aimed mainly at obtaining larger yields per acre. At the Plant Science Department of the University of Manitoba a team of researchers are crossing wheat, *Triticum,* and rye, *Secale*, to produce a new grain which they call Tricale. The variety of wheat is Durham, a bearded wheat that crosses readily with the bearded rye. The result is a grain that is high in protein, and has an unusually high yield – according to early claims, up to three hundred bushels per acre.

Economics, always the dominating factor, is having another interesting effect on grain research. Whereas the emphasis in the past was on the production of a hard, good-milling variety, needed for breadmaking in Europe and America, some scientists are wondering if they should now be working to achieve a different result. One of Canada's biggest customers for wheat, China, doesn't use the wheat for flour. Instead, they make it into puddings and other dishes, and often buy the cheaper, low grades of wheat that have been affected by moisture. This poses an intriguing question: why not produce a low-grade, soft wheat that will have a much higher yield than any of the present varieties, and so coup the Chinese market?

Another important field crop of the plains, introduced when wheat was hard to sell, is rape. Rape is a broad-leafed, flowering plant about two feet high, pollinated by both wind and bees. The seeds, small, round and hard, are forty per cent oil. Thus a bushel of rape seed (52 pounds) will yield over twenty pounds of oil which is used for making margarine, salad oil, shortenings, as well as lubricants for fine machinery. Rape grows well on the more moist aspen grove prairies, matures as soon as, or earlier than wheat, and can be planted and harvested with similar equipment. It will never replace wheat, but it does provide a ready alternative when wheat markets fail.

12 A RAVISHER FROM THE SOUTH

Prairie grasses and grains are afflicted with a number of diseases that, depending on weather and other conditions, do considerable damage. These diseases are caused by bacteria (black chaff and black point on wheat), viruses (false stripe and yellow dwarf on barley, wheat and oats, and aster yellows on numerous other crops), and parasitic organisms that cause rust, smuts, root rot, and leaf spots. Of all these diseases, the worst is rust.

Rust is caused by fungi that attack the stems and leaves of grass plants, including grain, and is particularly devastating to wheat. Fungi are plants that don't possess green colouring matter in their cells, and consequently are unable to produce their own food. They attach themselves to plants or animals from which they draw nourishment. Those living on dead matter are known as saprophytes, while those feeding on living organisms are called parasites. Rust is a parasite.

The factors which make rust a plague are threefold. In the first place, the spores that produce new plants travel on the wind, and there is always plenty of wind on the plains. Secondly, rust attacks during years when there is ample moisture for plant growth; during hot, dry seasons it doesn't thrive at all, but neither does the grain. Thirdly, rust has a great capacity for hybridization, producing new races of rust to take the place of those defeated by plant breeding. It seems impossible for scientists and farmers ever to win the fight against rust completely. At present they are barely holding their own.

There is nothing new about rust. It was mentioned in the Bible in several places under the names of "blasting" or "mildew." It is common in all countries where grain is grown, and was first reported in North America at the beginning of the eighteenth century. In the early days, in Quebec and Ontario, rust was a menace and, peculiarly, always seemed worse in fields surrounded by or adjacent to barberry shrubs. The early settlers could not fathom the underlying reason, but they knew enough to cut down and burn the wild barberry.

Without doubt, as soon as wheat was grown in the Red River settlement on the plains, rust made its appearance. In 1891, it was reported in several parts of Manitoba by a visiting agriculturalist, Dr. John Dearness. The Dominion Experimental Farm at Brandon reported outbreaks of stem rust during the wet year of 1896. In 1904, heavy infestations were reported by the pioneer farmers of Saskatchewan. From then on, "light rust years" and "heavy rust years" were recorded, the worst being 1916 when an estimated hundred million bushels of wheat were lost to rust.

From the beginning, plant scientists in Canada have studied rust extensively and they've learned a great deal. The most insidious characteristic of the fungus is that in two of its three development stages, "red" and "black," it is highly contagious. The red, or summer stage, appears on stems and leaf sheaths of the green plants when they are moist from rain or dew. Red spores (urediospores) lodge on the plant and germinate within a few hours, penetrating the plant with germ tubes through stomata, the minute breathing pores of the plant.

Once beneath the epidermis of the stem, the germ tube branches out with thread-like roots that spread among the plant cells, as root hairs spread among soil particles. They suck nourishment from the living cells and, within four or five days, produce new spores that erupt through the epidermis like a rash of pimples. These spores become windborne and begin the cycle on other plants. Since the entire process takes only seven or eight days, it is easy to comprehend how many plants can be infected during the growing season.

When the plants ripen and the stems are no longer green, the rust produces black spores (teliospores). These remain dormant for a period lasting up to six months; in this stage the rust passes the winter. In the spring the black spores germinate on the wet green stocks, feed on the growing plant, and produce more spores which are shot off into the air. But these spores, unlike the red ones, do not grow on grasses. Their sole host is the leaf of the barberry shrub. Each black spore produces a tube that penetrates the surface of the barberry leaf, and grows in much the same way as the red spores on the wheat plant. In less than a week after penetration, small round pustules appear on the leaf of the barberry bush. These grow and enlarge, producing tiny vase-shaped structures that exude a nectar which collects on the surface of the pustule.

On the under-side of the pustules structures called cluster cups form; they contain the aeciospores. When the cluster cups (aecia) open, the spores are shot out into the air. Strangely, these spores cannot infect leaves of the barberry, but instead seek out the stems and leaves of wheat and other cereal plants where they produce the red summer-stage of the fungus and start the process all over again.

Since barberry is not native to the Canadian plains, and since the winter weather here is too severe for the black spores to survive, rust cannot survive the winter on the prairies. Each season there is an invasion of rust spores from the south, usually from the Mississippi valley, that inundate the wheat plains of southern Manitoba. The spores spread rapidly north and west until they may infest the entire crop. There are many varieties of rust and they tend to specialize. For instance, the rust that attacks wheat and barley does not attack oats. Another variety specializes in oats but avoids wheat. Still another variety specializes in rye. Also, each variety boasts numerous races, and each of these in turn concentrates on a particular variety of the grain, called a host by scientists.

Worst of all, the rust fungus goes through a sexual stage, which begins with the germination of the black spores on the barberry leaves. The two sexes of many different races of fungi readily hybridize, and produce new races of rust. Fortunately, rust does not destroy the entire wheat crop, but it does affect the yield and grade drastically. Because rust fungi draw their food from the green, growing plant, they deprive that plant of the nourishment it needs to develop plump, healthy seeds. Besides, as the fungus grows on the stem and leaves of the plant, it destroys the food-manufacturing cells close to the surface. Growing rust also uses up water needed by the plant, and the evaporation of water caused by eruptions of rust pustules is greater than the volume normally lost through the epidermis of the plant.

Although the wheat plant will mature and produce seeds, the kernels, starved of nourishment, are shrivelled and much smaller than those from a healthy plant. It takes a far larger quantity to make a bushel, and they never attain "Grade No. 1 Northern." Also, the damaged straw becomes brittle and may break before the grain is harvested, causing a further loss of yield. It is impossible to gauge losses due to rust accurately, but by comparing good yields with rusted yields, fairly accurate figures can be established. Dr. D. R. Knott, of the crop science department of the University of Saskatchewan, estimates that in 1965 and 1966 the rust loss, in his province alone, amounted to one hundred million dollars.

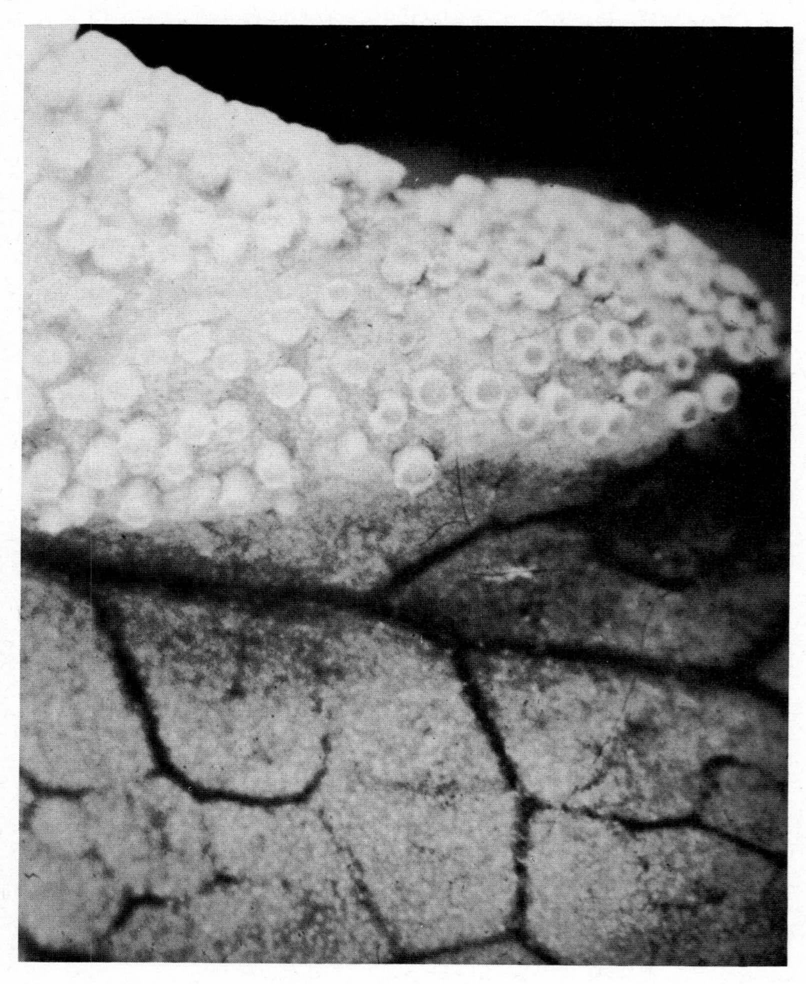

Clusters of stem rust form on a barberry leaf in the spring stage of the disease. The cups produce a stream of spores which infect wheat. When crop scientists produce a rust-resistant variety of wheat, the rust takes a decade to return.

Naturally, an enemy as destructive as rust has been fought by grain growers from the beginning. Because the disease is not passed on by the grain seed, there is no point in treating the seed with chemicals, as in the case of smut. Because the spores are wind-borne and come from regions beyond the Canadian border, little can be done to stop the incredibly rapid spread of the disease. Nor can the farmers of the West control it through the destruction of barberry shrubs. These plants, on which the spores thrive and hybridize in the third stage of the fungi's life cycle are rarely found in western Canada. Since 1950 a great deal of research has been carried out towards developing a fungicide to be sprayed on the growing wheat, absorbed by the plant, with sufficient antagonism to rust to prevent infestation. So far the required formula has not been found.

This has left plant breeding as the most effective weapon against rust. Some varieties of wheat have become immune to different races of rust. The task of the plant breeder is to seek out rust-resistant varieties. Unfortunately, the rust-resistant variety seldom possesses the other qualities necessary for success on the western plains – high yield, early maturing, good bread-making qualities, and drought resistance.

It is easy to understand that the permutations and combinations of producing the desirable qualities of wheat are many. Nature can produce a new race of rust in one season, while it takes at least ten seasons for scientists to produce, test and distribute a new variety of wheat. Thus, the introduction of Thatcher wheat, corresponding with the end of a drought cycle, was one of the most significant developments on the plains.

Thatcher wheat, developed at the University of Minnesota, and introduced into Canada in 1935, was the first really rust-resistant wheat. Soon all farmers were planting it and congratulating themselves that the problem had been solved. But then, in the wet years following the last war, rust damage began to reappear. It was first noticed in southeastern Manitoba, and gradually worked its way west until it covered the entire area.

Another new strain of wheat was developed at the Winnipeg Laboratories of the Canadian Department of Agriculture. It was called Selkirk wheat, a cross between the stem-rust resistant McMurachy, the leaf-rust resistant Exchange, and the excellent milling variety Redman. Selkirk was developed to counter a particularly virulent and rapidly spreading variety of rust – Race 15B – which first emerged about 1950.

Soon the majority of farmers in Manitoba, where rust is always worst, were seeding Selkirk, and it grew in popularity in Saskatchewan. But by 1965, the worst rust year in decades, Selkirk wheat was helpless against new strains of the pest – it had lasted only ten years. But scientists are still in the fight, using all the skill and knowledge they can muster.

By cross-breeding Thatcher with other varieties, a team at the University of Manitoba produced a brand new variety which is resistant to both leaf and stem rust, and has the other qualities a good wheat must have. After extensive field testing, it was licensed for distribution in 1965, and many farmers are hopefully trying it. Its name is Manitou. How long will Manitou resist the stem and leaf destroying rust? Crop scientists say about ten years and possibly even less. The process of natural selection which produces new rusts matches the efficiency of the scientists.

13 WILDFLOWERS AND WATERPLANTS

Associated with the grasses throughout the prairie regions are forbs, wildflowers, weeds and waterplants. Often the words are interchangeable. There are hundreds of them, but only a few of the most common will be mentioned here. Forb is the name given to a broad-leaved plant or herb that grows between clumps of grass, either on the range, along the margins of grain fields, or on the roadside and wasteland. Sometimes they are eaten by livestock, sometimes shunned; but they are an important part of the prairie cover.

Pasture sage is one of the more common forbs of the short grass and mixed grass prairies, occurring very rarely in the aspen grove prairie; it's a take-over plant. The branching, fibrous root, runners that produce new plants, great quantities of tough seeds, and an unusual tolerance to drought, permit the sage to grow when some grasses will not. And when grasses are overgrazed to such an extent that their roots have been weakened, the sage rapidly takes over. Luckily it provides as much nourishment as the best grasses, but because of certain aromatic oils, cattle will eat it only during autumn and winter. When the "bloom is on the sage," the abundant yellow flowers give off clouds of pollen which keep hay-fever afflicted cowboys sneezing throughout September.

Wild roses are abundant on the plains, and the prickly rose, *Rosa acicularis*, which grows on the open range and around the edges of poplar bluffs, is the floral emblem of Alberta. It is a short shrub with a delicate, pink flower. Livestock, particularly sheep, will graze on it and it has nutritive value. A great variety of birds feed on the hips and thus carry the seeds to new grounds. Prairie boys often munch the petals of the delicate flowers, and the red skins of the hips, when they are ripe. Little girls used to assiduously collect the petals, put them in jars, and make sachets of their sweet perfume.

The western snowberry is most important in the floral pattern of the plains. The small white berries that remain on the stem after the snow falls are a staple food for prairie chicken, Hungarian partridge and other birds that winter on the plains. Some seeds, found in their droppings, germinate better than seeds that just fall to the ground. Probably passage through the bird's digestive tract helps to break down the dormancy of the seed. As a result, snowberry plants find a home wherever grass and other plants have been destroyed and, as mentioned, prepare the way for willows and aspen poplars.

Another member of the rose family brightens the foothills and Cypress Hills, and appears more rarely in moist, cool locations. It is the yellow rose, sometimes called buckbrush, or more properly, shrubby cinquefoil. The sturdy shrub grows up to three feet tall and, from June until December, produces a lot of small, yellow, rose-shaped flowers. Its deep-seeking root protects it from eradication by grazers and browsers alike.

The plains area has a good representation of legumes that perform the important function of replacing, through the action of root tubercles, nitrogen in the soil. Ground plums creep between grass plants, close to the turf, and produce good-sized plum-shaped fruit, which Indians used to eat, and livestock still do. Unfortunately, cultivation and overgrazing have made this useful plant quite rare.

Sweet vetch is still a common wild plant in the foothills and Cypress Hills; wild peavine flourishes in the bushes as elsewhere in Canada; and the silvery lupine, or wolfbean, likes the same regions. Neither alfalfa nor sweet clover are native to the plains, but since their introduction from Europe, have become very common both as cultivated forage, and as wild forbs growing on the ranges. White and red clover grow almost anywhere they can gain a foothold, but prefer areas where precipitation exceeds seventeen inches per year.

A great number of other forbs may be classified as weeds or wildflowers, depending on the point of view. The ubiquitous dandelion is the best representative. It grows everywhere. If there is plenty of moisture it grows tall and lush; if moisture is scarce it is small and close to the ground. Although roundly cursed by lawngrowers everywhere, the dandelion could stake a fair claim to being one of the most useful plants on the plains. Livestock eat it all summer long, growing fat on its abundant leaves, while the yellow flower is rated highly by beekeepers as a honey producer.

That is only part of the dandelion's usefulness. The succulent green leaves are used for salads in the spring, whereas pioneers collected bushels of the flowers to make a tasty and potent wine.

The most typical of all prairie wildflowers is the crocus. The blanket of pale purple that covers the pastures and range-land in early spring is almost beyond imagination. Blooming before the grass covers it, the tiny crocus is barely six inches tall. As soon as the snow melts from the hillsides it is there, telling the prairie dwellers that after six months of cold, windy, miserable winter, spring has arrived. Then, when the flowers have died and gone to seed, the growing grass protects the plant from wind and storms. But the prairie crocus isn't a crocus at all, bearing no relationship to the cultivated garden crocus. Properly, it is called the pasque flower, but when the children of Manitoba voted almost unanimously to have it as their floral emblem, they were voting for the "crocus."

The floral emblem of Saskatchewan, on the other hand, is a

HOW NATURE SOWS AND SPREADS HER PLANTS

Many seeds are dispersed by wind and animals. Dandelion seeds parachute over great distances; maple seeds perform a twirling glide to earth; cockleburs hook onto the fur of cattle; snowberries pass through the digestive system of birds; and acorns are carried by squirrels and jays.

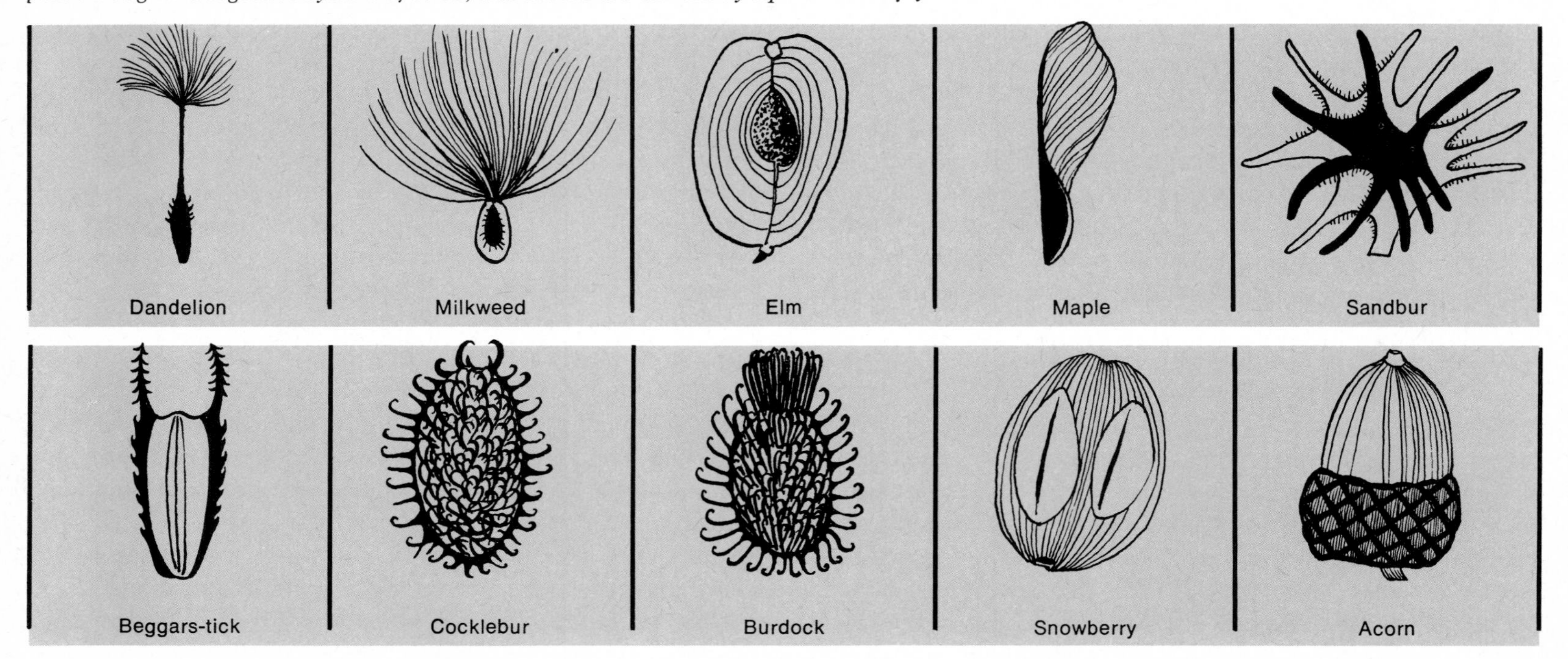

plant which is hardly typical of the prairies. For one thing, the tiger lily, or prairie lily, likes moist conditions, and the prairies are essentially dry. However, in the wet ditches along railway tracks and in the damper parts of the aspen grove prairie the plant is still fairly plentiful.

In some of the drier parts of the plains cacti find a natural home. They grow in isolation among tufts of short grass, and in the sandy areas where grass does not strike roots. The prickly pear, *Opuntia polyacantha*, produces a delicate yellow flower resembling that of the rose, while the purple cactus, *Mamillaria vivipara*, produces a reddish-purple bloom with a pineapple-shaped centre.

Weeds, the great pest of the prairies today, were largely unknown before the land was converted to crop growing. Their seeds came in the bags of grain from Europe, and at first were so few the farmers ignored them. So they grew and multiplied and, in some cases, completely crowded out the crops.

The perennial sow-thistle, for example, is an import from Scotland. By 1920 it was a pest in the Red River Valley. It spreads locally by means of fast-growing rootstocks which run under the surface to shoot up new plants. Each seed is attached to a tiny parachute, to catch the prairie winds. In this way the thistle spread westward until, by the 1930s, there were so many patches of it in the grain fields that it was classed as the primary noxious weed.

Pigweed, wild mustard, wild oats, and a host of others, short and tall, have cost the farmer dearly. For years he fought them with hoe, harrow, cultivator and rod weeder, barely holding his own. Today the prairie farmer fights with new, deadlier weapons – chemical sprays that destroy weeds on contact. What they do to soils and the other plants that grow on them is yet to be determined.

For so dry a land, there is an astounding number and variety of water plants on the plains. The great number of sloughs and the thick, rich muck that accumulates in and near them supports grasses, sedges, rushes, water-weeds and flowers. The stagnant water teems with plant life that forms the nucleus of food for an equal abundance of animal life. The most spectacular of all the water plants is the common reed grass, that grows twice as high as a tall man, and spreads from creeping rootstalks in the marshes surrounding the Lake Winnipeg group, particularly on the delta at the south end of Lake Manitoba.

Other sloughs throughout the prairie have a quantity of plant growth dependant on the degree of alkalinity. The fresh-water sloughs support thick growths of grass, on and near their shores. Chief among these are common slough-grass, wild barley, awned sedge and smartweed. All of these are cut by the farmer when the sloughs dry up, and go by the common name of slough hay. In the knee-deep muck at the margin of the sloughs hardstem and softstem bulrushes wave in the breeze and give perching room to redwinged blackbirds. Crowded into this environment are the cattails, whitetops, and spiked rushes, so succulent that horses wade knee-deep to eat them.

In sloughs with less than two feet of water the broadleafed smartweeds predominate and they too, make excellent hay. Out in deeper water the sloughs are full of duckweed, pondweed, white-flowered crowfoot, bladderwort and burrweed. Among them float the green, filamentous algae that are an integral link in the chain of food that supports animal life.

14 THE UBIQUITOUS ASPEN

Visitors to the city of Saskatoon are always surprised to see so many trees. "Why," they exclaim, "this is no prairie town. There are more trees on the boulevards and along the river bank than in many cities in southern Ontario." The reason for this may have something to do with the perversity of people. In the eastern cities where trees are common, householders clamour to have trees cut down because they interfere with lawn growing, construction of driveways, or simply the view. In western cities, on the other hand, grass is plentiful but trees are scarce, and tree planting has become an obsession.

The boulevards along the straight, wide streets of prairie cities are lined with elm, ash, box elders and oak. The numerous city parks are studded with trees, planted in straight rows and watered regularly. So precious are trees to the city dweller, that when the road builders in Winnipeg were about to cut down a huge elm to widen a street, they found themselves confronted by a ring of irate, red-faced housewives. The tree remained and the road went around it.

It would not always have been so. When the big inrush of farmers came to the plains, following the building of the railroads, many were from Ontario where tree cutting had been a necessary prelude to farming. Their natural inclination was to cut down the aspen groves on their land and pile up the trees for burning. It was a disastrous practice, as subsequent dust storms proved, and now the aspen along with numerous other trees is greatly encouraged on the farmland. In Saskatchewan alone, federal, provincial, and municipal agencies plant over ten million trees a year.

The trembling aspen, one of the numerous poplars that grow on the prairie, is among Canada's most widespread trees. Wherever there are trees growing, on the coasts, in the mountains, on the Mackenzie Delta, there you will find this white-barked tree with the hard, round, long-stemmed leaves that dance and rustle with every breeze. It is the first tree to establish itself in the burned-over forests, and it remains while birch, pine, ash, spruce, and other more durable trees of the region take over.

Aspen is well adapted for this job. It is a quick-growing softwood that can withstand any kind of weather. Besides an abundance of seeds, produced in catkins, carried by the wind and by birds, it propagates itself from root-suckers that are immune to fire and frost. Wherever the solid mat of grass roots is broken, the aspen is able to take up residence. On the southern plains the aspen grows in pure stands and also in association with willow, pine, spruce, and other trees. Seeking sun and abhorring shade, it thrives wherever there is enough moisture for its roots – on the margins of sloughs, along the banks of streams, in coulee bottoms, and even on the bald-headed prairie.

In many ways the aspen is an integral part of life on the plains. Its bark provides winter food for rabbits, mice, and other rodents, while beavers eat it all year round. Deer and elk browse on its leaves, buds, and stems. Crows, hawks, owls, and a multitude of smaller birds nest in its branches; and it has always been a boon to man.

THE VITAL SLOUGH

An integral part of the prairie scene, sloughs like this one store the water which is absolutely essential for the wheat. Aspen groves act as a windbreak and give protection to birds and other animals.

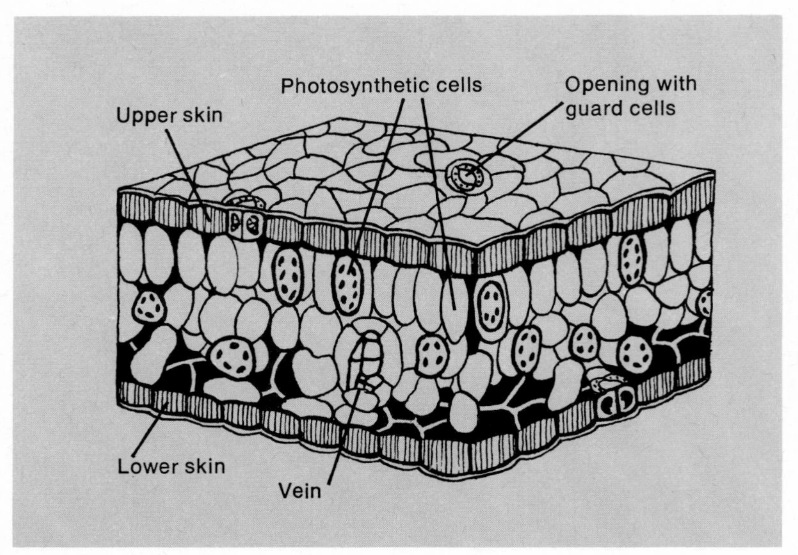

This enlarged leaf shows cells that contain the chlorophyll which, by photosynthesis, converts water and carbon dioxide into food.

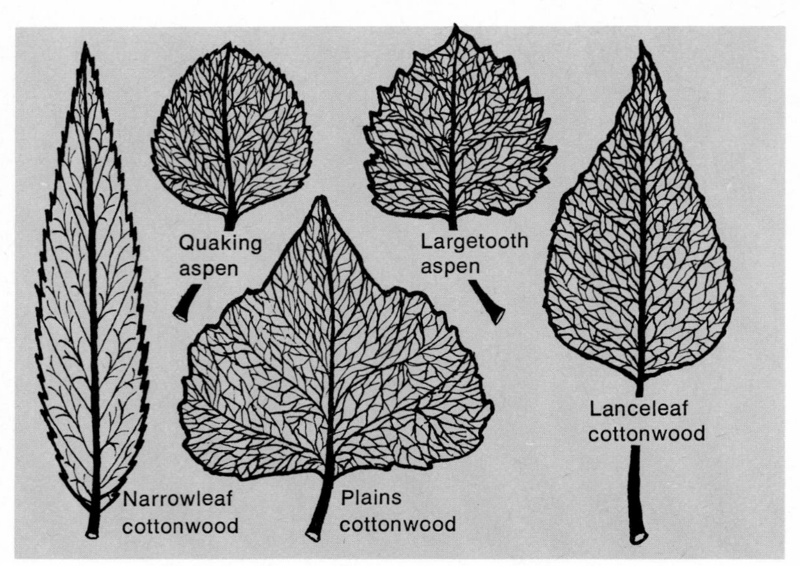

Leaves often help to distinguish between varieties within a single family of plants; all leaves illustrated above are from poplars.

The plains Indians, following the herds of buffalo, hauled along straight poplar poles for their teepees. Red River carts were made almost entirely of aspen, and the pioneer farmers built crude log cabins of poplar poles, or used them for roof frames on sod houses and barns. In pioneer times before coal was used, seasoned aspen wood was the principal fuel for heating and cooking. A week-long expedition to the poplar bush for the winter's supply of firewood was an autumn chore essential to all farmers.

As the first growth in a shelter belt around farmyards and fields, aspen couldn't be bettered. Often grown along with aspen for these purposes is the balsam poplar, or balm of Gilead. It is thicker and taller and longer-lived than the trembling aspen, and grows in the same type of soil. It is easy to distinguish the balsam poplar from the aspen by the shape of the leaves. Its end buds exude a spicy fragrance when crushed.

Cottonwoods, members of the poplar family, are found only in the dry southern sections of Saskatchewan and Alberta. They grow almost exclusively along the banks of rivers and streams. The Bow and the Milk and the Oldman and the Frenchman rivers have their share of cottonwoods. Like all poplars, their seeds are encased in long, cottony catkins, from which the trees get their name. The two varieties are easily distinguished. The plains cottonwood has a broad, triangular, coarse-toothed leaf, while the narrowleaf cottonwood has a leaf resembling that of the willow – long and narrow, growing in clusters.

Wherever polars grow, their first cousins, the willows, are likely to be found – but usually closer to water. The persistent willow also propagates from root suckers, or even from shoots pushed into the ground. Farmers use the tough, straight willow sticks as pickets in their fences. It's not unusual during a really wet summer to find these newly-placed fence posts sprouting fresh green leaves.

The sandbar willow, *Salix interior*, appears wherever wet sand accumulates, whether it is in the middle of the South Saskatchewan River, or on the gravelly beach of a lake. Its long, branching roots will even seek out subsoil moisture on sandy hills, where it prevents drifting. The basket willow, *Salix petiolaris*, often finds itself growing in two or three feet of water, in the spring or after a heavy rain, while the pussy-willow, *Salix discolor,* grows around sloughs and often takes over, along with slough-grass, when the water dries up.

Wolf-willow or silverberry, *Elaeagnus commutata*, a low shrub with elongated silvery leaves, plays an important role in

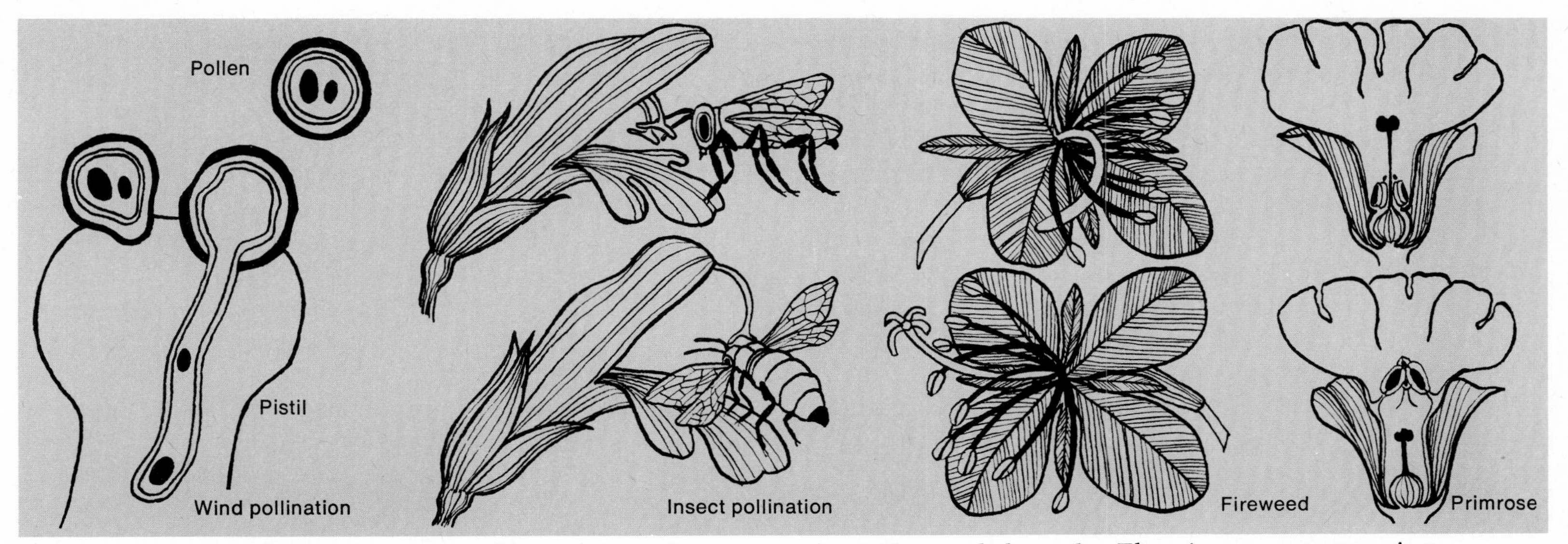

Pollen grains are most frequently transported from plant to plant by wind and insects. The pollen adheres to the hairy legs of the bee. In the fireweed pollen grains grow in long cords down through the pistil to reach the ovules. The primrose protects against self-pollination by having some flowers with a long pistil and short stamen and others with just the reverse.

spreading the aspen poplar. In winter the silver-coloured berries remain on the shrub and become, as the snow drifts deeper, the favourite food of jack rabbits. But they eat only the soft, outer covering, letting the stone drop onto the hard-packed snow. The wind blows the dry stones over snowbanks, and so spreads the seeds they contain.

These seeds in turn find a place to germinate in a weak spot in the wet spring grass. Here, by means of long, fast-growing rhizomes, they are propagated and spread, providing shelter for ground squirrels, gophers, badgers, and other digging animals. In this animal-cultivated soil the wind-blown seeds of the aspen take root and begin a new aspen grove.

The saskatoon berry, *Amelanchier alnifolia*, is one of the most important shrubs on the southern plains. It grows, often to tree size, wherever there is enough moisture – in shaded coulees, along river banks, and on the edges of aspen groves. It is a beautiful little tree, sometimes used as an ornamental shrub in eastern Canada, that produces an abundance of white blooms, followed by bunches of blue berries. These berries, which resemble blueberries, but are darker, drier and harder, are the favourite food of birds and browsing animals. The Dominion Department of Agriculture rates the saskatoon bush as "one of the best browse plants for all classes of domestic livestock and game."

Not only birds and animals depend on the saskatoon berry. Early traders, hunters and explorers learned from the Indians how to use them to make pemmican. First the berries were dried in the sun like raisins; then they were mixed with buffalo meat or venison, that had been dried and pounded into a fine powder; melted fat was poured over the mixture, which was stirred up and permitted to harden. A slab of pemmican the size of a plug of chewing tobacco would sustain a voyageur or hunter for a full day. It could either be boiled with herbs and vegetables, or eaten raw – the problem of refrigeration did not arise.

When the first settlers came to the plains, fruit of any kind was at a premium. Wild strawberries and gooseberries could be picked in season, but it was mostly the saskatoon berries that provided much-needed vitamins and minerals, especially phosphorus.

Berry picking expeditions in late June were a must for most families. They would go to the river bank or coulee for the day and return with the buggy or wagon loaded down with washtubs full of the precious fruit. Preserved in quart sealers, the berries were consumed as dessert and used for pie-making during the long, cold winter. Chokecherries too, considered poisonous by many eastern Canadians, were used extensively on the plains for making jellies, jam, and even a palatable and potent wine.

The caragana deserves special mention because of its wide use on the plains for hedges and shelter belts. Of all trees, it seems best able to withstand drought, and during the fateful year 1937, when many other trees gave up, the caraganas turned a little yellow around the edges but remained staunch.

The Manitoba maple or box elder, although scorned by most eastern Canadian lawnmakers, is an important shade tree throughout the plains. It grows fast, it withstands the coldest winter, and its short trunk and widely branching limbs provide ample shade. It is the mainstay of urban boulevards and lawns, and is always found in farm shelter-belts.

Fruit trees are becoming common throughout the prairies. For many years it was assumed that apples, pears, plums, and other orchard trees couldn't stand the extreme winters. But the agricultural departments of the prairie universities have developed fruit trees that thrive on the plains if properly cared for. An extensive fruit tree programme, carried out by the government, the Kiwanis Club, and other agencies, has persuaded many prairie farmers to consider the feasibility of orchards.

Along with the poplars, willows and shrubs that are native to most of the prairie regions, there are areas where other trees grow. For instance, the flood plains of the Red, Assiniboine, and Souris Rivers support stands of Manitoba maple, lance-leaved ash, and American elm.

The camper will find that the predominant tree in the camp grounds around Winnipeg or Portage la Prairie is the bur oak. This short, branching, rather gnarled tree rarely reaches a height of more than forty feet. It extends into Saskatchewan for a short distance along the Qu'Appelle Valley, and is the only member of the oak family native to the prairies.

In the Cypress Hills, where rainfall is heavier than anywhere else on the plains, the lodgepole pine is abundant. There are also some jack pine and spruce. On the hillsides and in the valleys, growing among the grasses and trees, are found many plants that do not appear elsewhere on the plains; exotic orchids for instance, along with ferns and the semi-tropical yucca grass.

But the natural habitat of most plains trees is in the wooded areas north of the aspen grove prairie. A journey north in Saskatchewan and Alberta leads to the mixed wood belt, the home of the poplar, white birch, spruce, tamarack, and jack pine, interspersed by large stretches of muskeg and marshland. Further north, in the colder drier regions of the Northwest Territories, the same trees become more stunted and sparse, until the tree line is reached near the mouth of the Mackenzie.

The northern forest is extremely valuable, not because the timber and pulpwood can be cut from it by man – there is little of this activity – but because it is the refuge of birds and animals that once were abundant on the plains. In Wood Buffalo National Park the sparse survivors of the once great flocks of whooping cranes build their nests and watch fretfully over their two eggs. The sandhill crane and trumpeter swan, which once nested on the prairie, now seek the safety of the bush.

The bison that once roamed the grassland in millions, now picks its living among the bushes in Elk Island and Wood Buffalo National Parks. The grey wolf, driven off the plains by poison and high-powered rifles, still dwells in the forests, as do the few remaining grizzly bears. But the story of the animal life of the plains is the story of another section, and it is largely a story of destruction.

THE BADLANDS

Following the course of the Red Deer River (from Stettler south to Steveville) the badlands provide a landscape quite unlike that of any other part of Canada. Crags, gullies and mesas rise from the dry valley bottom, beckoning the naturalist to explore the secrets of primeval life sealed in the rocks.

Hoodoos, the strange "monuments" of the Red Deer Valley, symbolize the territory.

A valley of naked rocks

In the Red Deer badlands erosion has excavated a valley up to a mile wide and four hundred feet deep. Volcanic ash, from the upheaval that built the Cordillera, turned to impervious bentonite and acted as a protective blanket over the softer rocks below. Glaciers broke into this system and since then the sun, rain, wind and frost have attacked beds of coal, shale, clay and sandstone faster than plants could take root to consolidate the soil. The result is a nightmare landscape of multi-coloured rock strata exposed in places like a huge scoop of Neapolitan ice cream. Yet the river bank, and coulees hidden among desolate crags, support an incredible variety of wildlife, from voles to browsing deer. Hawks and eagles soar aloft, snakes lurk in the shadows, and bobcats run unchallenged among the bleached and crumbling exposed fossils left by countless generations of remote ancestors.

◀ *The boulder precariously balanced on this bluff of rock will soon topple to join the treacly flow of debris.*

Caps of shale, forming hoodoos, overlying soft eroded sandstone and slightly more resistant ironstone, are but fleeting whims of nature in terms of time gauged by geological standards. ▶

Small projections in the river valley, akin to feeble teeth flattened by wear, are the remains of once grotesque hoodoos.

Standing proud as a mountain, this massive outcrop of soft rock is fast succumbing to the relentless forces of erosion.

The Chasmosaurus was a huge plant eater, vaguely resembling today's rhinoceros, that grew bony neck frills and three horns.

Exploring seventy-five million years

Life was abundant on the plains, in the sea, and in the surrounding swamps during the Cretaceous period. The lush vegetation was overshadowed by giant redwoods on the high ground. Like some of these trees, one family of reptiles developed giantism tendencies – the dinosaurs. Their remains were first discovered in the Red Deer Badlands in 1872. Since then one hundred skeletons, ranging from the fearsome five-ton Gorgosaurus to eighty-foot plant eaters, have found their way to many museums.

In this series of photographs Canadian palaeontologists use the latest techniques to collect fossils from the Cypress Hills.

Immediately after removal from the rock, brittle fossils are coated with shellac and wrapped in a plaster cast.

Getting bones out from an inaccessible site can require a makeshift sled, muscle power, lots of sweat, and determination.

At the museum the delicate work of assembling fragments begins. It takes four men about a year to completely assemble a skeleton.

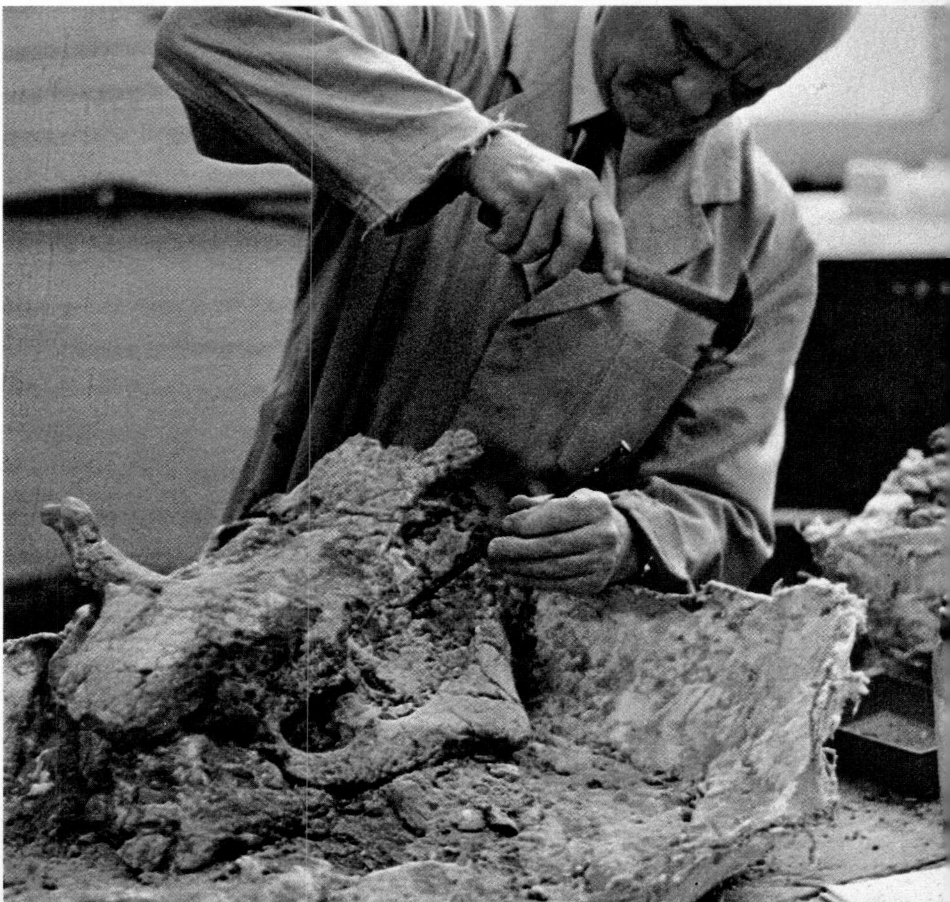

In the spring the male sharptailed grouse performs a noisy ostentatious courtship ritual on ancestral dancing grounds.

PART FOUR / **ANIMAL LIFE**

15 WILDLIFE OF THE OPEN SPACES

A ground squirrel bounces across the prairie followed by a slow but very persistent badger. The squirrel scoots down its hole and the badger begins to dig, not down the same hole but at a point where, by an enigmatic sense, he's estimated the squirrel would be. In a few minutes the badger has caught the squirrel and is eating it. How did the badger learn this, and how is it able to do this? By natural selection. All animals specialize and the badger specialized in digging. So, over millions of years of development, the best diggers have survived, and have developed the strongest claws and the most powerful fore-feet.

In other respects, too, the badger's adaptation to life on the plains is complete. Low to the ground and the same colour as the drying grass, it is hard to see. Thick, long hair keeps it warm on the coldest day. It breeds in autumn when there is time and opportunity, but the embryo doesn't begin to develop in the uterus until the middle of February. This puts the time of birth at about the first of April so that when the youngsters are ready to venture out the weather is fine again.

The badger eats just about anything that runs, crawls or creeps. When cornered it can fight like a demon, and if that doesn't work it can lift its tail and spray the enemy with an eye-destroying musk. In fact, if it weren't for man and the poison he spreads, nothing could dislodge the badger from its prairie home.

The forefoot of a full grown badger shows the long hard nail which enables it to dig swiftly in the hard prairie soil.

All other animals that run, fly, crawl or swim in the prairie region, have their own specialties that account for their presence. There are few tree climbers on the grasslands but many diggers. Birds nest, for the most part, in the tall, sheltering grass or in burrows, and sing from knolls, meadowlarks; strong grass stems, bobolinks; or on the wing, horned larks. The pronghorn antelopes are fleet of foot and keen of eye. They gather in herds for protection, and even give an alarm by complicated warning systems.

16 DENIZENS OF THE PAST

Most of the animals that developed in the plains region during the Paleozoic era were similar to those developing in the seas elsewhere. Fossil remains, whether near the surface or brought up in drill cores, show that animal life began on the plains more than six hundred million years ago, and developed through various stages until by the end of the Paleozoic era, 230 million years ago, a great number of invertebrates, fishes and amphibians lived both in and out of the water.

During the Mesozoic era reptiles, like dinosaurs, grew to prodigious size; the sea was filled with fish, and warm-blooded mammals appeared on the land. With a gradual change in climate the dinosaurs finally disappeared. They had no hair on their bodies to protect them from the cold, and were far too big to crawl into holes and sleep all winter. The vegetation that supported their monstrous appetites had dwindled – and so the dinosaurs finally succumbed.

The smaller reptiles and amphibians took over, and warm-blooded mammals of varying sizes and shapes continued to evolve according to their natural bent. If, by some magic, a modern prairie dweller could be transported back in time some forty million years, he would find himself in a weird and terrifying environment. He would not, as many fanciful drawings of

The fastest of the American animals, the pronghorn, with its hollow horns is not a true antelope. It can attain top speeds of sixty m.p.h. and runs easily at forty m.p.h. The white rump patches can be used as warning signals.

those times suggest, be completely surrounded by a horrendous group of mammals chewing each other or loitering in groups.

But, as he walked over the grassland and between the trees and through the marshes, he might well encounter a great variety of creatures. Certainly they'd not be man-shy because no manlike creature was to make its appearance for many millions of years. But most of them would be extremely wary of anything larger than themselves, as all small animals must be to survive.

Springing away from him over the plains he might have seen a small antelope, *Leptomeryx*. These were among the first grass-eaters whose distant relatives have survived on the plains to the present day. Or he might see a small, long-necked mammal, *Poebrotherium*, which was an early camel-like mammal. These animals continued to evolve through millions of years, until they were among the most numerous on the plains.

An animal that may not have run away was a fierce sabre-toothed cat, *Dinictis*, which preyed on the antelope and other plant-eaters. In the sky huge vultures soared, waiting for their share of the kill. The traveller may have caught a glimpse of a fat, big-faced creature, *Subhyracodon,* the first true rhinoceros. And near it, perhaps a long-necked relative, *Hyracodon,* another rhinoceros that, although more fleet of foot, finally became extinct.

He might easily have seen turtles and herons and crocodiles, looking very much as those creatures do today. Descendants of the herons and turtles have survived, but today – except for bones that are found on the plains – signs of crocodiles point to the past. There were also relatives of our pigs, *Entelodon*, and huge, bear-like carnivores called *Hemipsalodon.*

If our visitor to the past farmed anywhere near Regina, all of these creatures would be familiar to him; he would have seen pictures and bones during a holiday visit to the Saskatchewan Museum of Natural History. The excellent display there explains that the animals pictured are the most prominent of more than forty species whose remains have been discovered to date.

One of the mammals in the display is of particular interest to the old prairie farmers because, until recently, the descendants of this beast were the most important mammals on the plains. The *Mesohippus*, a small, three-toed mammal that looked like a short-haired sheep, was actually one of the ancestors of the modern horse.

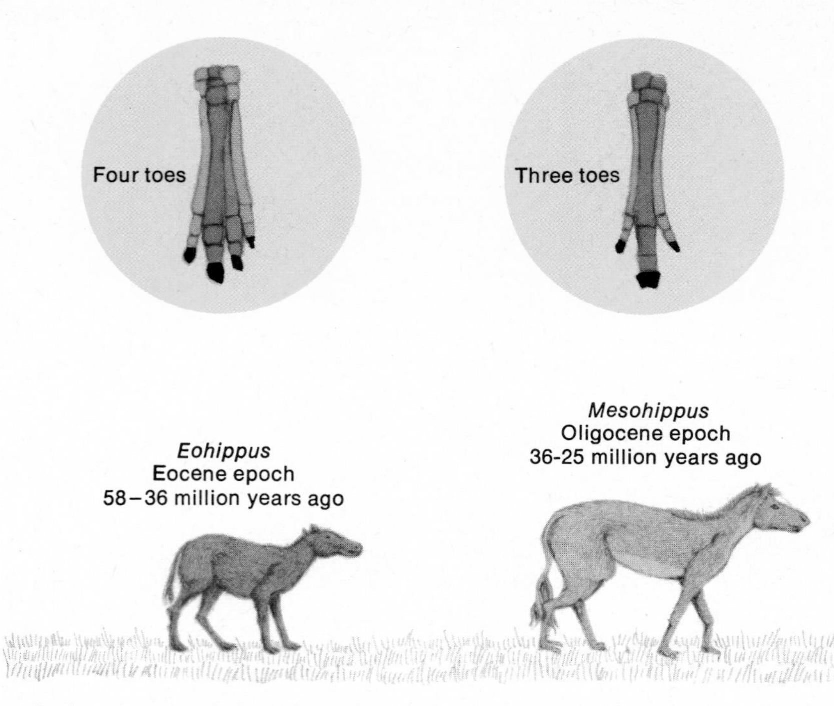

The horse is a native of the western plains, perfectly adapted to the environmental changes from swampy forests to dry grasslands.

Because the bones of many different representatives have been found on the plains, the story of the evolution of the horse is fairly complete. The earliest record goes back about sixty million years to a tiny grazing creature which has been named *Eohippus.* It roamed the woodlands of Alberta and Saskatchewan on toed feet, that kept it from sinking into the soft earth. The small, low-crowned teeth, that have been found in its skull, indicate that it ate the leaves of low bushes. But it couldn't climb or dig or fight or create a smell; to foil enemies it just ran – and running develops strong legs.

In rock strata some twenty million years younger there are no more bones of *Eohippus*, but those of a descendant, *Mesohippus.* The legs are longer and better developed, and had fewer toes. Most significant, the centre toe had become dominant while the two side ones were much shorter and smaller. The teeth indicate that it was still munching leaves.

Ten million years later a descendant of *Mesohippus* was much larger and stronger of leg. From years of digging the centre toe into the turf to gain speed, it had become harder and

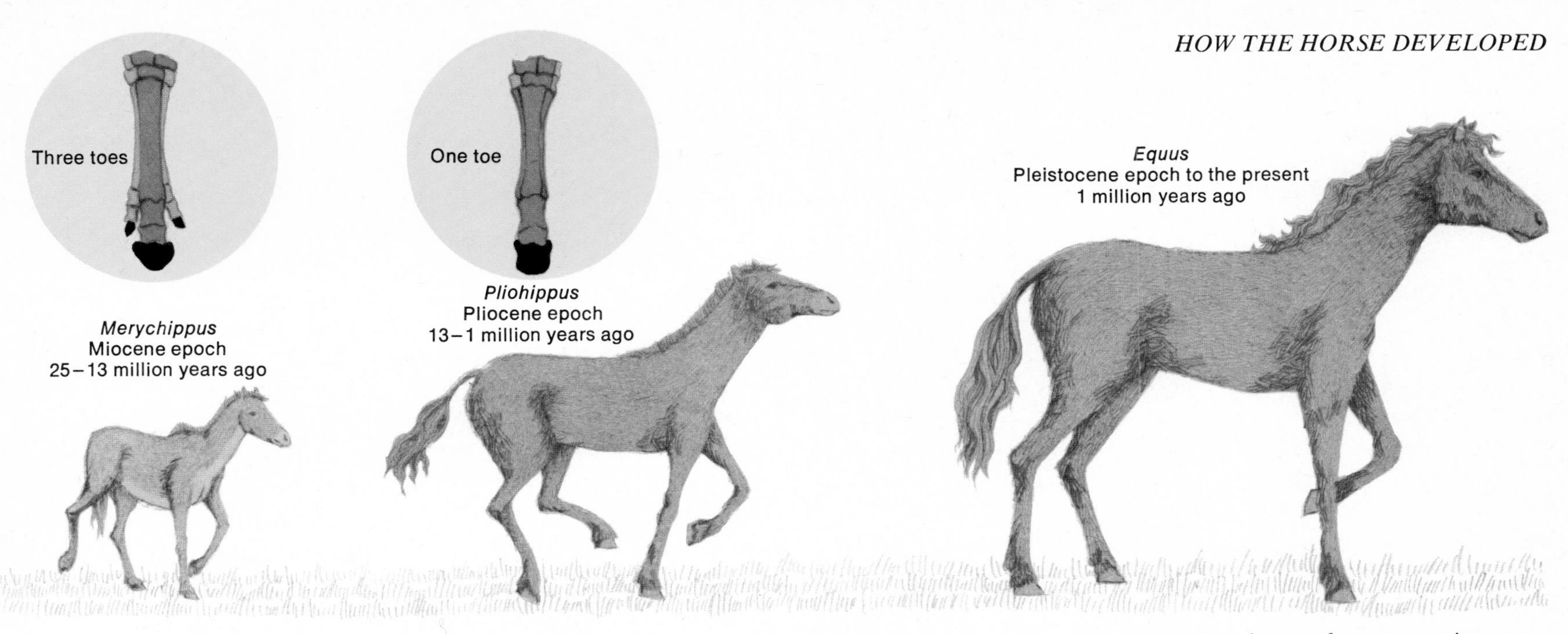

The sixty-million-year evolution from Eohippus, *a browser the size of a bobcat, to* Equus, *the sleek modern horse, shows a consistent development of the brain, strong grinding teeth, and modification of four toes into broad hooves for added stability and speed in running.*

sharper; in short, more like a horse's hoof. The teeth had changed too, having long crowns to allow for much wear by the tougher grass that had replaced the forest. This one has been named *Merychippus.*

By early Pliocene times, twelve million years ago, the evolutionary process had developed a horse-like creature, *Pliohippus*, which had no obvious side-toes and whose middle toe had enlarged to a strong hoof. It had bigger grinding teeth and sharp front teeth for biting through the tough grass stems and leaves. For protection, covering the back of its longish neck it had probably developed a mane of thick hair. About the size of a small pony, it could not only gallop like the wind, but also packed a good punch with hind or fore-feet.

In the rock strata of a period ten million years later are found the bones of *Equus*, the true horse, tall, fleet and powerful. And a fortunate thing it was for man that it didn't become extinct somewhere along the way, for it is difficult to think of what modern man's history would have been without the horse to carry him into battle, pull his plough, transport him from place to place, help build his railways – in short, before the advent of the gasoline engine, to provide almost his only power for work and land transportation.

By late Pleistocene times an amazing variety of mammals inhabited the western plains. There was a great woolly mammoth which stood twelve feet high at the shoulder and carried two enormous tusks, each of which weighed as much as an average man, 168 pounds. There were mastodons and an ancestor of the camel, and a woodland muskox. The moose, looking very much as it does today, munched away on the leaves of trees. The bison arrived on the scene about fifty thousand years ago, having migrated from Asia.

As the great glaciers receded, within the past eleven thousand years, most of these mammals, together with many smaller ones, returned to the northern plains. The woolly mammoth seems to have disappeared about eight thousand years ago, and the mastodon sometime within the last five thousand years. The bison still remains, but only on sufferance of man who has taken over his domain.

The creatures of the grasslands

About 20,000 indigenous pronghorns, mistakenly called antelopes, feed on sagebrush, and can leap in spurts of 60 m.p.h. Coyotes and badgers stalk ground squirrels while the bull snake explores a prairie dog town in search of a meal. A weasel sinks its teeth into the skull of a lemming and the mink patrols streams at night, alert to movement and the croaking of frogs. The broad vistas which at times seem "empty" are in fact teeming with life.

◄ *The reddish brown colour of the prairie dog is an effective camouflage. They dig burrows of about 12 feet deep with a main entrance plus a few side doors. Farmers consider them a menace to crops.*

top: Western toad
bottom: Bullsnake

Boreal chorus frog with extended vocal pouch.

This mink has probably escaped from a trap. Over six million domestic and wild mink are killed annually.

Weasels are the most vicious of carnivores. This least weasel, about 6 inches in length, has caught a lemming.

top: Coyote
bottom: Snowshoe hare

top: Thirteen-lined ground squirrel. bottom: Deer mouse

The badger is a strong fighter and an excellent hunter. He buries extra kills for later meals.

17 GRAZERS AND PREDATORS

Of all the amazing mammals that roamed the plains over the millions of years that have passed, for aggressiveness, adaptability, and numbers none could surpass the American bison, usually called the buffalo. It took over the plains and made them its own. All the food needed was right at its feet, and the head was slung low so that it could graze constantly, without even bending down. Needing no burrow or nest or shelter, it carried in the form of a thick, shaggy coat all the protection needed against the worst prairie blizzard. Here was the perfect plains dweller.

Estimates of the number of buffalo that inhabited the plains vary from sixty million to seventy-five million. Nobody is certain, but early explorers tell of watching a herd go by for days on end. Their paths still remain in parts of the uncultivated plains, as do the big boulders (called erratics because they were carried and scattered across the plains from the Canadian Shield by the great glaciers) against which the buffalo scratched their itchy hides. There are great depressions, called buffalo wallows, where the huge beasts rolled until they had worn away the grass. The bones of the slain buffalo were so plentiful that they were the first cash crop of settlers, who gathered them by wagonloads and shipped them east, where they were used in the process of refining sugar.

The buffalo was a big beast; bulls weighed up to a ton and were strong enough to break down a fairly large tree just by walking into it. This great size and strength, together with sharp crescent horns, made them a match for the wolves that constantly dogged the herds. The young and weak were protected by placing them in the centre of a circle with the bulls facing outward on the edge. Buffalos kept the grass cropped and fertilized the soil. They prevented excessive growth of aspens by knocking over the big ones and trampling on the saplings.

The buffalos even got on well with the plains Indians, who depended almost entirely upon them for meat, skins for their teepees, horns for decorations, leather for trousers, jackets and mocassins. The Indians killed buffalos with arrows, by driving them over cliffs, and by catching them in pounds, but they made little impression on the herds. It wasn't until the Indians obtained guns and could trade a buffalo hide for a tin-cupful of cheap whisky, and until sportsmen from the East, and abroad, shot them by the thousands, that the buffalo disappeared as a wild animal.

Some were saved, however, and can be seen in Elk Island Park near Edmonton, in Wood Buffalo National Park, and in numerous zoos. Many laments have been voiced about the disappearance of the great buffalo herds, but the simple fact is that there was no more room for them. They needed the same land for their grazing that the settlers needed for their farming.

On the other hand, elk, properly called wapiti, white-tailed deer, and moose survived in the wild state because they inhabit poplar groves and woodlands where the soil is of little use for farming. But one grazer has continued to live with farmers and ranchers – the pronghorn antelope. It doesn't even overgraze the range land because it does not care much for grass. The pronghorn evolved on the western plains and has stayed there. Unrelated to the fleet-footed antelope of Africa, it has no relatives anywhere.

Antelopes can still be seen from the Trans-Canada Highway in the short-grass country west of Swift Current. But mostly they keep away from roads, feeding peacefully on the hillsides, on patches of sage in the badlands, sometimes intermingling with cattle. Of all mammals they are best adapted to life on the plains. Their food consists almost entirely of sagebrush, but they'll eat weeds and other forbs and occasionally grass.

They have eyes as big as those of a horse; they can see an intruder miles away. Then, up goes the warning signal on the rump, a rosette of white hairs that can be raised, and away leaps the herd of antelope at speeds of up to sixty miles an hour. This warning signal can be seen by another antelope four miles away, and affords good protection against coyotes and other natural enemies. Unfortunately, it can also be seen by a stalking hunter who, with his highpowered rifle aimed through a telescopic sight, can pick off his quarry from an even greater distance.

The pronghorn has a trachea of exceptionally large diameter and runs with its mouth open so that it can keep going in leaps of up to twenty feet for fifteen miles without stopping.

Antelope fawns, born in early spring, for the first few days lie perfectly still in the long grass, depending upon their soft tan colouring to protect them. They will not move, even if handled. The mother hovers within a quarter of a mile and pays no attention to the fawn, except to feed it. When four days old the fawn's legs are so strong that it can outrun a man, and with its mother rejoins the herd.

Somewhere along the evolutionary path the pronghorns developed the capacity of shedding their hollow horns annually, as deer shed their antlers. They are the only hollow-horned ruminants in the world to do this. The pronged horn is in the form of a sheath that grows over a bony core. Both sexes have horns and shed them in the fall. Pronghorns have further adapted to the dry country in which they live by their ability to go for long periods without drinking, obtaining needed water from the plants they eat.

Another prairie mammal that should be dealt with at length, because it is peculiar to the prairies, is often confused with other species: Richardson's ground squirrel, *Citellus richardsonii*, known to prairie farmers simply as the "gopher." There are also true gophers on the prairies, but they are rarely seen. The northern pocket gopher, *Thomomys talpoides*, is a small, dark-coloured, buck-toothed rodent with huge, fur-lined pockets on its cheeks. A tremendous digger, it lives almost entirely underground. Most prairie people call it a "mole".

Another mammal that must inevitably vanish from the prairies – as has the grey wolf, the grizzly bear, the wolverine, the puma, the otter, and a host of others – is the coyote. This most cunning member of the dog family, whose musical howl is as much a part of the plains as the crocus, has always been regarded by farmer and rancher alike as Public Enemy No. 1. It all goes back to the early days, when the first settlers, plagued by drought, hail, frost, tornadoes, grasshoppers, and dust, couldn't chance losing a single chicken, duck or calf to a hungry coyote.

From the beginning the coyote has been trapped, shot,

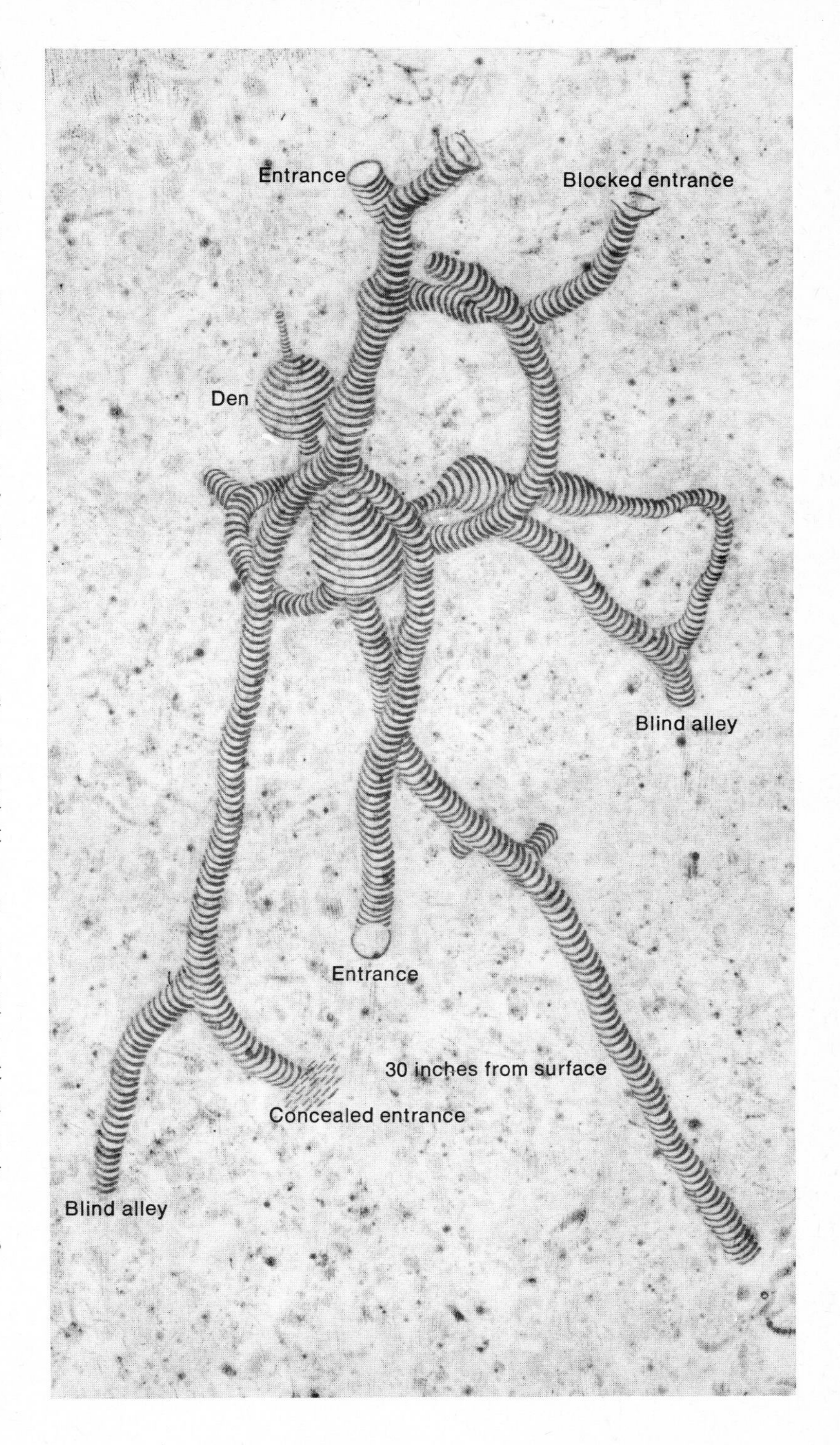

Richardson's ground squirrel, a guileless grain-nibbler about eight inches long, is almost impossible to catch once it has entered into its maze of passages which includes nurseries, dens and blind alleys.

poisoned, hunted by packs of dogs and – most recently – from aeroplanes. Despite constant persecution, the coyote has survived. Why? Because in each generation of coyotes there have always been a few wary of poison, and able to escape the gun. And the offspring of these cunning coyotes have been born with just a little more guile than their forebears. Many years of this have produced an animal of unbelievable sagacity.

The coyote looks like a small grey wolf, or like a small, lean, scraggy collie dog. Its ears are big and keen, its nose long, and its teeth sharp. The tail is bushy and carried at half mast, never curled over the back, as wolves sometimes do. Its eyesight is keen. It can outrun any dog except a wolfhound, and can outfight most larger dogs. Full of curiosity it may even stand watching men at work, but only if they are unarmed.

There are three subspecies on the plains. The smallest, weighing about twenty-five pounds, lives, and hunts gophers, rabbits, mice, birds, and anything else it can catch, in the southern part of Saskatchewan and Alberta. A larger one with more brown in its coat lives farther north on the prairies, and as far north as the Mackenzie District. Another species which lives in the sub-Arctic weighs up to seventy pounds, or almost three times as much as its southern cousin.

Apart from its incredible cunning, the coyote has several other points in its favour in the battle for survival. It is prolific, raising six or seven pups at a time, and both parents look after the young until they are able to hunt for themselves. It will eat just about anything that moves and much that doesn't move. Thus it is the supreme scavenger of the plains, cleaning up the livestock or game that has not survived the winter. Usually coyotes hunt in pairs, with one blundering after a swift-footed jack rabbit or antelope and chasing it right into the jaws of the other one, lying in wait.

The famous "prairie dog" so often associated with the plains, has never been seen by most prairie dwellers. There is only one community of the black-tailed prairie dogs, *Cynomys ludovicianus*, consisting of a number of colonies, twenty miles southeast of the village of Val Marie, Saskatchewan, almost on the U.S. border. But the prairie gopher (Richardson's ground squirrel) is everywhere on the plains, especially near wheat fields. A greyish-brown rodent, about ten inches long with a light-coloured, pencil-like tail, it burrows deep into the ground, but spends most of its time running about on the surface, eating grain in all its stages of development.

In contrast with the coyote, the gopher is dull-witted and has a stupid habit of sitting at the edge of his hole, chirping and jerking its tail, (hence the name flickertail) before scuttling to safety. Apart from that it is a favourite food of hawks, badgers, weasels, coyotes, rattlesnakes, and other predators. Farmers have been setting out poison for it since the first grain was planted on the prairies, and children have been paid a bounty of from one to two cents a tail.

How has it managed to survive? In the first place, there is an unlimited supply of food right on its doorstep. It never has to go more than a few feet to obtain all the grain it wants. In the second place, with a gestation period of less than a month, it raises an immense family of up to a dozen young at a time. As befits a grassland dweller, the gopher's burrow is a masterpiece of engineering. It has several rooms, including a hibernating chamber and a nursery, constructed so that heavy rains will not pour into any of these. Although a sitting gopher makes a good target for a boy with a twenty-two rifle, it isn't considered a worthy trophy by real hunters.

A close relative of Richardson's, usually referred to as the "striped gopher", is the thirteen-lined ground squirrel, *Citellus tridecemlineatus*. It is a little smaller, has a bushier tail and, as the name suggests, is striped. In habits and diet it resembles the more notorious cousin. Besides destroying crops, gophers in western Alberta particularly, play host to ticks that carry Rocky Mountain spotted fever, a form of plague fatal to man.

But the gopher, along with other diggers, plays an important role in the uncultivated grassland. Digging stirs up and aerates the soil. Although ground squirrels have always been plentiful, the common brown or Norway rat, that infests barns, corncribs, and dwellings of eastern Canada, was unknown on the plains until the late 1920s. They have gradually worked their way west, and now are as much a menace in granaries, barns and homes of the plains as in eastern Canada.

Mice and voles are plentiful on the plains, as elsewhere, and play their important part in the food chain of mammals, birds, and reptiles. The ubiquitous mouse is the deer mouse, while the sagebrush vole and the prairie vole are more common in the south.

18 WINGS OVER THE SLOUGHS

Birds live where there is food for them. As to climate, birds are adapted in truly remarkable ways to cope with it. Their bodies are covered with the finest natural insulation known: down and feathers. Their metabolism is so rapid that they can turn food into heat and energy almost immediately. Perhaps most important of all, birds can migrate for the winter to a region of warm weather and abundant food.

The southern plains with their grasses, forbs, and scattered trees make a perfect environment for birds, both large and small. For the seed eater there are grasses, weeds, and the grain fields. Berry eaters thrive on snowberries, rose hips, hawthorns, saskatoon berries, pincherries, chokecherries, and many others. The great number of rodents, large and small, feed the hawks, owls, and shrikes; while the insect eaters find enough mosquitoes, ants, and grasshoppers to satisfy the most voracious appetite. And in the sloughs, usually closely associated with grain fields, there is a supply of food for swimming and wading birds.

Although, by their very nature, the prairies have been hospitable to the largest North American birds, three of them have been forced to retreat – the whooping crane, the sandhill crane and the whistling swan. The whooping crane, largest of all, standing four feet tall, having a wingspread of seven to eight feet, was perfectly adapted to the plains environment. A long-legged, long-necked, long-billed wader, it dwelled near sloughs or marshes, feeding on the molluscs, crustaceans, frogs, salamanders, and small fish found there.

As befits a dweller of the wide open spaces, it was noisy and showy, and loved privacy. From its five-foot-long windpipe, coiled about the breastbone like a trumpet, it could emit whoops that were audible for miles. Standing on a knoll, peering with its yellow eyes from its red crown and face, black legs and wingtips contrasting with the snow white of the rangy body, it could be seen for miles. And, as if that was not enough, it performed a noisy, rumbustious mating dance that attracted the attention of everything within range.

Since they were relatively unmolested – coyotes and other predators occasionally robbed the big nests, but mostly the cranes could fend them off – the whoopers laid only two eggs

The cormorant is able to remain below the surface up to thirty seconds while gaffing fish with the hooked tip of his bill. The pelican engulfs the catch in its throat-pouch, later tossing the fish into the air to swallow it head first. Unlike the merganser, a duck whose bill is lined with sharp serrations for gripping its catch, these two have no nasal passages and breath through their mouths.

and frequently raised only one offspring. Besides that, they mated for life and showed amazing constancy. If one of the pair was injured or killed the other would stay by its side instead of seeking safety and, even if it escaped the same fate, would never mate again.

Despite these characteristics, the whooping cranes were common from the Gulf of Mexico to the Arctic, and each spring at mating time made the plains resound with their cavorting. But, with the arrival of the white man, the whooper was doomed. Many sloughs and potholes were drained and the whooping crane, unlike its smaller relative the sandhill crane, could not adapt to a diet of grain. At the same time, its size and noisiness made it a ready target for hunters. And so its range was pushed farther and farther north, and the numbers decimated, until today these birds have almost been exterminated. Their nesting place along the Sass River in Wood Buffalo National Park is a protected area, as is their wintering ground on the salt flats of the Aransas Wildlife Refuge near Austwell, Texas, on the Gulf of Mexico. But each spring and fall the birds embark upon the long migration flight across unprotected territory, often in company with sandhill cranes for whom there is an open season and, although conservationists in both Canada and the U.S. are doing their best to protect them, the migration period has become a time of great anxiety.

The smaller sandhill crane was also driven from its nesting grounds on the plains. Like the whooping crane, it is a wading bird that now nests in the Nipawin area of central Saskatchewan and migrates south every fall. Although it managed to adapt to the coming of agriculture by switching its diet to grain, this has been its undoing. So fond has the crane become of grain that a wheat farmer can lose as much as $3,000 worth of crops in a single season (based on insurance claims). As a result, the Saskatchewan government declared an open season on the birds from September 1st to 17th, issuing two thousand licences for hunting in a restricted area beween Lost Mountain and Quill Lakes. In one season 2,564 of these birds were shot. Thus, in any conflict between man and bird, the bird will inevitably lose.

Trumpeter swans, the other displaced birds, once nested on the central plains as well as in the western mountains. These beautiful large birds were seen by the early trappers and traders swimming majestically on shallow lakes and sloughs, scooping up crustaceans and parts of aquatic plants from the bottom

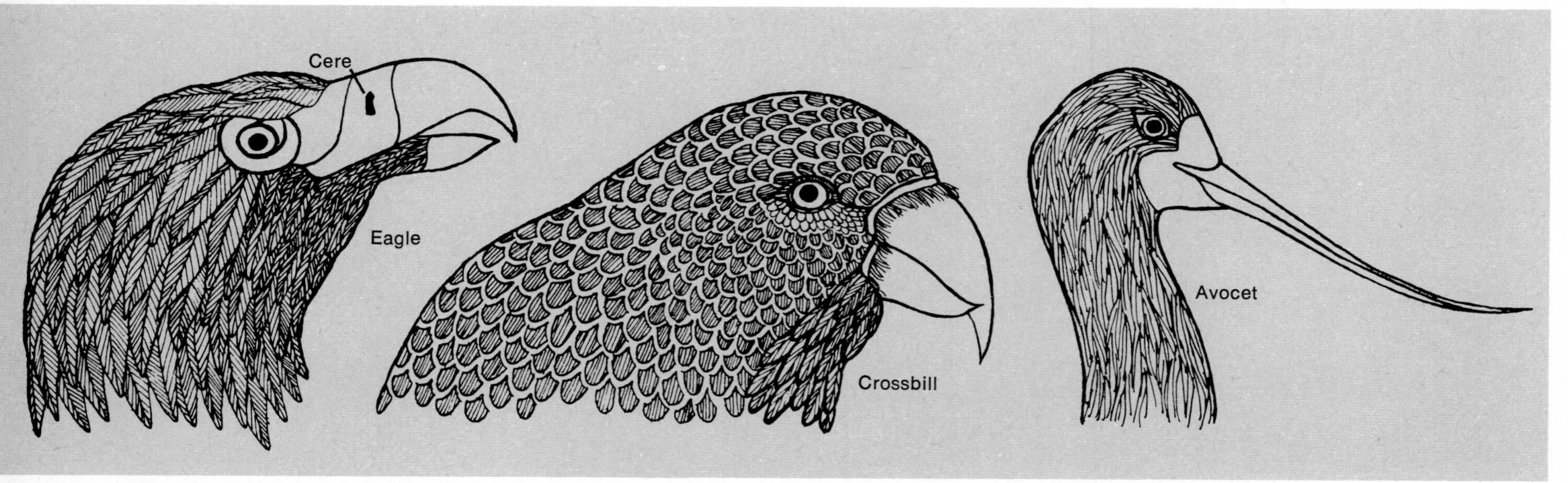

The gracefully curved bill of the avocet acts as a pair of fine pliers while it probes the pebbles of the shore for molluscs and crustaceans. The crossbill lives in evergreen forests where it pries open pinecones to extract the seed with its sloping, bent mandibles. Eagles, like all birds of prey, have strongly hooked beaks to aid their talons in tearing a quarry. The base of the beak is covered by a "cere."

with their black, sieve-sided bills. Their nests were piles of reeds and rushes, usually on top of an old muskrat house, and in them each pair of swans raised from five to seven cygnets. They were perfectly in tune with their niche.

But a plump swan made an easy target, and a good meal for a hungry settler. This alone would never have decimated the flocks had not the Hudson's Bay Company and other traders paid good money for densely feathered swan skins. When they were in style as muffs and costume decorations, thousands appeared on the London market.

Today a few swans find sanctuary at the Delta Waterfowl Research Station, Manitoba, in the Cypress Hills Park, and in a protected region near the town of Sexsmith in the Peace River country. But the largest flock winters at Lonesome Lake in the western mountains of British Columbia. The big, ungainly, throat-pouched white pelicans, that have wing spreads up to nine feet, still find space to nest on the plains, undoubtedly because they prefer isolated islands in lakes to sloughs in farmers' fields. They are not too particular as to terrain, nesting in such diverse localities as Lavelle Lake in the woods of Prince Albert National Park, and Lake Newell, just off Highway 1 in the mixed grass prairie east of Calgary.

The double-breasted cormorant, another fish-eater, is often found on the same barren islands with the pelicans. To some, both pelicans and cormorants may seem out of place on the prairies, since both are usually associated with the ocean, but the ample flying space and feeding grounds make the prairies a natural home for both species. Similarly, no region in North America is more hospitable to ducks than the Canadian plains.

In the prairie region, along with a smaller section of the U.S. plains, breed eighty per cent of the continent's mallards and pintails, and other ducks breed there in comparable concentrations. In fact, of all the North American ducks, only the eider, oldsquaw, wood, and black ducks are strangers to the plains. Many a motorist driving across the plains and seeing thousands of ducks, in isolated pairs, or huge flocks, depending on the season, asks himself: Why so many ducks? The answer can be summed up in one word – sloughs.

The prairie sloughs are the perfect place for ducks to nest, feed, loaf, and congregate. And sloughs are incredibly abundant. In other parts of Canada, notably southern Ontario, rain and snow-water tend either to sink into the sandy or gravelly subsoil, or run away in the numerous streams. On the plains the heavy clay soil holds the water in low places until the summer is far advanced. Thus, in the spring of a wet year, there are as many as one hundred and fifty sloughs per square mile, or in the whole of the southern plains well over eight million.

The soil of the sloughs is exceptionally fertile. Over the years the richest soil of the field is washed into the sloughs and supports a tremendous growth of duckweed and numerous other plants. Most of the water plants make good food for ducks, while the rushes, sedges, and cattails provide ideal cover for nests.

Naturally, where there is an abundance of plant life there will be an abundance of animal life. The slough water is thick with crimson water mites, grey-green amphipods, snails, water fleas, and the larvae of mosquitoes, dragonflies, and other insects. It has been estimated that a fertile prairie slough contains ten times the animal life of an equally big body of water in eastern Canada.

So the ducks, who relish the cool, crisp air of the plains, flock to the sloughs in early spring and stake out their territories. Some, such as canvasbacks, redheads, and ruddy ducks, live on the water and build their nests in the sedges and rushes near the shore. Mallards, pintails, teals, and shovelers prefer to build their nests in the grasses on the shore. Mallards and pintails will build nests as far as a mile away from a slough, and obtain most of their food from farmers' fields, using the water mainly for courting and loafing.

Canada geese also nest on the plains but, being more wary, tend to go farther north away from the prairie farmland. One of the most interesting groups of nesting wild geese can be easily seen within the city limits of Regina, barely a stone's throw from the busy Trans-Canada Highway. Along with killdeer, coots, sandpipers, terns, yellow-headed blackbirds, eared grebes, and many others, they are the guests of the Saskatchewan government in the Wascana Bird Sanctuary.

Associated with ducks are the crows and magpies, who feed on their eggs and young. Swainson's hawks and marsh hawks also feed on young ducks. Associated with the same grainfields that feed many of the ducks are three other grain-eaters peculiar to the plains – the sharp-tailed grouse, the greater prairie

The birds arrive

An unlimited food supply turns the plains into a bird paradise not only for slough water fowl, like the Canada goose, but also for birds of the northern forests and shores, both migrant and resident. Cormorants from the east, grebes from the west and avocets from the south are joined by swans and ducks in spring for the annual pageant of nuptials. They gather to mate and loaf, sing, dance and savour the freedom of the open spaces.

Young double-crested cormorants venture from their scraggy nest.

Whistling swans and Canada geese.

left: Horned grebe in nuptial plumage.
right: An avocet surveying a full clutch.

left: Bonaparte's gull wearing its hangman's mask for courting and nesting in the northwoods.
right: The western grebe haunts the lake shores with its plaintive call.

left: Swainson's hawk—a prairie rodent killer.
right: The calm and elegant cedar waxwing.

KEEPING TABS ON MIGRATION

Modern bird banding started two centuries ago with the use of red string. Now combined Canadian-U.S. operations band about 600,000 birds annually. A whole flock of Canada geese, like the bird in our photograph, can be snared in a boom net, shot by remote control over the heads of the birds while grazing. Wildlife officers then measure and weigh the birds before clipping a band on the leg. About eight per-cent of the bands are recovered – mostly from game birds which have been shot. The information gained is analyzed by an electronic index system, devised to learn more about bird species and their migration. Amateurs have tagged many songbirds and, in total, more than a million bands have been returned, graded in fourteen sizes – from less than one-tenth to almost an inch in diameter. By this method, arctic terns have been traced to South Africa, a distance of 10,000 miles.

chicken, and the Hungarian partridge. The first two are native to the plains; the third was imported from central Europe and, like other immigrants, soon adapted itself to the new land.

The sharp-tailed grouse, *Pedioecetes phasianellus*, is a ground-nesting, ground-feeding bird of the order Galliformes that is found on the prairie and in the aspen groves. Its elaborate courtship dance, during late April and early May, is carried on entirely by the males, and is a means of selecting the most vigorous rooster, who then mates with most of the females of the flock. The dance is described by one writer as being performed on traditional dancing grounds, that may be in the middle of a farmer's field: "to the accompaniment of squeaks, hoots, clucks, and beeps, the males pair off and, with heads bowed and tails erect, perform the allemande-left and dosido."

The sharp-tailed grouse can survive fairly well in conjunction with man, but must have sufficient long grass or stubble in order to hide from its enemies, the hawks and owls, that are constantly on the lookout for them. The greater prairie chicken, sometimes called the pinnated grouse, *Tympanuchus cupido*, inhabits more open terrain than the sharp-tailed grouse, and is larger and brownish in colour, with heavy bars on the underside.

The Hungarian partridge, or grey partridge, presents a perfect example of a bird's adaptation to a new environment. Smaller than either of the two grouse mentioned above, the "Huns" are also faster-flying and trickier. Their colour blends perfectly with the dry grass of fall. When they land in the stubble or slough grass they duck their heads and run at great speed, bursting into the air like bullets, when approached. Thus they make a difficult target for hunters. They are able to exist on small weed-seeds scorned by other grouse, and during the long cold winter nights huddle close together on the ground, sharing their body heat. They are prolific egg-layers as well, and often raise clutches of twenty or more young.

The sage grouse, which inhabits the short-grass region and feeds mostly on sage, is the largest of all the plains fowl. Males that weigh up to eight pounds, put on the most elaborate mating dance of all on the largest "drumming grounds." Besides ruffling their beautiful tail feathers, they inflate neck pouches to a grotesque size to demonstrate their strength and vigour. Only the best among them mate with the females who patiently await

A pair of trumpeter swans, now rare, give vent to their emotions during courtship at the Delta Waterfowl Research Station, Manitoba.

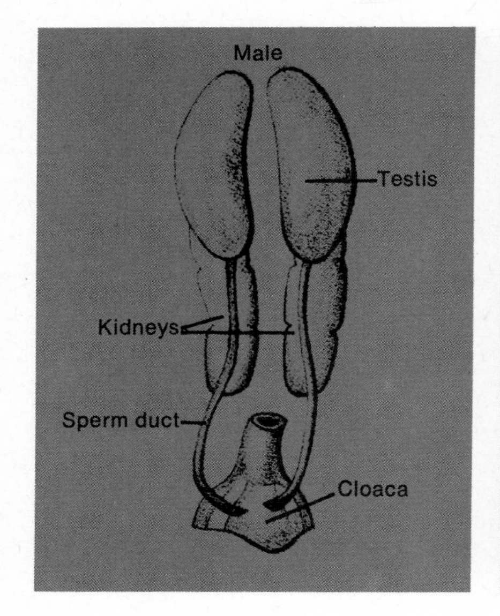

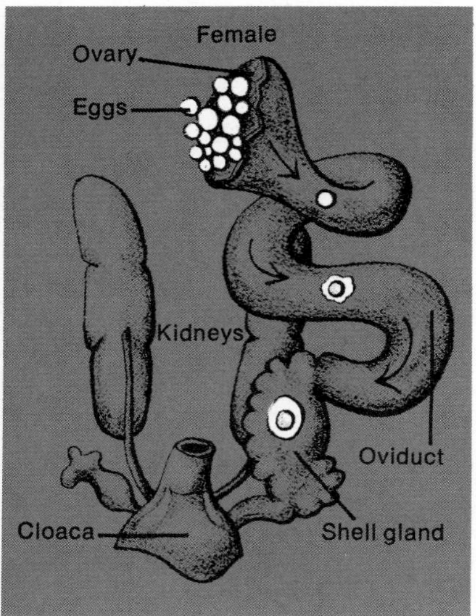

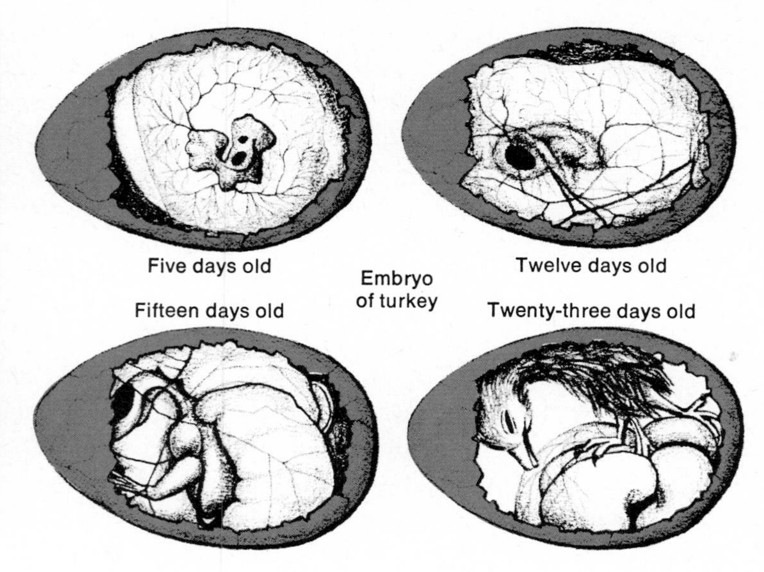

HOW BIRDS REPRODUCE
The sperms of male birds are discharged through the cloaca (which also evacuates waste) into that of the female. They fertilize eggs that have started travelling down the oviduct toward the shell gland, where they collect yolk, egg white, and a protective calcium coat.

HOW THE EGG DEVELOPS
During incubation (eleven to eighty days) embryos feed on the egg white and the yolk sac which becomes suffused with blood-vessels. The porous shell allows the developing chick to breath, and supplies lime for the growth of its bone structure.

their turns, and the supreme cock or flock-master may mate with four out of five of the hens. In this way the vigour of the species is maintained.

Naturally where there is an abundance of rodents and ground birds, birds of prey are plentiful. The great horned owl lives and hunts on the plains during the summer, while the snowy owl is a winter visitor from the North. Both feed extensively on Hungarian partridge. The much maligned buteos, once common on the prairies, are now becoming quite rare.

A good example of predacity is presented by the ferruginous rough-legged hawk, *Buteo regalis,* sometimes called "gopher hawk". Bird experts estimate that one rough-legged hawk consumes as many as 450 ground squirrels in a single season, thus saving more than thirty-five bushels of wheat. The hawks nest on the ground in huge piles of sticks, usually on the bank of a coulee, which they use year after year. Thus the eggs and young are prey not only to magpies and crows but also to coyotes, rattlesnakes, and, worst of all, farmers with guns. As a result, the birds disappeared almost completely in 1940, and only a few nesting pairs remain.

The golden eagles, who nest on the cliffs of the badlands along the Red Deer River and in southern Saskatchewan, are barely holding their own on the plains. Their great size and the fact that they are susceptible to poison set out for rodents have greatly reduced their number. Although many ranchers assiduously believe that eagles steal their lambs and calves, careful studies show that their diet consists of about two-thirds jack rabbit and cottontails, with various birds and carrion making up the rest.

Even where sheep-raising is common and hundreds of lambs are abroad the eagles practically never attack them. But unfortunately, verified evidence of this kind can't stand up against folklore, superstition, and a natural prejudice that has branded the eagle as a vile-smelling killer of the innocent.

19 THE RATTLESNAKE COUNTRY

In conjunction with the birds and rodents of the plains, a number of reptiles join the food-web. Descending from the reptiles of the Triassic and Jurassic periods, they have over millions of years adapted themselves to changing conditions on the plains. Many that could not adapt have disappeared. The remainder have managed to precariously co-exist with man. How much longer they can do so will depend upon man's attitude.

The most characteristic prairie reptile, although not found on the eastern plains, is the prairie rattlesnake. Its range lies within thirty-five miles of the U.S. border in western Saskatchewan and Alberta, along the banks of the South Saskatchewan as far east as Saskatchewan Landing, and in the badlands.

The prairie rattlesnake is a typical pit viper, with the sensitive depression on each side of its flattened head, between the nostril and the eye. These snakes pick up radiant heat vibrations from warm-blooded animals as far as a foot away, so they can strike with deadly accuracy in pitch darkness. The hollow striking-fangs at the front of the jaw fold back in grooves along the roof of the mouth when the jaws are shut. The poison which is injected into the victim destroys red blood cells and breaks down tissue, so that the digestive process is begun before the prey is swallowed. Its effect is not as instantaneous as the paralysing poison of the cobra, nor as deadly.

Prairie rattlesnakes reach a length of four feet, and can be distinguished by the greenish-grey colour (to match the grass) and the dark brown blotches along the back (to resemble stones), as well as the rattlers on the tail. It's impossible to tell the snake's age by counting the rattlers because the snake does not grow one a year, as is generally supposed, but renews them each time it sheds its skin, and this depends on a number of factors such as the availability of food and weather conditions. Besides, older snakes usually lose some of their end-rattles. Newborn rattlesnakes have only a tiny button at the end of their small tail, but in proportion to their size they are just as poisonous as their parents.

For food the rattlesnake depends mainly upon gophers, but

THE ARMOURY OF A RATTLESNAKE

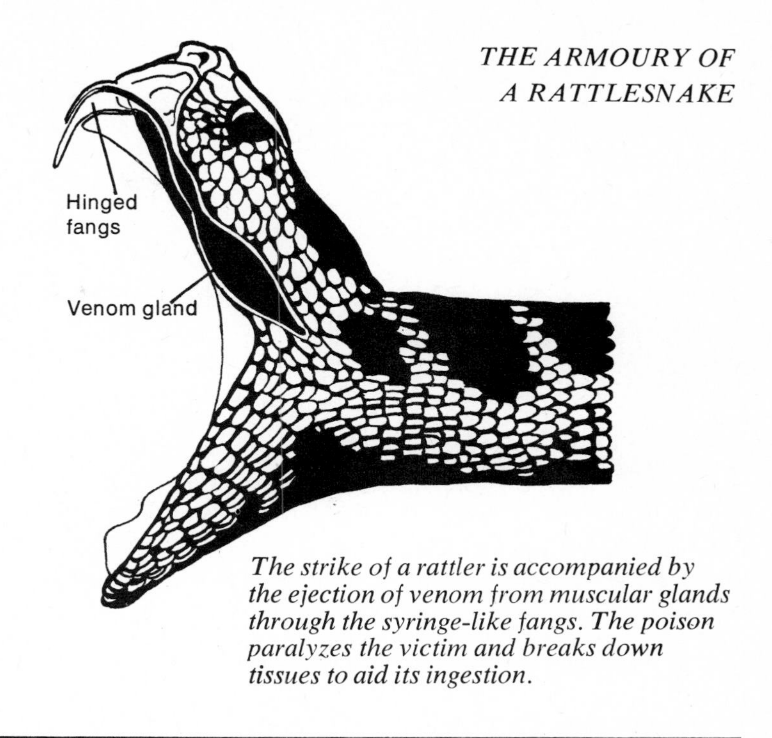

The strike of a rattler is accompanied by the ejection of venom from muscular glands through the syringe-like fangs. The poison paralyzes the victim and breaks down tissues to aid its ingestion.

When a rattlesnake is approached, loosely jointed segments at the tip of the tail are vibrated to sound a warning buzz or "rattle" Young snakes start with a single button and grow an additional segment with each shedding of the skin, which occurs several times a year with young snakes.

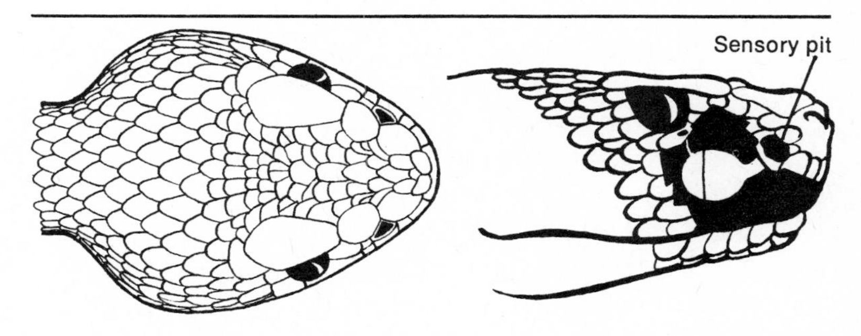

Rattlesnakes, like all reptiles, are cold-blooded, but sensory pits beside the nostrils detect heat from warm-blooded animals eighteen inches away and enable the snake to strike accurately in the dark.

also feeds on mice, frogs, birds, and any other living thing it can catch. It has a most efficient and safe manner of feeding. First it strikes the victim with a hammer-like blow, piercing its hide with the needle-like fangs. Then, to avoid injury to its delicate face, it backs off and waits for the victim to die before swallowing it whole. A rattlesnake will only strike a target too big to swallow, such as cattle or humans, if it is surprised and cannot escape. This is most likely to happen during the spring skin-shedding time when, for a short while, the snake is partially blind and easily confused.

The Saskatchewan Department of Natural Resources warns persons bitten by a snake not to run, not to drink whisky, and not to panic. Rather, they say, sit still, apply a tourniquet between the bite and the heart, make a shallow incision over the wound with a sharp, sterilized blade, and apply suction to remove as much of the poison as possible. They also warn against picking up a recently killed rattler, as reflex action remains in the muscles for some time, and a man can be bitten by a dead snake.

The bullsnake is larger than the rattlesnake, and is also blotched, but has a pointed head and no rattles. It eats the same food as the rattlesnake but squeezes the prey to death before swallowing it. It is found from Estevan west, and north to the edge of the aspen grove prairies. There is a colourful story that used to be told to prairie newcomers that bullsnakes mated with rattlesnakes to produce a more powerful and deadly specimen than either – that is a fable.

In winter snakes of the plains crawl into an abandoned rock-filled well, old excavation, gravel pit, or hole of some kind that will take them below the frost line, where they remain dormant but not asleep throughout the cold season. Hundreds of snakes gather for this purpose, and co-exist without conflict. In one excavation east of Estevan, Saskatchewan, more than a thousand red-sided gartersnakes were found in one old coalmine shaft.

Looking like a relict from the Permian period is the short-horned lizard, *Phrynosoma douglassi*. Their one-inch long young are born alive and soon learn to scurry across hot, dry ground, like their parents. These creatures love heat and when they burrow into the ground it is to keep warm. When angered, horned lizards can squirt a tiny drop of blood from the corner of their eyes. They are found in the extreme south, principally in the Cypress Hills.

The amphibia of the prairies are especially adapted to the water conditions. Thus there are none of the big green bullfrogs that live in the lakes and permanent swamps of eastern Canada. The largest frog is the leopard frog, *Rana pipiens*, that lays its eggs in a gelatinous mass in sloughs. The adult frogs however, prefer dryer land and are most often found in the pastures or fields where they feed on insects, and themselves provide food for snakes, badgers, prairie chickens, and a host of others.

One of the first signs of spring on the plains, long before all the snow is gone, is the penetrating chorus of frog music that goes on day and night. This is the mating song of the smallest, noisiest, and most abundant frog of all, the boreal chorus frog, *Pseudacris triseriata*. They keep up their singing into early July, whenever there is enough rain to keep them happy. In dry seasons they are never heard. A member of the tree frog family, the boreal chorus frog sometimes climbs up the stems of grasses or rushes. It is especially equipped to do this by tiny disks at the end of each digit.

A spring singer that is often seen is the great plains toad, *Bufo cognatus*. It breeds in mud puddles or temporary sloughs during heavy rains in late spring and summer. After that, this squat, brown, heavily warted amphibian takes up residence in a field or garden and spends its time darting out an incredible tongue to catch spiders, flies, slugs, worms or bugs.

Of all the amphibia of the plains, the best adapted to the dry regions is the plains spadefoot. This species breeds, not necessarily in spring but whenever there is enough water. After a heavy rain the toads gather quickly, attracting each other with short, sharp bleats that can be heard a mile away, breed, and lay their eggs in temporary puddles and ditches. The development of the tadpole is incredibly fast, since it must be accomplished before the water dries up. When there is no water, the spadefoot does not breed at all, and will dig itself backwards into the ground with the handy spade on each back leg, remaining there until it rains enough to provide more puddles.

Another digger during dry spells is the tiger salamander, *Ambystoma tigrinum,* found as far north as Prince Albert. This one grows to lengths of from eight to ten inches, and like the frogs lays its eggs in sloughs, ditches, and shallow lakes, such

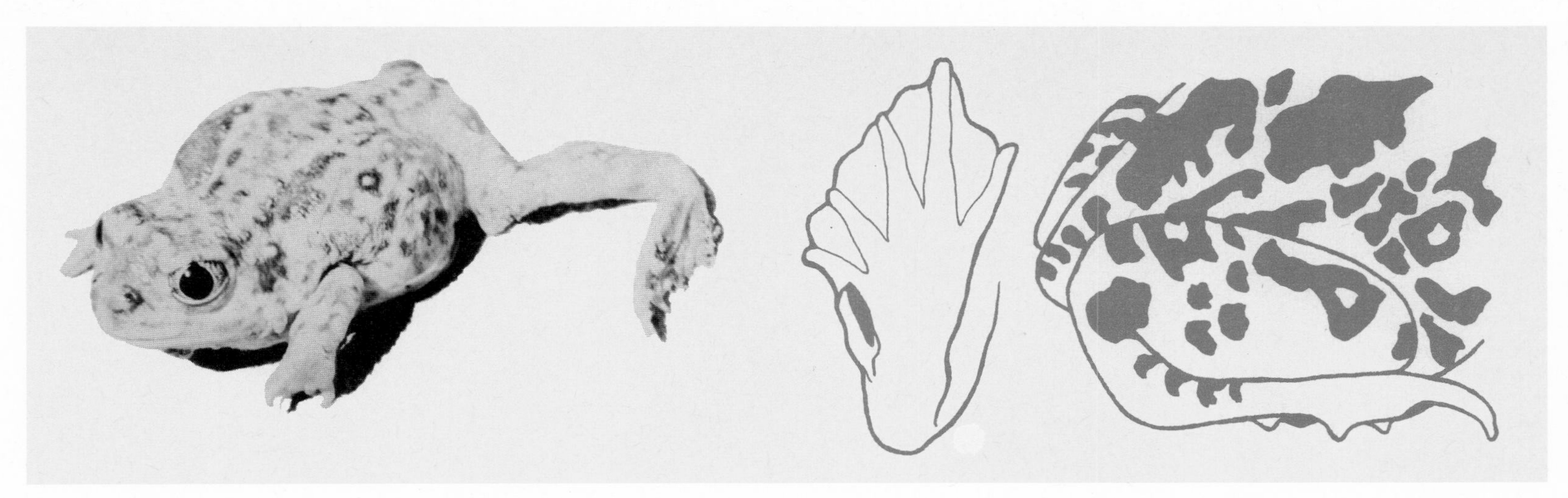

The two-inch plains spadefoot has a pronounced bump between close-set bulging eyes with vertical pupils similar to those of a cat.

Spadefoots dig into dry ground with wedge-shaped spurs on their hind-feet; they emerge after a summer downpour and breed prolifically.

as Old Wives Lake. The larva in its later stages has bushy, external gills at the base of the head, and resembles a small eastern mudpuppy. The tiger salamanders retain the gills until they are sexually mature, and even after they have left the slough may have small vestiges of them. On moist evenings in some locations they'll come out onto the highway, to be squashed by passing cars. They are amazingly tolerant to cold, and have been seen migrating over ground covered with snow.

Since late Devonian times, fish have thrived in the seas, rivers, lakes, and marshes of the plains. Even today, with less water than ever before, there is still a great variety of fish. The fish in the rivers and lakes of the northern plains are species identical with those caught in the lakes and rivers of the Canadian Shield. Great Slave and Great Bear Lakes, for instance, provide great quantities of commercial whitefish and lake trout. Therefore, this account will be concerned primarily with fish native to the southern plains – the prairies.

As previously noted, most of the water of the prairie regions collects in temporary, semi-permanent, or permanent sloughs. The water in these is stagnant and supports no fish. This leaves the Saskatchewan-Nelson river system, the rivers of the extreme south, that flow into the Missouri system, and a great number of freshwater lakes ranging in size from Lake Winnipeg to those a mile or less in length. Since the waters of the rivers and many of the lakes are heavy with silt, the most common fish are those that like murky conditions.

One of the most numerous of these is the northern pike, *Esox lucius*, or jack fish as it is called by most plainsmen. The northern pike is big, prolific, laying up to 200,000 eggs in a season, powerful, and has an unbelievable appetite. It will devour anything from tiny insect larvae to muskrats, ducks, mice, or whatever happens to fall into the water. From the time it is an inch long it begins to swallow other fish, often those just slightly smaller — a one-and-a-quarter inch pike is recorded as having swallowed a one-inch fingerling. The pike accomplishes this remarkable feat by swallowing the other fish by degrees, digesting the part in the stomach to make room for the rest; even large pike have been observed swimming about with the tail of another fish protruding from their mouths.

The pike that live in the colder lakes of the northern prairies, like Montreal, Cold and Dore Lake, are good to eat and are sought after by anglers, particularly from the U.S.

Many kinds of suckers, family Catostomidae, are found in lakes that are too stagnant for other fish. No matter what the condition of the water, or the nature of the food it contains, the sucker will do well. The sucker's mouth is on the underside of its head, and shaped so as to take in food from the bottom of the lake.

The "horned toad" is in fact a reptile that grows to four inches long and is partial to ants. This short-horned lizard inhabits hot, arid regions and can squirt blood from the corners of its eyes.

Various members of the perch family, Percidae, thrive in the majority of the plains waters, the most common being the pickerel. These voracious fish – each one will eat as many as three thousand smaller fish annually – make up for their destructiveness of other fish by being very tasty. But the fish most closely associated with the plains are the small, silvery, beautifully-shaped goldeyes, *Amphiodon alosoides*. They thrive in the muddy, fast-running Saskatchewan River. Since these waters empty into Lake Winnipeg, it holds a large number of them; but rarely are goldeyes found east of Lake Winnipeg.

For years eager children and adults too, caught goldeyes in the South Saskatchewan, either with throw lines weighted by means of railroad spikes, or bamboo poles and a cork float. But they never were very good to eat, being soft, mushy and full of bones. Then someone discovered that by smoking the same goldeye slowly and carefully over a smouldering oak fire it became a gourmet's delight. Now it brings a big price in the best restaurants of New York and elsewhere under the name of Lake Winnipeg goldeye, and is the mainstay of a large fishing industry.

As is inevitable with success, the Lake Winnipeg goldeye has its imposters. One of the fish substituted is the lowly cisco which is normally used as mink feed. Smoked and dyed it looks like the real thing, but there is one certain way of telling the difference. If there are no teeth in the mouth, it's not a goldeye.

Occasionally a fisherman will land another fish in the Saskatchewan that is hard to credit. As he pulls it in he is soon aware of something much bigger than a goldeye, and when it comes to shore he will look in amazement. It may be from three to six feet long, have an ugly, up-turned snout with whiskers, and a body covered with rows of sharp, tough shields. It looks like something from another world and it is – the lake sturgeon, *Acipenser fulvescens*, a direct descendent of the chondrosteans of the late Devonian period.

Lake sturgeon in the Saskatchewan River take twenty years to reach maturity; they spawn at seven-year intervals.

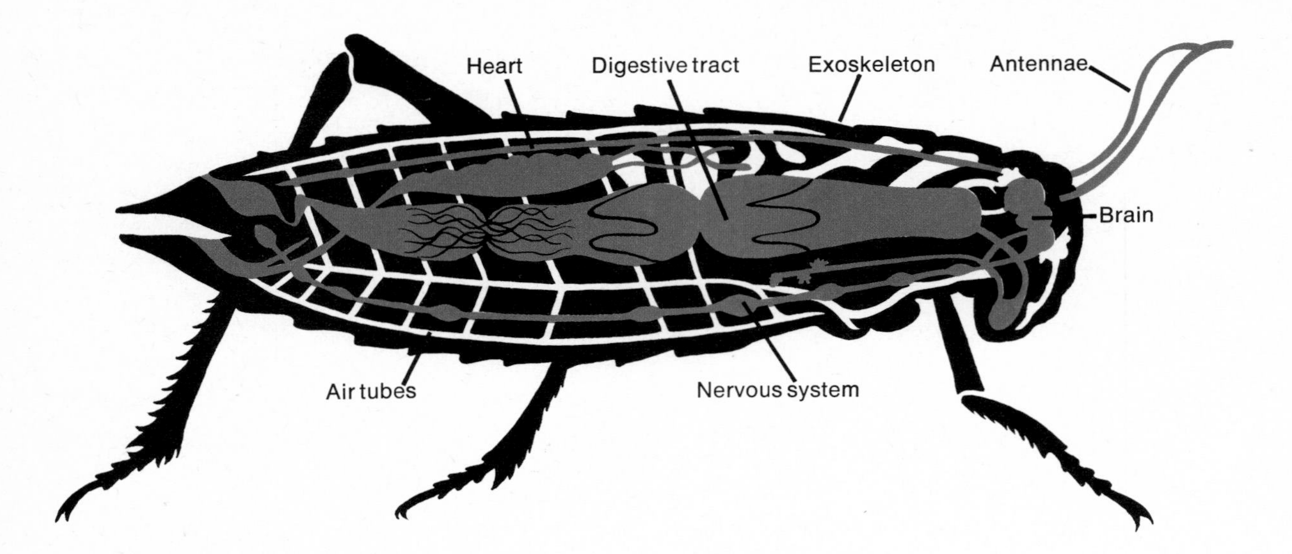

INSIDE-OUT CREATURES
Endowed with a heart, brain, and nervous system, insects, including grasshoppers, grow skeletons, not inside, but around their bodies. Holes in this exoskeleton, called spiracles, are connected to a network of air tubes that enable the insect to breathe.

20 INSECTS: THE OLDEST SETTLERS

Of all plains dwellers those that have been there longest in their present form, more than 225 million years, are the insects. These small creatures are so well adapted to life in the cold, having developed perfect methods of lying dormant through the long winters, that they frequently challenge the mammals, including man. In fact, if man ever completely destroys his present environment, and himself, the insects will probably survive. It would be impossible to discuss the thousands of different species that thrive on the plains and so we shall concentrate on a few that are particularly well adapted to life in the grass.

The first and most typical of these, as the name suggests, is the grasshopper. At the outset it is well to clear up any confusion between grasshoppers and locusts – there really is none. Locusts are grasshoppers that form dense swarms and march or fly in close-knit groups. The famous Rocky Mountain locusts, which pioneers tell of seeing in such dense clouds that they darkened the sun, have disappeared from the plains. The last one on record was seen in the Red River Valley in 1905. The grasshoppers that plague the farmers today are home grown, raised right beside or in the grain fields on which they feed.

There are more than eighty different species of grasshoppers on the plains, but of these, two do most of the damage – *Camnulla pellucida,* the clear-winged grasshopper, sometimes designated the roadside grasshopper because the eggs are laid in mature grasses along the edges of fields or in pastures; and *Melanoplus sanguinipes,* the redlegged or stubble grasshopper. Two others that do considerable damage are *Melanoplus bivittatus,* the two-striped grasshopper and *Melanoplus packardi* or Packard's grasshopper.

The grasshopper is perfectly adapted to life on the prairies. In the first place it has wings, enabling it to fly from his enemies, powerful hind legs to leap with, and compound eyes that see in several directions at once. Like all insects, its skeleton forms the outer shell of the body, made up of chitin, a tough, light, chemical-resistant, flexible substance, and sclerotin which is hard as fingernails. All of this is covered with wax that prevents moisture from penetrating to internal organs, and essential body moisture from getting out.

Unlike most insects that go through a complete metamorphosis – egg, larva, pupa, adult, eating different foods at each stage – grasshoppers skip the dormant stage completely and eat the same food from the time they emerge from the egg. And that food is all around them. In late summer and early fall the female grasshopper lays hundreds of eggs in little waterproof capsules in the ground. These eggs are equipped with a timing mechanism (diapause) that prevents them from hatching pre-

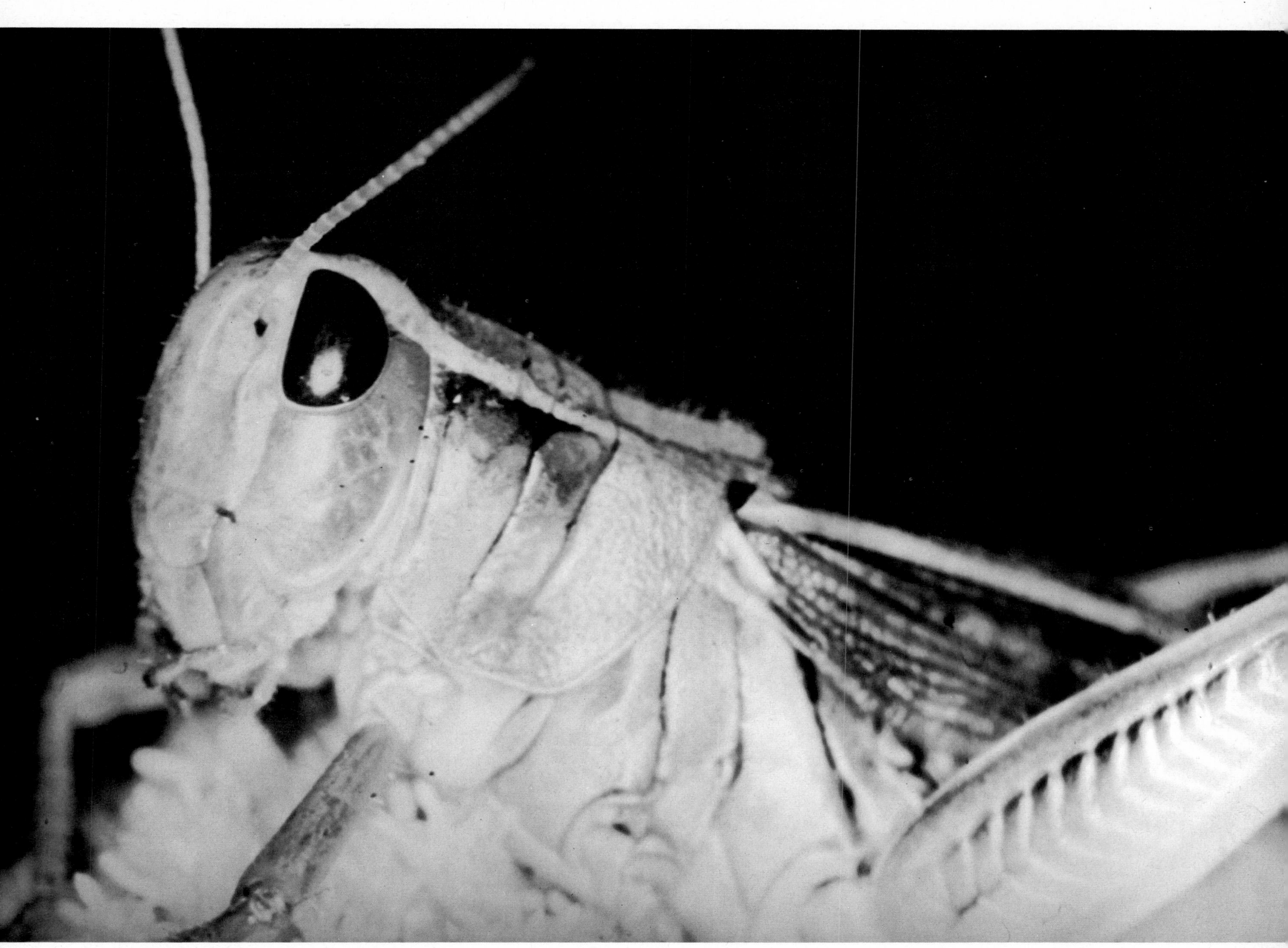

This short-horned grasshopper, enjoying a meal of goldenrod, becomes a menace when it attacks grain crops with its strong mandibles.

maturely during any warm spell that might occur in late fall or winter. In early spring they hatch as small worm-like nymphs that squirm their way to the surface where they immediately shed their coats and become diminutive black grasshoppers without any wings.

They immediately begin to eat the newly sprouting grass – or wheat – and keep on growing and eating all summer. Five times they shed their skins, and after the last shedding they are equipped with wings. The male has the ability to make a rasping noise with his hind legs, that attracts the female – and the whole process begins again. The rate of grasshopper reproduction is staggering. Some species put as many as twenty eggs in one capsule. Official checks, after a warm summer, reveal up to 10,000 eggs in one square foot of ground. The cost of damage that grasshoppers do to crops runs into millions of dollars.

Many natural controls limit grasshoppers. Almost all ground-feeding birds dig up and devour the eggs, as do ground squirrels, skunks, mice, gophers and other rodents. Birds eat the grasshoppers themselves at every stage of development. Seventy-nine grasshoppers were counted in the crop of one Hungarian partridge. There is a tiny wasp that feeds its young on grasshopper eggs by depositing its own eggs inside the capsule with a long, needle-like ovipositor. The hunting wasp captures a young grasshopper, paralyses it with a sting, lays an egg in the insect and pushes the grasshopper into a hole in the ground, so that when the young wasp arrives it will have fresh meat. Robber flies catch adult grasshoppers in full flight, as do kingbirds and other flycatchers. A fungus disease also destroys millions of grasshoppers.

But the greatest natural control is weather. Grasshoppers do best on hot days, and when these occur in early spring they hatch quickly and do an enormous amount of damage. But if the weather turns cold the nymphs will not eat at all and millions perish from starvation. Also, cold weather in late summer and early fall cuts down egg laying. Therefore, grasshopper populations fluctuate drastically from season to season, building up to a serious epidemic in cycles of about eleven years.

Farmers spray their fields with DDT and the more deadly dieldrin which kills grasshoppers but also contaminates the soil (see Section 5). But poisoning has little effect on subsequent infestations. As Dr. P. W. Riegert of the Entomology Section, Canada Department of Agriculture Research Station, University of Saskatchewan, points out: "We can control grasshopper damage, but we'll never control the grasshoppers." Only weather can do this. For example, after a wet, cool fall and a harsh winter the grasshopper damage of 1966 was only one-quarter of that in 1965.

Among other insects that lay their eggs in the ground and feed on grasses, three should be mentioned – the cutworm, the wireworm and the armyworm. The wireworm and the cutworm eat the roots, seeds and lower stems of the plants, while armyworms crawl out of the ground and eat the leaves and heads. Cutworm and armyworm adults are moths, while the adult of the wireworm is the black click beetle. When turned on its back it gives a little "click" and flips over onto its feet again.

Due to large expanses of stagnant water on the prairies, mosquitoes are particularly plentiful. They breed in sloughs by billions, even in such small stands of water, found in old tin cans, jars or abandoned automobile tires. Extensive control programmes have been carried out by spraying oil onto sloughs and ditches and by "fogging" the streets of cities and camp grounds.

Blackflies, *Simulium arcticum*, the scourge of the northern plains, as of the Canadian Shield, also lay their eggs in water, but the water must be fast-running and aerated. The eggs are laid in June but don't hatch until very early the following spring. The tiny larvae cling to rocks, and quickly develop into adult flies that are abroad and biting before all the snow has gone. The tiny blackflies have such an insatiable appetite for blood and attack in such numbers that they can kill caribou, deer or domestic stock by causing an oedema that fills the lungs.

Thousands of other insects that fly, hop, crawl and burrow, are all part of the food and life patterns. For millions of years they have co-existed with mammals, birds, reptiles, amphibians and plants, each adapting to and helping to develop its own niche. Man with his weapons, tools, and chemicals has already destroyed much of the bird, mammal and reptile life, and unless he mends his ways, will quickly exterminate the others. Thanks to the great numbers of eggs they lay and their ability to adapt even to poisons, it is extremely doubtful whether this will ever have much effect on insects.

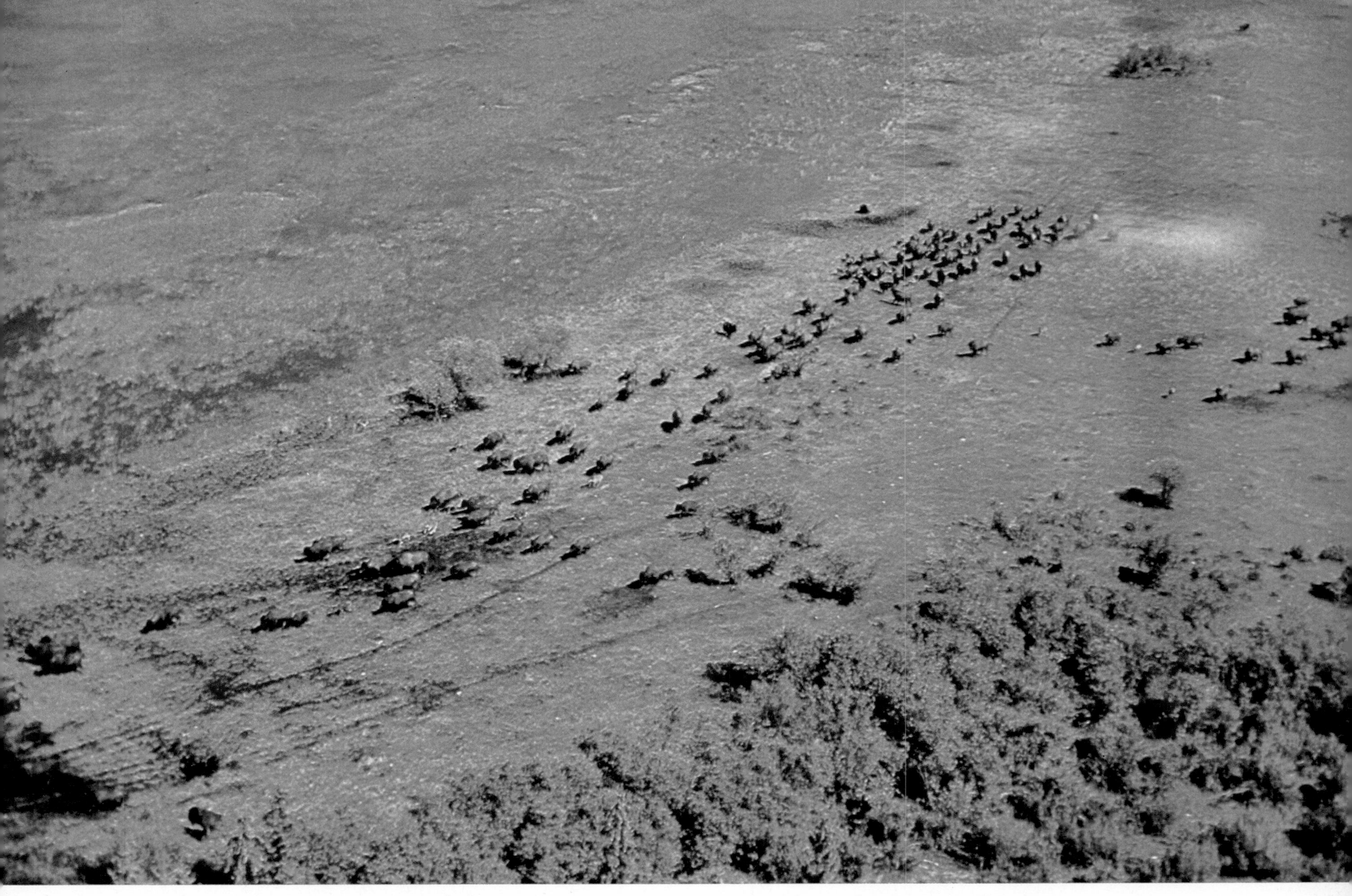

Shaggy buffaloes, bulls weighing up to a ton, run at 30 m.p.h. from a circling airplane.

A CHANCE FOR SURVIVAL

Wood Buffalo National Park—all 17,300 square miles of it—provides a sub-arctic preserve for the last herds of wild buffalo and a rigidly protected home for the whooping crane, barely surviving to return each year to this unspoilt region.

A harsh environment

Early explorers identified well over four hundred species of plants within this sub-arctic forest region. From the remote Caribou Mountains, rising to 3,500 feet, Wood Buffalo Park stretches across the 9,000-square-mile Alberta Plateau, dotted with sink holes, down to the salt plains along the Slave River. An area of low sandhills stretches from the Peace River south to the Birch Mountains and west to the meadows of Lake Clair, the shallow remains of a once large glacial lake. Seventy per cent of the park is covered by mixed woodland; marsh prairie and lakes make up the rest. The climate is harsh, the average July temperature of above 90° falls to 60° below zero in winter. Swarming insects make summer even more difficult for man.

Sink holes, caused by the solution of limestone beneath the surface, are known as Karst topography and often form pools.

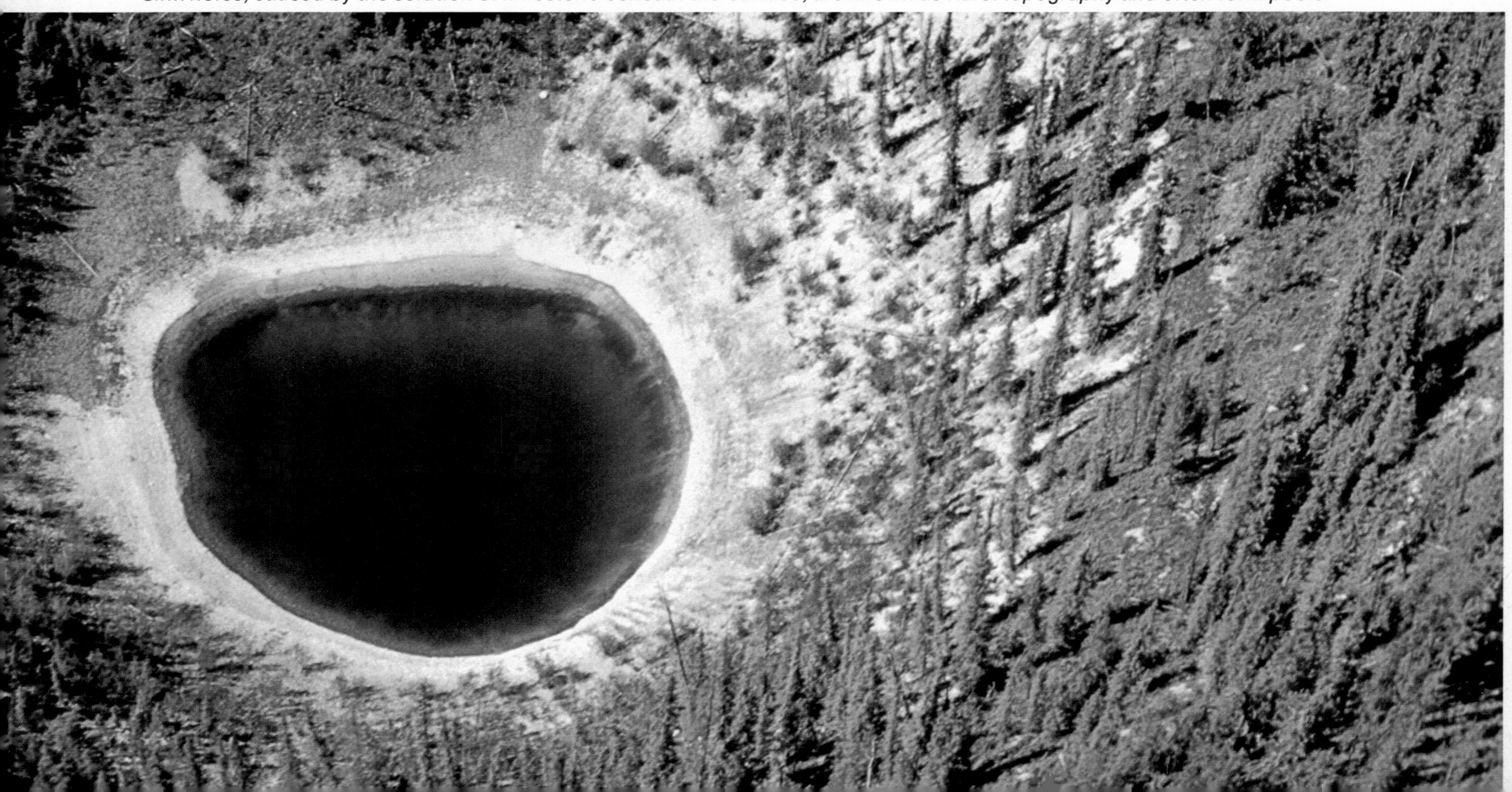

This shallow dried-up lake bed south of Fort Smith acts as an evaporation basin for saline water from the Alberta Plateau.

The almost pure sodium chloride accumulating at the base of the salt plains escarpment can be gathered by the wagon load.

Spruce trees growing on a blanket of sphagnum moss and sedge can stretch to the horizon in an endless pattern of circles.

These limestone strata on the Peace River jut up in a perfect syncline, a rare formation in an area of horizontal layering.

Monarch of the plains

The bison, commonly known as the buffalo, verged on extinction in 1890. The herds that once roved in hundred of thousands now number 12,000, the majority of the protected flock living in Wood Buffalo Park. Timber wolves, drowning in spring and disease keep the number of animals within the capacity of the grazing land. The bison in the park and its vicinity is a hybrid of the region's wood bison and the plains bison which started to interbreed about forty years ago. At present the meadow sedge of the delta area between the Peace River and Lake Clair attracts the largest concentration of animals. Bisons graze throughout the year, even fifty degrees below zero, but scurry for forest cover when the icy winds reach 10 m.p.h. Hunting is confined to the needs of the local population and, at the annual round-up, some are slaughtered to cull the herd.

The broad shoulders of these placid shaggy-maned grazers reach the height of a man and their horns can span almost three feet.

Gregarious bisons follow well-trodden trails from pastures and drinking holes to wallows and "rubbing trees" in the woodland.

Fiercely protected calves, born in summer, join the herd four days after birth; they renew one-tenth of the stock each year. ▶

The fight to save the whooping crane

Canada's tallest birds, standing four feet high, are hovering on the brink of extinction. Their only permanent breeding ground lies within the park boundaries. The cranes normally lay two eggs, but seldom rear more than one chick. Wildlife officers each year attempt to salvage the unwanted but fertile eggs and several of these have hatched thriving young in captivity. In autumn the birds migrate to Texas and the following spring leave the fledglings to make their own way. The mortality among the young birds is high.

With a majestic wing spread of eight feet, white whoopers are recognized by their outstretched neck and legs. ▶

Site of Sass River nesting ground. The cranes nest in this desolate place far from civilization.

Announcing their arrival with loud whoops, a pair of cranes prepare to settle for the short sub-arctic summer. A warm dry season encourages mating.

This readily distinguished young whooper feeds alongside its near relative, the sandhill crane.

The young cranes quickly match their parents in size, and start to wade in shallow marshes where they feed mainly on aquatic insects, and berries.

The whooping cranes begin their 2,000-mile journey south just before the sub-arctic winter descends again on the plains.

PART FIVE / **CONSERVATION**

21 MAN, THE WANTON DESTROYER

During the early 1900s the amount of damage done by man to the land, water, air, and wildlife of the plains was still small, but there were a number of disturbing portents.

One early spring day in 1921, when the snow had gone from the exposed places, but still lingered in the shade, a group of teenagers and their younger admirers were loafing on a knoll near the standpipe at the corner of Second Avenue and Twenty-third Street in Prince Albert, Saskatchewan. Nearby was a hole, probably the cellar of an earlier shack, that had been filled with rock and other debris. Suddenly one of them noticed a bleary-eyed, red-sided gartersnake poke its head out between two rocks, sense the warmth, and crawl into the light. It was followed by another, then another and yet another. They too felt good that at last it was spring – but not for long.

The biggest galoot let out a whoop and grabbed one of the snakes by its spindly tail. With a quick flick of his wrist he snapped it, as you would a whip, and broke its back. He dropped the squirming wreck and grabbed another one, and as quickly as he could pick them up he disposed of more than twenty of the helpless reptiles before they could know what was happening. The red-sided gartersnake was one of the few reptiles to find its way so far north.

People used to swim in both branches of the North Saskatchewan River. The water was muddy – prairie water is always muddy – however it didn't smell or taste bad. But downstream from the swimming areas the cities' sewage systems dumped household wastes into the stream. There weren't many flush toilets, and practically no factories, so that the fast-flowing rivers easily handled the load.

Hunting down coyotes with a pack of dogs and a snowmobile was a favourite rural sport in the 30s. The government bounty was $25 for each pair of coyote ears then, and besides, every farmer knew that coyotes were a pest to be exterminated. The pack was led by a wolfhound who would catch a coyote and hold it at bay until the others got there for the kill. Harrassed farmers shot "chicken hawks" – in fact, red-tailed hawks – if they landed within a mile of a chicken yard. There were plenty of mice and gophers around farmyards too, but the farmer never stopped to think that the hawk was probably after them.

Brushing out poplar bluffs and draining sloughs was a common practice among early settlers. During the short time that he's settled in the West, man has gone a long way towards destroying his natural environment. Now there are signs that he is becoming aware of the waste and is trying to do something to stop and repair it. But time is a crucial factor.

22 THE WINDS OF WRATH

Three things damage the soil of the prairies – wind, fertility depletion, and chemical poisoning. Of these, the one that has caused the most damage in the past is wind. A Canada Department of Agriculture pamphlet points out that soil drifting is caused "by wind blowing across an unprotected surface that is dry, loose, and finely granulated." It goes on to state that dust particles, less than 0.1 millemetres in diameter, are dislodged by wind, lifted in the air, and carried for many miles. Particles up to 0.5 millemetres in size are lifted and then dashed to earth with such force that they pulverize the soil. Larger particles creep and roll along the surface. In other words, a dust storm develops, that blows away topsoil and leaves the ground barren.

When the first pioneers came to the plains they sought out the lighter, sandy soils, not because they didn't know better but because the power they had – oxen and horses – couldn't pull ploughs through the heavier clay soil. Besides, the topsoil was so heavily matted with grass roots that it seemed unlikely ever to blow away. Then, to provide more land for wheat, they cut down and burned the aspen groves.

Year after year they ploughed the land, turning the roots and stubble under, exposing the unprotected soil. Gradually the soil began to lift and blow and drift. Many farmers abandoned the light soil and, with tractors were able to plough the heavier soil. But gradually, as deep ploughing continued, this soil too became pulverized and began to lift in the wind. Drifting has always been worst on summer-fallow fields. These are fields – usually comprising half the farmer's land – that, instead of being sewn to crop, are cultivated all summer long to control weeds and conserve moisture. The land is then ready for sowing immediately the ground thaws in the spring. On summer-fallow, the yield of wheat is increased by about forty per cent. But it is also the soil most susceptible to heavy spring winds.

All this came to a disastrous climax during the 1930-40 period, when the prairies were hit by the worst drought in history. The blowing dust buried fences and farm machinery, piled up against barn doors, completely denuded some fields, and even drifted into the houses. The drifting was so bad in the south that thousands of disillusioned families left farms they had lived on for years, loaded what they could on trucks or even hayracks, and migrated north into the bush country, where there was at least some protection from the relentless wind.

But so deep is the topsoil on the best land that when the rains came again and fertilizers were used it produced as well as ever. The farmers moved back, and in a succession of wet years, all but forgot the disaster. Today when the winds blow strongly, the soil still drifts. Dr. D. A. Rennie of the Department of Soil Science, University of Saskatchewan, estimates that nine million acres still suffer from erosion, in his province alone, with a probable loss of forty-five million bushels a year. But the situation has never become as critical as it was during the thirties. Why?

There are a number of reasons. One is a tree planting programme sponsored by the government and various other agencies, that has seen millions of trees planted in shelter belts each year. Another is the practice of sowing as much of the poorest land as possible to permanent pasture.

Strip farming has also increased. This is done by dividing the field into strips of from five to twenty rods wide, depending on the texture of the soil, running at right angles to the prevailing wind. Every second strip is cultivated, leaving plenty of long stubble on the others. This prevents the wind from ever getting a clean sweep across the field and taking the topsoil with it.

Also the use of chemical weed killers has reduced the need for extensive cultivation on summer-fallow, that tended to pulverize the soil. But the principal reason for the reduction in soil drifting is the disappearance of the plough. This implement — for years the symbol of agriculture — was actually the worst enemy of the western farmer. For the ploughshare turned the topsoil over completely and buried the trash – and trash is now the by-word of the western farmer.

By trash the Department of Agriculture means the straw and roots that remain after the grain crop is harvested. Whereas a farmer used to be judged by how clean and "black" his land looked between plantings, now he strives to have as much trash on it as possible, up to two tons or more per acre. It looks untidy, but it catches flying dust and prevents drifting. The implements that can best conserve trash, such as the wide-blade cultivator, the sweep machine, and the rod weeder, have replaced the plough.

Whereas the eastern farmer likes to see his field nice and smooth and even, the western wheat-grower prefers his lumpy and uneven, with good-sized clods. By using a one-way disc instead of a plough, the clods are turned up and stay in place. Discs fitted with seeder boxes are used for sowing grain on trash-covered fields, as are stubble-mulch drills that will seed through quantities of trash.

This excerpt from a bulletin issued by the Department of Soil Science and Saskatchewan Soil Survey, University of Saskatchewan, tells another part of the story. "It is conceivable that with more universal adoption of moisture conserving practices, such as conservation of crop residues at or near the surface, minimal and shallow tillage during periods of high evaporation, judicious control of weeds, practices conducive to maximum retention of snow-fall over the field and maximum conservation of snowmelt, the storage of an additional inch of water on either fallow or stubble land could readily be achieved; this should be reflected in an upward adjustment of yields of approximately twenty-five per cent."

But there is still evidence that the lessons of the past have not been learned by all. In a letter from Meadow Lake, in October, 1967, a thoughtful resident says: "This leads to what to me is the saddest development in the north. More and more land is being cleared for farming. Right now you will pass acres and acres of trees that have been bulldozed and put in piles for burning. A few years ago there was little wind here. Now the wind can be as bad as anywhere on the prairie and dust storms are becoming more and more frequent."

Although conservation of water has always been a problem on the prairies, for a long time little thought was given to soil fertility. The prairie soil was the most fertile in the world, and that was that. But seventy-five years of intensive cropping have taken their toll, and today fertilizing is as essential a part of crop cultivation as seeding.

The three soil nutrients that are usually lacking in soil and must be replaced by commercial fertilizers are nitrogen, phosphorus, and potassium. The code on the bag of chemical fertilizer, as prescribed by the Canadian Fertilizer Act, must state what percentage of each is contained in the mixture. Thus 11-48-0 means that the fertilizer contains eleven per cent nitrogen, forty-eight per cent phosphate, and no potassium. In Saskatchewan all the formulae end in "0" because the land is amply supplied with potassium. But the other two nutrients must be replenished yearly. In the past ten years, use of fertilizers on farm land has increased by ten times to an annual consumption of more than 700,000 tons.

But there is another and greater threat to the soil than lack of fertility – contamination by chemicals. Twenty years ago insect pests, such as grasshoppers, were fought with poisons spread around the edges of the fields, and weeds were controlled by cultivation. Today, both of these pests are controlled by chemicals that are regularly sprayed on the land.

While it is known that this spraying of the soil with poisons kills some harmful creatures, ranging in size from microscopic bacteria to ten-inch earthworms, little is known about its effect on beneficial organisms in the soil. This is what an official publication of the Canada and Saskatchewan Departments of Agriculture says on the subject: "The live weight of these organisms may be as high as five tons per acre. Micro-organisms are responsible for decomposing the organic materials added to soils, consequently releasing plant nutrients formerly tied up in crop residues. The activity of these organisms has a profound effect on soil productivity, controlling in particular the availability of nitrogen and micronutrient or trace elements."

Little research is being done to ascertain to what extent these essential organisms are being destroyed or inhibited by poisons.

Spraying from the air is the most efficient method of killing crop pests. Only time can tell whether the selective poisons used will do irrevocable harm to the soil, wildlife, cattle and, ultimately, man.

But the same official publication gives this warning: "Many insecticides, notably the chlorinated hydrocarbons, dieldrin, aldrin, endrin, heptachlor, and DDT, are very persistent and may leave residue on crops or soils which could contaminate foodstuffs, including meat and dairy products."

In 1962, after approximately one and a half million acres of southern Manitoba farmland had been treated with the chemical dieldrin, the Manitoba Department of Agriculture and Conservation made tests for contamination. As a result, they found traces of the poison in milk from cattle that had access to the treated land. Several farmers were taken to court for violating the Food and Drugs Act and thousands of pounds of contaminated butter were seized. In May 1963, the Manitoba legislature passed a pesticide control act calling for pesticide residue testing, and licencing of pesticide dealers. But the act, it is admitted, cannot completely prevent the careless spraying of poisons on fields.

The soil scientists concerned admit that a "vast amount of damage" is being done, not enough research is being devoted to this hazard to the very life and usefulness of soils, and that there is little co-ordination between soil chemists and the "chemical killer people."

There is still another threat to prairie soils that arises from the increasing industrialization of the region. Thirty years ago, the great complaint about the prairies was its one-crop economy. Almost everybody worked on the farms or ranches, or provided services for farmers and ranchers. If the rains didn't fall and the grass and grain didn't grow, the region was smitten with economic ruin.

But with the discovery of oil and potash all this changed. Oil wells appeared among the wheat fields and on the range. In Saskatchewan potash mines have been dug in the middle of some of the best agricultural land in the province, such as Esterhazy, Belle Plain, Saskatoon, Unity, Allan. Associated with the wells and mines are gasoline refineries, the sulphur plants, chemical plants, and potash refining plants, all of which are known polluters of air, water, and soil.

At present the potash mines and refineries are being watched closely. In the first place, by the nature of potash mining, tremendous amounts of materials are taken out of the ground, all from one layer, and nothing is put back. Potash company officials are convinced that sufficient material is being left between the tunnels to safeguard against cave-ins. Others are not so positive about this. They point out that there are layers of unstable, unconsolidated materials between the potash beds and the surface, and are genuinely concerned about wholesale sinking of the land.

A more apparent threat is the residue from the potash refining process, both that which comes out of the smoke stacks, and that which is piled on the ground. Roughly half of the salt brought up from the mine is common salt, sodium chloride. This means that if in one year a plant produces a million and a half tons of potash which is shipped away to market, it also produces a million and a half tons of table salt for which there is no market. Presently this is being piled on the ground in immense dirty grey pyramids. But as anyone who has ever gargled knows, salt readily dissolves in water and so it is gradually being distributed over the fields. Too much salt can ruin soil by reducing the availability of water and upsetting the nutrient balance.

Another hazard is the dust fall-out from the refining process itself. These salts spread even farther than those dumped on the ground, and are much more difficult to control. The Soils Chemistry Department of Saskatchewan University tests the soil around the mine before production begins and regularly thereafter, but soil pollution from these causes is a long, cumulative process, and by the time definite conclusions can be reached the damage may have been done.

23 THE TURBID WATERS

One morning, in the fall of 1953, a housewife in Prince Albert, Saskatchewan, turned on the hot water tap to run herself a bath. Instead of the usual clear water, the tap yielded a dark brown substance that smelled unlike anything she'd ever smelled before. It soon became evident that the water all over the city was the same. It was off-colour and it stank. Something had definitely got into the Prince Albert water supply.

But Prince Albert gets its water from the North Saskatchewan River and what could be cleaner than fast running water. With the exception of the cities of Battleford and North Battleford about one hundred miles upstream, there was no city of any size between Prince Albert and Edmonton, Alberta. Surely the contamination, whatever it was, couldn't have come all the way from Edmonton to foul the water at Prince Albert – but it did.

In desperation, a committee appointed by the city council went to Edmonton and took samples from the North Saskatchewan River, where the Canadian Chemicals Company was dumping effluents into the river. These were submitted to the Saskatchewan Department of Public Health, for testing and comparison with samples of water taken at Prince Albert. The official report stated in part that "the present data comprise convincing evidence that the volatile contaminants in the North Saskatchewan River water are due mainly to chemicals in the sewage of the Canadian Chemicals Company." And Edmonton is at least four hundred miles away by river.

This awakened the people of the plains to the facts of water pollution. It showed them that the wide, fast-running Saskatchewan is not immune, as they had always thought, to any and all types of contaminants. For years the major cities have been dumping their raw sewage into the river, taking care of course to have sewer outlets downstream from drinking water intakes. They believed implicitly that running water would purify itself in a couple of miles. Now they know it will not.

When the Saskatchewan Water Resources Commission held public hearings in four major cities, during May 1967, they learned some more facts about the condition of Saskatchewan water. The rural municipality of Cory, which is immediately downstream from the fast-growing city of Saskatoon (population 125,000), testified in its brief that: "medical opinions have been obtained from time to time by the Council, indicating that the South Saskatchewan River is polluted within the boundaries of the Municipality, to the point where it is a danger to health." For this reason, the municipality has had since the 19th of May, 1942, a court injunction barring Saskatoon from dumping sewage into the river until said sewage is: "sufficiently purified and deodorized so as to remove and avoid all menace to the public health and so as not to create a nuisance."

Twenty-five years later the city of Saskatoon is still dumping inadequately treated sewage into the river, always giving as the reason that it simply couldn't afford a proper sewage disposal plant. (In presenting his brief, the Saskatoon representative thanked the Municipality of Cory for their tolerance.) Saskatoon's problem is compounded by the new Gardiner Dam, at Outlook, which in summer can reduce the river flow from 10,000 cubic feet per second to 1,300 cubic feet per second, thus cutting down the waste-carrying capacity by eighty-seven per cent. At such times, citizens say, the river stinks.

In another brief to the Commission, Mr. Hugh Arscott of Saskatoon, who spent part of the summer of 1966 exploring the Red Deer and South Saskatchewan by boat, testified that he was: "shocked at the great number of junk yards and garbage dumps that desecrate and contaminate the shores. A constant stream of filth drains into the water course. At Estuary, close to the junction of the Red Deer and South Saskatchewan Rivers, the river surface was blobbed with orange-brown suds. They swirled up into great, dirty cones in the centre of whirlpools. The bushes on either side of the river hung heavy with accumulated filth." He stated that a chemical plant on the Red Deer River: "is spewing large quantities of industrial waste back into the stream," but he named the city dwellers who flush their toilets into the river, as the real villains of river pollution.

Further north, farmers near Lloydminster, on the Alberta-Saskatchewan border, were forced to form an anti-pollution association to defend themselves against household and industrial wastes from that small city. They complained to the Commission that much of the vegetation and nearly all trees lining waterways had been killed, that Neal Lake, about three miles from Lloydminster, had been converted from a pleasant recreation spot to a "smelly cesspool and scene of desolation," and that cattle had died from drinking polluted water.

The capital city of Regina has no river running through it and depends upon water from Buffalo Pound, a lake about forty-five miles northwest of the city, and from wells. Due to runoff into the lake from cottages and from fields heavy with fertilizers and pesticides, the lake was hit by an "algae bloom" in the winter of 1965, that killed thousands of fish. Although authorities described the condition as "unusual," the people of Regina tended to be upset about the purity of their drinking water, which had taken on a definite odour.

Briefs from towns and municipalities throughout the province described the water pollution problem as critical. Words such as vile, foul, rotten, were common in describing the condition of the water. The causes outlined, boiled down to three: 1) the dumping of raw home sewage into rivers and streams; 2) the effluent from chemical plants, petroleum and potash refineries, pulp mills, and other industries; 3) the runoff from land heavy with fertilizers, insecticides, and herbicides.

In Alberta, pollution of the branches of the Saskatchewan River are not so serious simply because the Alberta cities and towns are upstream from Saskatchewan communities. But the problem of runoff is basically the same as that in Saskatchewan, complicated by the fact that Alberta has many more oil refineries and chemical plants.

Manitoba, which has far more water than either of the other two provinces, still has an increasing water-pollution problem. The Red and Assiniboine Rivers, which meet in the city and into which the metropolitan municipalities dump their wastes, have been described as "open sewers." Although many people blame this on communities south of the U.S. border, in the case of the Red River, many others recognize that Metropolitan Winnipeg, which comprises thirteen municipalities and has a population of half a million, is the real villain. Winnipeg does not use the Red or Assiniboine Rivers for its water supply, but obtains this from Shoal Lake, about one hundred miles away.

What Winnipeg does to the rivers is, even the officials admit, an outrage. From the time of the first fur trader, the rivers had been used as sewers. Everything that wasn't wanted went into them and was carried off to be lost in the vastness of Lake Winnipeg. But, as the communities grew and flush toilets came into use, and tanneries, slaughterhouses, hospitals, and hundreds of other establishments dumped more and more waste into the rivers, the water became increasingly dirty. To quote from an official source: "Beginning in 1930, pollution in the Red and Assiniboine Rivers was at an all-time high. The effects of the discharge of untreated wastes from the developed area, coupled with a cycle of low river flows, made the situation intolerable."

So something was done about it – namely, the Greater Winnipeg Sanitary District was created. Unfortunately, there was an escape clause in the act passed and six of the nine municipalities that then made up the metropolitan area withdrew. However, three of them came back and the District began the job of cleaning up the rivers. But they are still behind, never quite able to keep up with the number of people and industries moving into

Beyond its northward bend, sixty miles from Saskatoon, the South Saskatchewan meets the three-mile-wide Gardiner Dam, with control shafts the size of a railway tunnel. The 140-mile-long reservoir holds water sufficient to cover eight million acres one foot deep.

the area. The Manitoba Department of Health has given the city until 1971, to fully treat all sewage dumped into the river.

To help pay for new plants, the city levies a surcharge on industries with excessive effluents. Thus a sugar beet factory, whose pollution load is equivalent to that of 150,000 persons, has paid as much as $100,000 a year. The city is building secondary sewage disposal plants as fast as possible, and expects that by 1971, the deadline set by the Department of Health, the situation will be under control. "Of course," one official remarked ruefully, "we'll never return the river to its pristine purity."

Most water control experts believe that the only solution to the water problem on the plains is a joint control commission of the three prairie provinces, with the Federal government providing advice and money. In the meantime, all prairie cities are faced with the same problem – how to attract industry and at the same time prevent industry from fouling the waters.

In the matter of water conservation, the prairies have done better. In Alberta, dams on the St. Mary, Belly, Bow, and Red Deer Rivers have provided two million acres of irrigated land on which sugar beet and other crops flourish. In Saskatchewan, smaller irrigation areas were provided at Val Marie, Swift Current, and Maple Creek. And in 1967, the Gardiner Dam was completed on the South Saskatchewan, with a potential irrigation range of 200,000 acres.

In Manitoba the problem is as much one of flood control as water conservation. To control floods on the Assiniboine, fifteen in the last fifty years, a reservoir has been built at Shellmouth, Manitoba. To allow Lake Manitoba to act as a storage reservoir for the area, a diversion has been built at Portage la Prairie, and to protect Winnipeg from floods like that of 1950 – 8,200 homes flooded; damage $114 million – the Red River Floodway has been built around the entire metropolitan area. At the same time, water conservation projects have been engineered at Rivers, Neepawa, Deloraine, and other places, and most of these can be used for irrigation.

People of the prairies recognize today, as they always have done, that scarcity of water is their biggest problem. There just isn't enough water, either falling from the clouds or entering the region by way of glacier-fed rivers, to satisfy the agricultural and industrial needs. For this reason their attitude is very cool towards the grandiose so-called "continental" scheme, that would divert waters presently running into the Arctic, into canals taking much of it southward to the United States. This N.A.W.A.P.A., North American Water And Power Alliance programme calls for, among other things, the establishment of great reservoirs in the Canadian Cordillera and for a canal that would run south through the states of Montana, Idaho, Nevada, and California, with branches going through Utah and Arizona into Mexico. Another canal would run across the prairies to Lake Superior.

Dr. Trevor Lloyd, head of the Geography Department of McGill University, describes it as "an exercise in sophomore civil engineering, which has received far greater attention than it ever deserved;" and Dr. W. R. Derick Sewell, Department of Economics, University of Victoria, warns against the effect of this "world's largest reservoir and aqueduct system" on the geology of the Rocky Mountain trench, and even on the climate of the prairies. Prairie people just say that "we're going to need all the water we can get, right here at home."

Prairie dwellers have always been proud of their fresh air. Phrases like "the wind blows free" and "skies are not cloudy all day" have always been taken at face value, and until recently they had a right to be accepted without reservation. A personal experience will help to illustrate what has happened in the past 23 years.

When I left the prairies in 1944, there was little industry. Oil hadn't been found in any quantities, and potash wasn't even a word. After two years in Toronto breathing air contaminated with factory fumes, I returned for a visit in the early spring. I remember getting out of my berth when the train stopped briefly at South Saskatoon, and stepping out onto the platform. Immediately I felt the difference between this air and that of Toronto. It smelled better than any air I'd smelled in two years. My nose told me I was home.

I returned again in 1967, but this time I could not detect any difference in the air. At Saskatoon, a new fertilizer plant was filling the air with stench. At Regina, the refineries in the east end of the city cast a dirty pall over the sky, and in Winnipeg, from a window in the Royal Alexandra Hotel, I could see only a couple of blocks.

I didn't get to Calgary, but a newspaper story from that city quoted the Medical Officer of Health as saying: "On several occasions each month, during the fall and winter, a decidedly whisky-coloured pollution pall can be noted hanging over that area of the city located in the valley of the Bow River. The time has come where every unnecessary source of air pollutants must be eliminated. Clean air is not cheap air."

Since most provincial and municipal officials on the prairies still consider that air pollution is something that happens in other regions, no research has been done to determine the exact amount of pollution. City officials who may be aware of pollution are reluctant to do much about it. As one official put it: "We are in the business of attracting industry to Manitoba, and we must co-operate with industry in everything we do."

Manitoba has no air pollution act as such, but according to a regulation under the Public Health Act air contaminants mean dust, fly ash, fumes, smoke, gases, or a combination thereof. Section 13 of the regulation states that: "it shall be unlawful and a nuisance for any person to cause, suffer or permit smoke or dust or cinders or fly ash or fumes or gases or offensive odours to discharge or escape from any building or premise to the detriment or annoyance of others."

Yet, as soon as you leave Winnipeg airport, heading downtown, you are hit by an odour that is certainly offensive. It comes from the feed processing plants, one of which is half a block from a large hotel, but nothing is done about it. The city's largest department store, on Portage Avenue, burns soft coal, and at times pours out volumes of black smoke that obscure the sky. Refineries foul the air with sulphur dioxide, although there are specific regulations against this.

The regulations have no teeth. They state that a medical health officer or sanitary inspector can, if he gets no response from the offender, refer the matter to the Minister of Health and Public Welfare of the Province, who "upon receipt of the complaint shall cause an investigation to be made and direct the manner in which the nuisance shall be abated." The persons affected feel that an act should be passed that will provide for stiff penalties, and which – recognizing that industry is essential to the province – will not put the entire onus for cleaning up the air on individual companies.

In Saskatchewan an air pollution act was proclaimed in February, 1967. It specifically defines air pollution as: "the presence in the outdoor atmosphere of an air contaminant in quantities that may cause discomfort to or endanger the health, safety or welfare of persons or that may cause injury or damage to property or to plant or animal life."

The act provides for definite penalties – for an individual a fine of not less than $5 nor more than $25; for a corporation not less than $100 nor more than $500. But the important factor is, that as the offence continues, each day is considered separately, and may be fined accordingly. On the positive side, the act provides for the setting up of an air pollution advisory committee, made up of engineers and other specialists in air pollution, to assist individuals and companies in controlling their pollutants.

In Alberta there is evidence that air is being seriously polluted, in at least some areas, by fall-out from gas processing plants. Reports from the Red River Valley, in November, 1967, quoted farmers as complaining that two plants near Alix and Nevis were poisoning the air to the extent that: "cattle are dying, becoming infertile, slipping their calves, suffering from internal poisoning, respiratory infection and eye irritation." Apart from this, the farmers claimed that hay and grass were losing food value and becoming harmful as feed; that formerly fertile pasture was being eroded and turned into wasteland by fumes and fall-out. They also complained that humans were suffering from severe respiratory trouble, sore throats, nausea and illness, and that a constant disagreeable odour of sulphur and hydrogen sulphide gas permeated the air.

The gas companies involved stated in reply that they were operating within standards set by the Provincial government, and that the air was regularly checked both by the companies and by the Environmental Health Service of the Department of Public Health. One company official was quoted in the Edmonton *Journal* as saying that: "it seems difficult to have this type of operation and the money it pours into the economy without affecting someone."

Editorially, the *Journal* wondered whether, if the companies were operating within government regulations, the provincially-set regulations were realistic, and stated: "There's at least a possibility that, while the two plants haven't violated the limits, the limits themselves aren't sufficient to guarantee healthy living conditions in the province."

The Alberta Advisory Committee on Pollution Control is made up of representatives from industry, municipal governments, universities and the Provincial government. Everywhere harassed civic officials pose the same question: "How do we clean up the air without driving industry out of our city, or our province, or for that matter, our region?"

For years the prairies suffered from a one-crop economy dependent upon the vagaries of the weather. Almost all manufactured goods came from industrial Ontario and Quebec. Cities like Saskatoon and Regina had no factories at all. Their air was pure but their economy shaky. For years prairie leaders planned and contrived to attract industry, without much success until oil and potash were discovered. Now the cities have refineries, chemical plants, fertilizer factories, and even steel mills. But the air is getting worse all the time.

The solution, as voiced by many people on the plains, lies with over-all regulations that apply to all communities, all provinces. Then no industry could threaten to move, or not to come at all, if the standards of one province are more stringent than those of another. Federal rulings, they argue, apply to marriage laws, abortion laws, and so on; Ottawa must therefore institute laws regulating water and air pollution for the whole country.

24 THE VANISHING BEASTS AND BIRDS

It has always seemed to me that in their attitude towards nature prairie farmers tend to be hard-headed and pragmatic. Perhaps it is because in their work their relationship with nature has been more of a struggle than a pleasure. It's difficult to see anything that is attractive in a ground squirrel that is eating your crops. A sudden hail storm that flattens the wheat isn't likely to evoke raptures about the grandeur of nature. A grasshopper isn't a scientific wonder – it is a pest. And that applies to a flock of sandhill cranes destroying half your wheat. Prairie poets write few odes to "gentle nature."

They tend to be wary of wildlife. During a recent visit to the Saskatchewan Museum of Natural History, I watched a pleasant-looking farmer's wife stop in front of the prairie chicken display. Most people would say the birds are handsome. Her lips compressed into a grim line and her only comment was: "There they are – the pests!" At the same time, game birds and animals have always been plentiful and the authorities see in them a good source of income. They will do almost anything to attract wealthy hunters to the area.

For instance, although the pronghorn antelopes are scarce, there is still a hunting season for them. Between twelve hundred and twenty-five hundred licences are issued each year in Saskatchewan, and as this is one of the few places on the continent where antelopes can be shot, there is great competition for them. To be absolutely fair to everyone, the licences are given out by lottery, with as many as four thousand eager hunters from all parts of the province jamming the auditorium of the Museum of Natural History to see who will be the lucky ones. It's such a good show that a large audience of non-hunters gather to watch the fun.

There is also an open season for sandhill cranes in Saskatchewan. Mr. T. A. Harper, of the Department of Natural Resources of Saskatchewan, pointed out that this is not entirely because the birds are a nuisance to the farmers, but because they are a good game-bird and the hunters have a right to get a crack at them. However, the hunting range is restricted to the area between Last Mountain and Quill Lakes, and the department has patrols posted to make sure that none of the almost extinct whooping cranes, that often migrate with the sandhill cranes, are shot by mistake.

Despite these precautions, the Canadian Audubon Society took a very strong stand against the open season. In an editorial they pointed out the danger of accidentally shooting whooping cranes with the sandhill cranes, and the advantage of protecting wheat fields by scaring the birds off, rather than killing them. The editorial ended with a strong plea to recognize the sandhill cranes as "a vibrant, vital part of our lives." There is still an open season.

Although naturalists and others have pointed out, time and time again, that the coyote is undoubtedly the best rodent killer on the plains, these animals are still destroyed with the blessing of the government. All it takes is a complaint from a farmer or rancher that he's being molested by coyotes – usually this means he's seen a coyote near his farm – and the Wildlife Branch sends a man with poison.

As a result of one wholesale poisoning programme in southern Saskatchewan, almost all the coyotes were eliminated from one area. Immediately the rodent population increased to an alarming degree. Since there will be predators wherever there is food, this was followed by an influx of red foxes. The ranchers soon decided they would rather have the coyotes than the thieving foxes.

Although hawks and owls are protected in most other parts of Canada, they are only partially protected on the prairies. During the winter months it is legal in some provinces to shoot the goshawks, great horned owls, and snowy owls. One worried naturalist reported that he had seen dead owls along the road in winter, where motorists had stopped their cars, pointed guns out the window, and shot the birds off telephone poles. The reason for all this carnage? Owls like to prey on Hungarian partridge, and the "Huns" are the hunters' darlings. Crows, magpies, blackbirds, cowbirds, grackles, and English sparrows can be legally shot at any time.

Naturalists are violently opposed to the wholesale use of insecticides, particularly the strong poisons sprayed into the air to kill mosquitoes. On one occasion forty dead ducks were picked up in the Wascana Bird Sanctuary. When the naturalists attempted to discover if the deaths were caused by spray, the authorities refused to give them samples of the poisons used.

Parallel with the continuing destruction of wildlife, there are counterforces working to abate and repair the damage. In Regina and Winnipeg there are large, modern, well-equipped museums of natural history where the public can see stuffed birds and animals in natural poses and in simulated surroundings. Numerous books describing the mammals, insects, and reptiles are available at reasonable prices, and in each there is a strong stand for conservation.

On the Alberta Game Farm, a few miles from Edmonton, visitors can see, live in cages and in large enclosures, almost every bird and mammal that is native to the plains, along with a great number that are not, including camels, zebras, Siberian tigers, Tibetan yaks, Peruvian llamas, Sicilian donkeys, and a pair of rare white rhinoceroses.

No part of Canada is better supplied with game preserves and bird sanctuaries than the plains. The national and provincial parks, water-fowl research stations and private sanctuaries provide protection for elk, bison, deer, ducks, geese, cranes, herons, and innumerable smaller birds.

The Canadian Wildlife Service is active on the plains, as elsewhere in Canada, conducting experiments on birds and animals so that they can better protect them. In Wood Buffalo National Park, for instance, they keep close tabs on the huge herd of bison. Periodically the animals are herded into compounds where they are checked for bovine tuberculosis, brucellosis, and various parasites. They are inoculated and permitted to run free again. Recently an outbreak of that dreaded disease of animals and humans, anthrax, was detected in the herd, both inside the park and on the other side of the Slave River, in the Grand Detour and Hook Lake areas. Over five thousand animals were vaccinated, and those whose blood tests revealed the presence of *bacillus anthracis* were destroyed and their bodies limed and buried.

Since traces of DDT and other poisons have been found in infertile eggs of eagles and hawks, the Wildlife Service is carrying out extensive research on the effect of herbicides and pesticides on birds of prey.

The problem of conserving wetlands on the prairies, as breeding grounds for ducks, has also been taken up by the Wildlife Service. Farmers and ducks tend to be incompatible. Not only do the flocks of ducks eat grain, but the sloughs where birds nest and loaf are often in the middle of grain fields. Wherever possible, the farmer tries to drain these and sow them to grain. To discourage this, the Wildlife Service has a programme whereby a farmer is compensated for the grain he would grow on the drained slough.

Also, in co-operation with the Delta Waterfowl Research Station, Ducks Unlimited, and the University of Manitoba Botany Department, the Wildlife Service is conducting one of the most thorough investigations on wildlife needs, habits, and conflicts ever tried in Canada. The Wildlife Service also co-operates with other agencies in the most expensive and extensive operation to save a wild species ever conducted anywhere – the Save-the-Whooping-Crane programme.

The international Whooping Crane Conservation Association, with headquarters in Hereford, Arizona, has members in both Canada and the United States (1968 president, Fred Bard, Director of the Saskatchewan Museum of Natural History), and spends considerable time and money to preserve the few remaining whooping cranes. One of their most ambitious projects has been "Operation Egg Hunt." Described as the "most significant breakthrough in the history of the research-propagation effort," the programme had Dr. R. C. Erickson and Mr. Glen Smart fly to Wood Buffalo Park, descend by helicopter near whoopers' nests, and take one egg from each of six of them. It was reasoned that, since the cranes rarely hatch more than one of their two eggs, this would not seriously affect the natural hatch. The eggs were taken back to the Endangered Species Research Section of the Patuxent Wildlife Centre near Washington, D.C., where five of them were successfully incubated.

Can the whooping cranes be saved? Far more important is the question of whether the soil of the prairies will be fit to grow food in, the water fit to drink, and the air fit to breathe. And as the population increases and industry expands, will there be any place at all for the wild animals that now live on the plains? Or will one species after another be poisoned, shot, crowded out, annihilated?

The answer lies not only with a group of dedicated naturalists, or an understaffed government agency, but with all the people who live on the plains.

GEOLOGIC TIME SCALE

TIME	ERA	PERIOD	EPOCH
	CENOZOIC	QUATERNARY	PLEISTOCENE
		TERTIARY	PLIOCENE
			MIOCENE
			OLIGOCENE
			EOCENE
50			PALEOCENE
100	MESOZOIC	CRETACEOUS	UPPER LOWER
150		JURASSIC	UPPER MIDDLE LOWER
200		TRIASSIC	UPPER MIDDLE LOWER
250	PALAEOZOIC	PERMIAN	UPPER MIDDLE LOWER
300		PENNSYLVANIAN	
		MISSISSIPPIAN	
350		DEVONIAN	UPPER MIDDLE LOWER
400		SILURIAN	
450		ORDOVICIAN	UPPER MIDDLE LOWER
500 550		CAMBRIAN	UPPER MIDDLE LOWER

MILLIONS OF YEARS

THE ASCENT OF LIFE: 20, 19, 18, 17, 16, 15, 14, 13, 12, 11, 10, 9, 8, 7, 6, 5, 4, 3, 2, 1

THE ASCENT OF LIFE: 1, *protozoan;* 2, *jellyfish;* 3, *crinoid;* 4, *cephalopod;* 5, *climatius;* 6, *shark;* 7, *brachiopod;* 8, *seed fern;* 9, *dimetrodon;* 10, *brontosaurus;* 11, *plesiosaur;* 12, *tyrannosaurus;* 13, *taeniolabis;* 14, *diatryma;* 15, *hyracotherium;* 16, *brontotherium;* 17, *oxydactylus;* 18, *pliohippus;* 19, *mastodon;* 20, *man.*

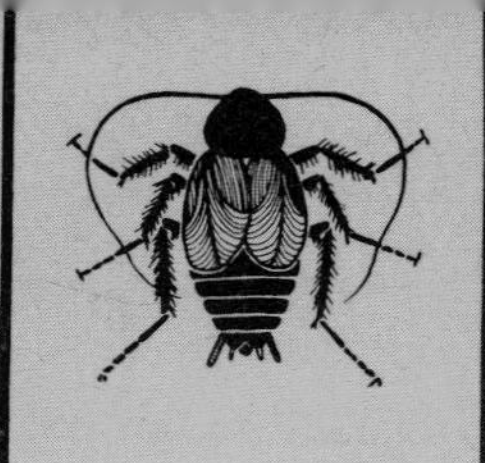

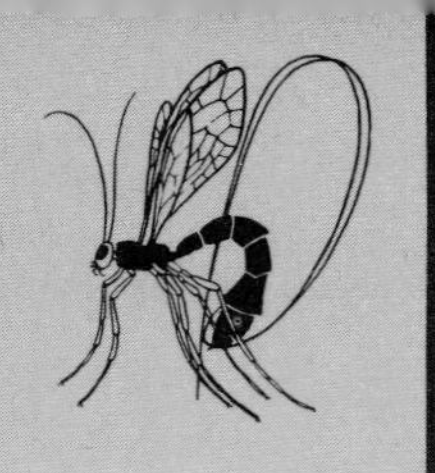

SHORT LIST OF ROCKS, PLANTS AND ANIMALS

The lists on the following pages have been compiled as a basic guide for amateur naturalists intending to explore the wealth of natural history of the Western Plains. These selected summaries cannot possibly cover all species — there are many thousands of insects alone — but an attempt has been made to include the common life forms and the natural phenomena peculiar to this region. Readers should find it useful to study the lists touching on their sphere of interest, checking off items they have observed during field trips. Those wishing to extend their search will find an extensive Bibliography on pages 153-5; references listed there contain more detailed information on specific subjects.

ROCKS

CENOZOIC ERA

PLEISTOCENE EPOCH

Erratics
Fine Sand
Gravel
Lacustrine sand, silt, and clay
Till
Varved clay

TERTIARY PERIOD

Conglomerate
Sandstone
Shale

MESOZOIC ERA

CRETACEOUS PERIOD

Conglomerate
Kaonlinized clay
Lignite
Sandstone
Shale, bentonitic
Shale, calcareous
Shale, non-calcareous

JURASSIC PERIOD

Calcareous shale
Limestone
Sandstone

TRIASSIC PERIOD

Impure limestone
Sandstone
Silty shale

PALAEOZOIC ERA

PENNSYLVANIAN PERIOD

Chert
Sandstone
Siltstone

MISSISSIPPIAN PERIOD

Carbonate rocks with evaporites
Dolomite
Limestone
Sandstone
Shale

DEVONIAN PERIOD

Brown dolomite
Dolomite
Dolomitic shale
Evaporites
Limestone
Sandstone
Shale (varying colours)
Shaly limestone
Siltstone

SILURIAN PERIOD

Dolomite
Limestone
Sandstone
Shale

ORDOVICIAN PERIOD

Conglomerate
Dolomite
Greenish shale
Limestone
Sandstone
Siltstone

CAMBRIAN PERIOD

Dolomite
Glauconitic sandstone
Limestone
Sandstone
Shale

MINERALS

The minerals listed are those most likely to be found in the regions named.

SOUTHERN MANITOBA

Bentonite
Cement (limestone)
Gypsum
Petroleum
Salt

SOUTHERN SASKATCHEWAN

Ceramic clay
Lignite
Natural gas
Petroleum
Potash
Salt
Sodium sulphate

ALBERTA

Bituminous coat
Bituminous sands
Ceramic clay
Natural gas
Petroleum
Sulphur

NORTHWEST TERRITORIES

Anhydrite
Gypsum
Lead
Petroleum
Zinc

INVERTEBRATE FOSSILS

CRETACEOUS

Pelecypoda
Arctica ovata
Callista deweyi
Cardium pauperculum

Corbicula cytheriformis
Corbicula occidentalis
Gervillia birugate
Inoceramus barabini
Inoceramus vanuxemi
Modiola attenuata
Nucula cancellata
Ostrea glabra
Ostrea subtrigonalis
Gastropoda
Campeloma cypressensis
Campeloma producta
Goniobasis sublaevis
Goniobasis webbi
Lunata obliquata
Lunata subcrassa
Ammonoidea
Acanthoscaphites nodosus
Baculites compressus
Baculites ovatus
Placenticeras intercalare
Placenticeras whitfieldi
Rhaeboceras (Scaphites) subglobosus
Plantae
Cones of Sequoia
Metasequoia (now includes *Taxodium)*
Populus
Sequoia
Viburnum

VERTEBRATE FOSSILS

PLEISTOCENE
Bison
Odocoileus
Equus
Camelops
Ovibos

UPPER MIOCENE
Wood Mountain gravels
Mylagaulus
Hypolagus
Amphicyon
Aelurodon
Pseudaelurus
Bassariscus
Merycodus
Aphelops
Merychippus
Gomphotherium

EARLY OLIGOCENE
Cypress Hills
Hyaenodon
Prosciurus
Palaeolagus
Mesohippus
Caenopus
Teleodus
Megacerops
Bothriodon
Merycoidodon
Leptomeryx

LATE EOCENE
Swift Current
Paramys
Mytonolagus
Hyopsodus
Protoreodon
Epihippus
Leptotragulus
Hyrachyus

PALEOCENE
Swan Hills
Ectypodus
Leptacodon

CRETACEOUS
Fishes
Myledaphus
Acipenser
Amphibians
Scaphereton
Reptiles
Baena
Basilemys
Trionyx (Aspideretes)
Champsosaurus
Leidyosuchus
Dinosaurs
Gorgosaurus
Albertosaurus
Tyrannosaurus
Kritosaurus
Prosaurolophus
Lambeosaurus
Corythosaurus
Tetragonosaurus
Parasaurolophus
Edmontosaurus
Stegoceras
Chasmosaurus
Centrosaurus
Triceratops
Edmontia
Euoplocephalus
Mammals
Stegodon
Cimolomys
Eodelphis

PLANTS

WATER PLANTS

HERBS
Richardson's pondweed
Potamogeton richardsonii
Sago pondweed
Potamogeton pectinatus
Western ditch-grass
Ruppia occidentalis
Horned-pondweed
Zannichellia palustris
American water-plantain
Alisma subcordatum
Broad-leaved arrowhead
Sagittaria latifolia
Canada waterweed
Elodea canadensis
Ivy-leaved duckweed
Lemna trisulca
Larger duckweed
Spirodela polyrhiza
Lesser duckweed
Lemna minor
Water persicaria
Polygonum natans
Yellow pond-lily
Nuphar variegatum
Large-leaved watercrowfoot
Ranunculus trichophyllus
Small yellow watercrowfoot
Ranunculus gmelinii
Vernal water-starwort
Callitriche palustris
Spiked water-milfoil
Myriophyllum exalbescens
Mare's-tail
Hippuris vulgaris
Greater bladderwort
Utricularia vulgaris

MARSH AND BOG PLANTS

SEDGES
Straw-colored cyperus
Cyperus strigosus
Awned sedge
Carex atherodes
Beaked sedge
Carex rostrata
Graceful sedge
Carex praegracilis
Water sedge
Carex aquatilis
Woolly sedge
Carex lanuginosa

GRASSES
Nuttall's salt-meadow grass
Puccinellia airoides

Tall manna grass
Glyceria grandis
Spangletop
Scolochloa festucacea
Common reed grass
Phragmites communis
Slender wheat grass
Agropyron trachycaulum
Nodding wild rye
Elymus canadensis
Tufted hair grass
Deschampsia caespitosa
Marsh reed grass
Calamagrostis canadensis
Marsh muhly
Muhlenbergia racemosa
Slough grass
Beckmannia syzigachne
Prairie cord grass
Spartina pectinata
Reed canary grass
Phalaris arundinacea

RUSHES
Baltic rush
Juncus balticus
Knotted rush
Juncus nodosus
Toad rush
Juncus bufonius

HERBS
Common horsetail
Equisetum arvense
Swamp horsetail
Equisetum fluviatile

Woodland horsetail
Equisetum sylvaticum
Common cattail
Typha latifolia
Broad-fruited bur-reed
Sparganium eurycarpum
Marsh arrow-grass
Triglochin palustris
Tall cotton-grass
Eriophorum angustifolium
Great bulrush
Scirpus validus
Prairie bulrush
Scirpus paludosus
Small-fruited bulrush
Scirpus microcarpus
Three-square bulrush
Scirpus americanus
Creeping spike-rush
Eleocharis palustris
Needle spike-rush
Eleocharis acicularis
Sweet-flag
Acorus calamus
Water calla
Calla palustris
Marsh-marigold
Caltha palustris
Pitcherplant
Sarracenia purpurea
March cinquefoil
Potentilla palustris
Purple avens
Geum rivale
Northern bog violet
Viola nephrophylla

Snakeroot
Sanicula marilandica

Water parsnip
Sium suave
Swamp cranberry
Vaccinium oxycoccus
Saline shootingstar
Dodecatheon pauciflorum
Tufted loosestrife
Lysimachia thrysiflora
Sea-milkwort
Glaux maritima
Buck-bean
Menyanthes trifoliata
Swamp milkweed
Asclepias incarnata
Wild mint
Mentha arvensis
Yellow monkeyflower
Mimulus guttatus
Marsh speedwell
Veronica scutellata
Elephant's-head
Pedicularis groenlandica
Marsh bellflower
Campanula aparinoides
Kalm's lobelia
Lobelia kalmii
Marsh ragwort
Senecio palustris

SHRUBS

Leatherleaf
Chamaedaphne calyculata
Labrador-tea
Ledum groenlandicum
Pale laurel
Kalmia polifolia

TERRESTRIAL PLANTS

SEDGES

Blunt sedge
Carex obtusata
Low sedge
Carex eleocharis
Sun-loving sedge
Carex heliophila

GRASSES

Awnless brome
Bromus inermis
Rough fescue
Festuca scabrella
Sheep fescue
Festuca ovina
Kentucky blue grass
Poa pratensis
Alkali grass
Distichlis stricta
Orchard grass
Dactylis glomerata
Purple oat grass
Schizachne purpurascens
Awned wheat grass
Agropyron subsecundum
Crested wheat grass
Agropyron cristatum
Quack or couch grass
Agropyron repens
Western wheat grass
Agropyron smithii
Hairy wild rye
Elymus innovatus
Wild barley or foxtail
Hordeum jubatum
June grass
Koeleria cristata
Hooker's oat grass
Avena hookeri
Poverty oat grass
Danthonia spicata
Plains reed grass
Calamagrostis montanensis
Sand grass
Calamovilfa longifolia
Redtop
Agrostis stolonifera

Timothy
Phleum pratense

Prairie muhly
Muhlenbergia cuspidata
Sand dropseed
Sporobolus cryptandrus
Indian rice grass
Oryzopsis hymenoides
Green needle grass
Stipa viridula
Spear grass
Stipa comata
Porcupine grass
Stipa spartea
Tumble grass
Schedonnardus paniculatus
Alkali cord grass
Spartina gracilis
Blue grama
Bouteloua gracilis
Sweet grass
Hierochloe odorata
Switch grass
Panicum virgatum
Big bluestem
Andropogon gerardi
Little bluestem
Andropogon scoparius
Indian grass
Sorghastrum nutans

HERBS

Common scouring-rush
Equisetum hyemale
Running-pine
Lycopodium clavatum
Prairie selaginella
Selaginella densa
Death camas
Zygadenus gramineus
Nodding onion
Allium cernuum
Western red lilly
Lilium philadelphicum
Yellowbell
Fritillaria pudica
Common camass
Camassia quamash
Soapweed
Yucca glauca
Star-flowered Solomon's-seal
Smilacina stellata
Fairybells
Disporum trachycarpum
Carrionflower
Smilax lasioneura
Common blue-eyed grass
Sisyrinchium montanum
Long-bracted orchid
Habenaria viridis
Wild mustard
Brassica kaber
Common nettle
Urtica gracilis
Nodding umbrellaplant
Eriogonum cernuum
Sand dock
Rumex venosus
Sheep sorrel
Rumex acetosella

Doorweed
Polygonum aviculare
Strawberry blite
Chenopodium capitatum
Orache
Atriplex patula
Winterfat
Eurotia lanata
Russian pigweed
Axyris amaranthoides
Red samphire
Salicornia rubra
Western sea-blite
Suaeda depressa
Russian-thistle
Salsola pestifer
Purslane
Portulaca oleracea
Common chickweed
Stellaria media
Blunt-leaved sandwort
Arenaria lateriflora
Field chickweed
Cerastium arvense
Depressed whitlowwort
Paronychia despressa
Smooth catchfly
Silene cserei
White cockle
Lychnis alba
White baneberry
Actaea alba
Wild columbine
Aquilegia canadensis
Low larkspur
Delphinium bicolor

Crocus anemone
Anemone patens

Prairie buttercup
Ranunculus rhomboideus
Smooth-leaved buttercup
Ranunculus abortivus
Tall meadow-rue
Thalictrum dasycarpum
Golden corydalis
Corydalis aurea

Stinkweed
Thlaspi arvense
Tumbling mustard
Sisymbrium altissimum
Wild radish
Raphanus raphanistrum
Shepherd's-purse
Capsella bursa-pastoris
False flax
Camelina sativa
Ball mustard
Neslia paniculata
Hare's-ear mustard
Conringia orientalis
Tower mustard
Arabis glabra
Western wallflower
Erysimum asperum
Pink cleome
Cleome serrulata
Clammyweed
Polanisia graveolens

Golden-bean
Thermopsis rhombifolia

Alumroot
Heuchera richardsonii
Bishop's-cap
Mitella nuda
Plains cinquefoil
Potentilla bipinnatifida
Prairie cinquefoil
Potentilla pensylvanica
Rough cinquefoil
Potentilla norvegica
Silverweed
Potentilla anserina
Ascending purple milk-vetch
Astragalus striatus
Cushion milk-vetch
Astragalus triphyllus
Ground-plum
Astragalus caryocarpus
Missouri milk-vetch
Astragalus missouriensis

Narrow-leaved milk-vetch
Astragalus pectinatus
Silvery lupine
Lupinus argenteus
Alfalfa
Medicago sativa
Alsike clover
Trifolium hybridum
Indian breadroot
Psoralea esculenta
Silverleaf psoralea
Psoralea argophylla
Late yellow locoweed
Oxytropis gracilis
Wild licorice
Glycyrrhiza lepidota
American hedysarum
Hedysarum alpinum
Wild white geranium
Geranium richardsonii
American vetch
Vicia americana
Large-flowered yellow flax
Linum rigidum
Seneca snakeroot
Polygala senega
Spotted touch-me-not
Impatiens biflora
Common mallow
Malva neglecta
Crowfoot violet
Viola pedatifida
Eveningstar
Mentzelia decapetala
Purple cactus
Mamillaria vivipara
Prickly-pear
Opuntia polyacantha
Fireweed
Epilobium angustifolium
Scarlet gaura
Gaura coccinea
White evening-primrose
Oenothera nuttallii
Yellow evening-primrose
Oenothera biennis
Wild sarsaparilla
Aralia nudicaulis
Plains cymopterus
Cymopterus acaulis
Cow-parsnip
Heracleum lanatum
Long-fruited parsley
Lomatium macrocarpum

Leafy musineon
Musineon divaricatum
Smooth sweet cicely
Osmorhiza longistylis
Squawroot
Perideridia gairdneri
Snakeroot
Sanicula marilandica
Lyall's angelica
Angelica lyallii
Pink wintergreen
Pyrola asarifolia
Mountain shootingstar
Dodecatheon cylindrocarpum
Starflower
Trientalis borealis
Spreading dogbane
Apocynum androsaemifolium
Showy milkweed
Asclepias speciosa
Franklin's scorpionweed
Phacelia franklinii
Western bluebur
Lappula redowskii
Tall lungwort
Mertensia paniculata
Hoary puccoon
Lithospermum canescens
Giant-hyssop
Agastache anethiodora
False dragonhead
Dracocephalum nuttallii
Western wild bergamot
Monarda fistulosa
Prairie ground-cherry
Physalis virginiana
Wild tomato
Solanum triflorum

Wild morning-glory
Convolvulus sepium

Butter-and-eggs
Linaria vulgaris
Blue-eyed Mary
Collinsia parviflora
Smooth blue beardtongue
Pentstemon nitidus

Kittentails
Besseya wyomingensis
Downy paintbrush
Castilleja sessiliflora
Scarlet paintbrush
Castilleja coccinea
Clustered broom-rape
Orobanche fasciculata
Common plantain
Plantago major
Northern bedstraw
Galium boreale
Harebell
Campanula rotundifolia
Spotted joe-pye weed
Eupatorium maculatum
Gumweed
Grindelia perennis
Common broomweed
Gutierrezia diversifolia
Flat-topped white aster
Aster umbellatus
Lindley's aster
Aster ciliolatus
Showy aster
Aster conspicuus
Smooth aster
Aster laevis
Rayless-aster
Brachyactis angusta
Hairy golden-aster
Chrysopsis villosa
Canescent goldenrod
Solidago canadensis L. *var. gilvocanescens*
Flat-topped goldenrod
Solidago graminifolia
Low goldenrod
Solidago missouriensis
Rabbitbrush
Chrysothamnus nauseosus
Rough fleabane
Erigeron asper
Prairie everlasting
Antennaria campestris
Tall everlasting
Antennaria anaphaloides
Povertyweed
Iva axillaris
Common ragweed
Ambrosia artemisiifolia
Cocklebur
Xanthium italicum

Black-eyed Susan
Rudbeckia hirta
Purple coneflower
Echinacea angustifolia
Long-headed coneflower
Ratibida columnifera
Prairie sunflower
Helianthus petiolaris
Oxeye daisy
Chrysanthemum leucanthemum
Tarweed
Madia glomerata
Colorado rubberweed
Hymenoxys richardsonii
Mountain sneezeweed
Helenium autumnale

Great-flowered gaillardia
Gaillardia aristata

Woolly yarrow
Achillea lanulosa
Pasture sage
Artemisia frigida
Leafy arnica
Arnica chamissonis
Entire-leaved groundsel
Senecio intergerrimus
Canada thistle
Cirsium arvense
Lesser burdock
Arctium minus
Chicory
Cichorium intybus
Yellow goat's-beard
Tragopogon dubius
Dandelion
Taraxacum officinale
Perennial sow-thistle
Sonchus arvensis
Blue lettuce
Lactuca pulchella
Skeletonweed
Lygodesmia juncea

Large-flowered false dandelion
Agoseris glauca
Scapose hawk's-beard
Crepis runcinata
White-lettuce
Prenanthes alba

SHRUBS

Low juniper
Juniperus communis
Low wild gooseberry
Ribes hirtellum
Wild red raspberry
Rubus strigosus
Shrubby cinquefoil
Potentilla fruticosa
Prickly rose
Rosa acicularis
Low sand cherry
Prunus pumila
Poison-ivy
Rhus radicans
Buffaloberry
Shepherdia argentea
Silveryberry
Elaeagnus commutata
Alternate-leaved dogwood
Cornus alternifolia
Lowbush-cranberry
Viburnum edule
Snowberry
Symphoricarpos albus
Twining honeysuckle
Lonicera glaucescens
Hoary sagebrush
Artemisia cana

VINES

Western virgin's-bower
Clematis ligusticifolia
American vetch
Vicia americana
Wild peavine
Lathyrus venosus
Virginia creeper
Parthenocissus quinquefolia
Riverbank grape
Vitis riparia
Hedge bindweed
Convolvulus sepium
Twinflower
Linnaea borealis
Wild cucumber
Echinocystis lobata

TREES

CONIFEROUS TREES

Jack pine
Pinus banksiana
Tamarack
Larix laricina
Black spruce
Picea mariana
White spruce
Picea glauca
Douglas fir
Pseudotsuga menziesii
Balsam fir
Abies balsamea

DECIDUOUS TREES

Balsam poplar
Populus balsamifera
Narrow-leaved cottonwood
Populus angustifolia
Trembling aspen
Populus tremuloides
Western cottonwood
Populus sargentii
Hoary willow
Salix candida
Peach-leaved willow
Salix amygdaloides
Pussy willow
Salix discolor
Beaked hazelnut
Corylus cornuta
River birch
Betula occidentalis
White birch
Betula papyrifera
Speckled alder
Alnus rugosa
Bur oak
Quercus macrocarpa
American elm
Ulmus americana
Western mountain ash
Sorbus scopulina
Saskatoon
Amelanchier alnifolia
Douglas hawthorn
Crataegus douglasii
Round-leaved hawthorn
Crataegus chrysocarpa
American plum
Prunus americana
Pin cherry
Prunus pensylvanica

Red-fruited choke cherry
Prunus virginiana
Common caragana
Caragana arborescens
Box-elder
Acer negundo
Lance-leaved ash
Fraxinus pennsylvanica

ANIMALS

INSECTS

SILVERFISH
THYSANURA
Silverfish
Lepisma domestica
MAYFLIES
EPHEMEROPTERA
Mayfly
Hexagenia bilineata
DRAGONFLIES AND DAMSELFLIES
ODONATA
Big green darner
Anax junius
Common bluet
Enallagma ebrium
Ruby-spot
Hetaerina americana
GRASSHOPPERS AND RELATED SPECIES
ORTHOPTERA
Clear-winged grasshopper
Camnula pellucida
Packard's grasshopper
Melanoplus packardi
Red-legged grasshopper
Melanoplus sanguinipes
Two-striped grasshopper
Melanoplus bivittatus
Praying Mantis
Paratenodera sinensis
Cockroach
Blatta orientalis

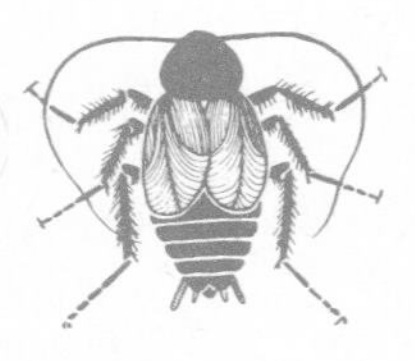

Field cricket
Acheta assimilis
Mormon cricket
Anabrus simplex
LICE
ANOPLURA
Crab louse
Phthirus pubis
Short-nosed cattle louse
Haematopinus eurysternus
LEAFHOPPERS, APHIDS AND SCALE INSECTS
HOMOPTERA
Potato leafhopper
Empoasca fabae
Six-spotted leafhopper
Macrosteles fascifrons
Cornleaf aphid
Rhopalosiphum maidis
English grain aphid
Macrosiphum granarium
Greenbug aphid
Taxoptera graminum
Pea aphid
Macrosiphum pisi
Potato aphid
Macrosiphum solanifoli
Sugar-beet root aphid
Penphigus betae
Western wheat aphid
Brachycolus tritici
Tomato psyllid
Paratrioza cockerelli
GRASS THRIPS
THYSANOPTERA
Grass thrip
Anaphothrips obscurus
TRUE BUGS
HEMIPTERA
Western chinch bug
Blissus occiduus
Lygus bugs
Liocoris borealis
Liocoris desertus
Liocoris rubroclarus
Liocoris unctuosus
Lygus lineolarius
Backswimmer
Notonecta undulata
Common bed bug
Cimex lectularius
Alfalfa plant bug
Adelphocoris lineolatus
Ragweed plant bug
Chlamydatus associatus

Rapid plant bug
Adelphocoris rapidus
Superb plant bug
Adelphocoris superbus

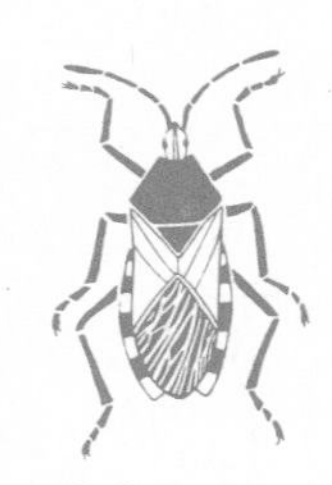

Squash bug
Anasa tristis

Chlorochroa sayi
Water boatman
Arctocorixa interrupta
Water strider
Gerris marginatus
NERVE-WINGED INSECTS
NEUROPTERA
Golden-eye lacewing
Chrysopa aculata
MOTHS AND BUTTERFLIES
LEPIDOPTERA
Army worm
Pseudaletia unipuncta
Bertha armyworm
Mamestra configurata
Wheat head armyworm
Faronta diffusa
Corn barworm
Heliothis zea
Flax bollworm
Heliothis ononis
Monarch butterfly
Danaus plexippus
Alfalfa caterpillar
Colias philodice
Tent caterpillar
Malacosoma americana
Western corn borer
Helotropha reniformis
European corn borer
Pyrausta nubilalis
Dark-sided cutworm
Euxoa messoria
Dingy cutworm
Feltia ducens
Pale western cutworm
Agrotis orthogonia

Sand cutworm
Euxoa detersa
Striped cutworm
Euxoa tessellata
Banded sunflower moth
Phalonia hospes
Diamond-backed moth
Putella maculipennis
Sunflower moth
Homoeosoma electellum
Tiger moth
Apantesis spp.
Case-making clothes moth
Tinea pellionella
Webbing clothes moth
Tineola bisselliella
Painted lady
Vanessa cardui
Red admiral
Vanessa atalanta
Beet webworm
Loxostage sticticalis
FLIES
DIPTERA
Bluebottle
Calliphora vicina
Bighead fly
Dorilas ater
Black fly
Simulium arcticum
Bot fly
Gasteriphilus intestinalis
Hessian fly
Phytophaga destructor
Horse fly
Tabanus atratus
House fly
Musca domestica
Moth fly
Psychoda alternata
Robber flies
Asilus prairiensis
Sand fly
Culicoides guttipennis
Soldier fly
Stratiomys unilimbata

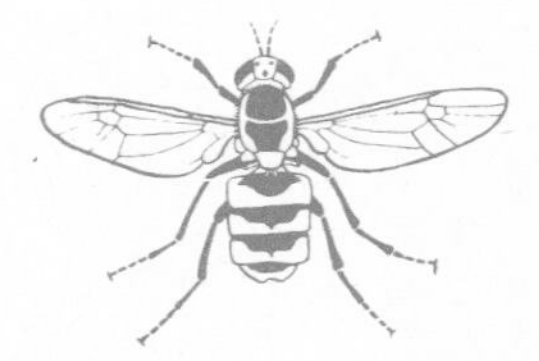

Vinegar fly
Drosophila melanogaster
Warble fly
Hypoderma lineatum
Sugar-beet root maggot
Tetanops myopaeformis
Sunflower maggot
Strauzia longipennis
Wheat stem maggot
Meromyza americana
Midge
Tendipes decorus
Wheat midge
Sitodiplosis mosellana
Spinach leaf miner
Pegomy hyoscyami
Mosquito
Aedes campestris

BEES, WASPS AND ANTS
HYMENOPTERA

Bumble-bee
Bombus species
Hairy flower bee
Anthophora occidentalis
Honey bee
Apis mellifera
Clover seed chalcid
Bruchophagus gibbus
Bald faced hornet
Dolichovespula maculata
Giant cicada-killer
Sphecius speciosus
Wheat stem sawfly
Cephus cinctus

Ichneumon wasp
Megarhyssa macrurus

Blue mud wasp
Chalybion caeruleum
Braconid wasp
Macrocentrus ancylivorus
Cuckoo wasp
Chrysis nitidula
Scelionid wasp
Scelio calopteni

BEETLES
COLEOPTERA

Blister beetle
Epicauta solani
Caragana blister beetle
Epicauta subglabra
Nuttall blister beetle
Lytta nuttalli
Carrion beetle
Silpha noveboracensis
Predacious diving beetle
Harpalus caliginosus
Dung beetle
Canthon pilularius
Flea beetle
Phyllotreta
Potato flea beetle
Epitrix cucumeris
Saw-toothed grain beetle
Oryzaephilus surinamensis
Hide beetle
Dermestes maculatus
Lady beetle
Adalia bipunctata

Colorado potato beetle
Leptinotarsa decemlineata

Red turnip beetle
Entomoscelis americana
Hairy rove beetle
Creophilus maxillosus
Sexton beetle
Nicrophorus marginatus
Common soldier beetle
Chauliognathus pennsylvanicus
Sunflower beetle
Zygogramma exclamationis
Alfalfa curculio
Sitona scissifrons
Firefly
Photinus pyralis
White grub
Phyllophaga spp.
Alfalfa weevil
Hypera postica
Pea weevil
Bruchus pisorum
Sweet clover weevil
Sitona cylindricollis
Prairie grain wireworm
Ctenicera aeripennis

FISHES

STURGEONS
ACIPENSERIDAE

Lake sturgeon
Acipenser fulvescens

SALMONS, TROUTS, CHARSES, WHITEFISH AND GRAYLING
SALMONIDAE

Brown trout
Salmo trutta
Rainbow trout
Salmo gairdneri
Brook trout
Salvelinus fontinalis
Dolly Varden
Salvelinus malma
Lake trout
Salvelinus namaycush
Common whitefish
Coregonus clupeaformis
Round whitefish
Prosopium cylindraceum
Blackfin cisco
Coregonus nigripinnis
Shortjaw cisco
Coregonus zenithicus
Tullibee
Coregonus artedi
Arctic grayling
Thymallis signifer

MOONEYES
HIODONTIDAE

Goldeye
Hiodon alosoides
Mooneye
Hiodon tergisus

PIKES
ESOCIDAE

Muskellunge
Esox masquinongy
Northern pike
Esox lucius

MINNOWS
CYPRINIDAE

Flathead chub
Platygobio gracilis
Lake chub
Couesius plumbeus
Finescale dace
Chrosomus neogaeus
Longnose dace
Rhinichthys cataractae
Pearl dace
Semotilus margarita
Northern redbelly dace
Chrosomus eos

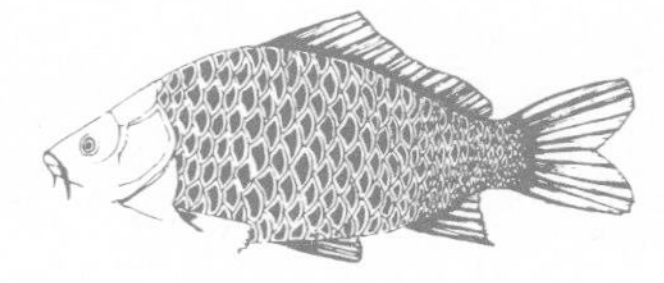

Carp
Cyprinus carpio

Brassy minnow
Hybognathus hankinsoni
Fathead minnow
Pimephales promelas
Blacknose shiner
Notropis heterolepis
Common shiner
Notropis cornutus
Emerald shiner
Notropis atherinoides
Golden shiner
Notemigonus crysoleucas
River shiner
Notropis blennius
Sand shiner
Notropis stramineus
Spottail shiner
Notropis hudsonius

SUCKERS
CATOSTOMIDAE

Bigmouth buffalo
Ictiobus cyprinellus

Northern redhorse
Moxostoma macrolepidotum

Silver redhorse
Moxostoma anisurum
White sucker
Catostomus commersoni
Mountain sucker
Catostomus platyrhynchus
Longnose sucker
Catostomus catostomus

Quillback
Carpiodes cyprinus

CATFISHES
ICTALURIDAE

Brown bullhead
Ictalurus nebulosus

Channel catfish
Ictalurus punctatus

Tadpole madtom
Noturus gyrinus

CODS
GADIDAE

Burbot
Lota lota

STICKLEBACKS
GASTEROSTEIDAE

Brook stickleback
Culaea inconstans

Ninespine stickleback
Pungitius pungitius

TROUT-PERCHES
PERCOPSIDAE

Trout-perch
Percopsis omiscomaycus

SUNFISHES
CENTRARCHIDAE

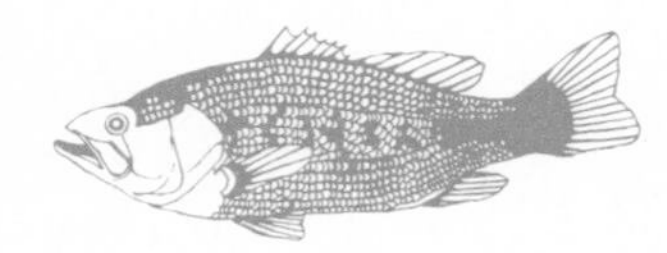

Largemouth bass
Micropterus salmoides

Smallmouth black bass
Micropterus dolomieui

Rock bass
Ambloplites rupestis

PERCHES
PERCIDAE

Blackside darter
Percina maculata

Iowa darter
Etheostoma exile

Johnny darter
Etheostoma nigrum

Log perch
Percina caprodes

Yellow perch
Perca fluviatilis

Sauger
Stizostedion canadense

Walleye
Stizostedion vitreum

DRUMS
SCIAENIDAE

Freshwater drum
Aplodinotus grunniens

SCULPINS
COTTIDAE

Deepwater sculpin
Myoxocephalus quadricornis

Spoonhead sculpin
Cottus ricei

Slimy sculpin
Cottus cognatus

AMPHIBIANS

Boreal chorus frog
Pseudacris triseriata

Leopard frog
Rana pipiens

Wood frog
Rana sylvatica

Tiger salamander
Ambystoma tigrinum

Plains spadefoot
Scaphiopus bombifrons

Canadian toad
Bufo hemiophrys

Great plains toad
Bufo cognatus

REPTILES

HORNED LIZARDS
PHRYNOSOMA

Eastern short-horned lizard
Phrynosoma douglassi

TURTLES
TESTUDINATA

Western painted turtle
Chrysemys picta

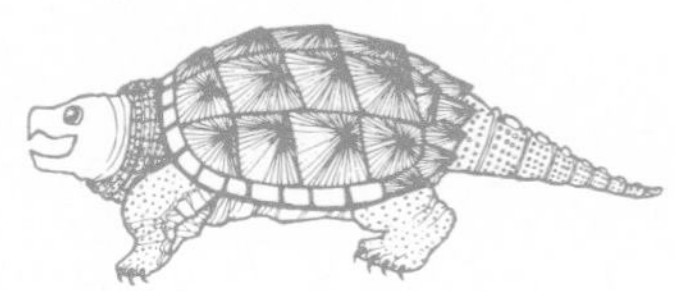

Common snapping turtle
Chelydra serpentina

SNAKES
SERPENTES

Bullsnake
Pituophis melanoleucus

Little brown snake
Storeria dekayi

Red-sided garter snake
Thamnophis sirtalis

Wandering garter snake
Thamnophis elegans

Western garter snake
Thamnophis radix

Smooth green snake
Opheodrys vernalis

Western hognose snake
Heterodon nasicus

Yellow-bellied racer
Coluber constrictor

Red-bellied snake
Storeria occipitomaculata

VENOMOUS SNAKES
CROTALIDAE

Prairie rattlesnake
Crotalus viridis

BIRDS

WATER, MARSH AND SHORE BIRDS

Common loon
Gavia immer

Red-throated loon
Gavia stellata

Red-necked grebe
Podiceps grisegena

Horned grebe
Podiceps auritus

Eared grebe
Podiceps caspicus

Western grebe
Aechmophorus occidentalis

Pied-billed grebe
Podilymbus podiceps

White pelican
Pelecanus erythrorhynchos

Double-crested cormorant
Phalacrocorax auritus

Great blue heron
Ardea herodias

Green heron
Butorides virescens

Little blue heron
Florida caerulea

Black-crowned night heron
Nycticorax nycticorax

American bittern
Botaurus lentiginosus

Least bittern
Ixobrychus exilis

Trumpeter swan
Olor buccinator

Whistling swan
Olor columbianus

Canada goose
Branta canadensis

Brant
Branta bernicla

White-fronted goose
Anser albifrons

Mallard
Anas platyrhynchos

Gadwall
Anas strepera

Pintail
Anas acuta

Green-winged teal
Anas carolinensis

Blue-winged teal
Anas discors

Cinnamon teal
Anas cyanoptera

American widgeon
Mareca americana

Shoveler
Spatula clypeata

Wood duck
Aix sponsa

Redhead
Aythya americana

Ring-necked duck
Aythya collaris

Canvasback
Aythya valisineria

Lesser scaup
Aythya affinis

Common goldeneye
Bucephala clangula

Bufflehead
Bucephala albeola

Oldsquaw
Clangula hyemalis

White-winged scoter
Melanitta deglandi

Surf scoter
Melanitta perspicillata

Ruddy duck
Oxyura jamaicensis

Hooded merganser
Lophodytes cucullatus
Common merganser
Mergus merganser
Red-breasted merganser
Mergus serrator
Whooping crane
Grus americanus
Sandhill crane
Grus canadensis

Virginia rail
Rallus limicola
Sora
Porzana carolina
Yellow rail
Coturnicops noveboracensis
Semipalmated plover
Charadrius semipalmatus
Piping plover
Charadrius melodus
American golden plover
Pluvialis dominica
Wilson's snipe
Capella gallinago
Long-billed curlew
Numenius americanus
Spotted sandpiper
Actitis macularia
Willet
Catoptrophorus semipalmatus
Greater yellowlegs
Totanus melanoleucus
Lesser yellowlegs
Totanus flavipes
Marbled godwit
Limosa fedoa
Avocet
Recurvirostra americana
Red phalarope
Phalaropus fulicarius
Wilson's phalarope
Steganopus tricolor
Northern phalarope
Lobipes lobatus
Promarine jaeger
Stercorarius pomarinus

Parasitic jaeger
Stercorarius parasiticus
Herring gull
Larus argentatus
California gull
Larus californicus
Ring-billed gull
Larus delawarensis
Franklin's gull
Larus pipixcan
Bonaparte's gull
Larus philadelphia
Sabine's gull
Xema sabini
Forster's tern
Sterna forsteri
Common tern
Sterna hirundo
Caspian tern
Hydroprogne caspia
Black tern
Chlidonias niger

Baird's sandpiper
Erolia bairdii
Pectoral sandpiper
Erolia melanotos
Belted kingfisher
Megaceryle alcyon
Traill's flycatcher
Empidonax traillii
Bank swallow
Riparia riparia
Rough-winged swallow
Stelgidopteryx ruficollis
Long-billed marsh wren
Telmatodytes palustris
Short-billed marsh wren
Cistothorus platensis
Common yellowthroat
Geothlypis trichas
Yellow-headed blackbird
Xanthocephalus xanthocephalus
Red-winged blackbird
Agelaius phoeniceus
Le Conte's sparrow
Passerherbulus caudacutus

Sharp-tailed sparrow
Ammospiza caudacuta
Swamp sparrow
Melospiza georgiana

BIRDS OF PREY

Goshawk
Accipiter gentilis
Sharp-shinned hawk
Accipiter striatus
Cooper's hawk
Accipiter cooperii
Red-tailed hawk
Buteo jamaicensis
Red-shouldered hawk
Buteo lineatus
Broad-winged hawk
Buteo platypterus
Ferruginous hawk
Buteo regalis
Golden eagle
Aquila chrysaetos
Bald eagle
Haliaeetus leucocephalus
Marsh hawk
Circus cyaneus
Harlan's hawk
Buteo harlani
Swainson's hawk
Buteo swainsoni
Rough legged hawk
Buteo lagopus
Osprey
Pandion haliaetus
Prairie falcon
Falco mexicanus
Peregrine falcon
Falco peregrinus
Pigeon hawk
Falco columbarius
Sparrow hawk
Falco sparverius
Barn owl
Tyto alba
Great horned owl
Bubo virginianus
Snowy owl
Nyctea scandiaca
Hawk-owl
Surnia ulula
Burrowing owl
Speotyto cunicularia
Barred owl
Strix varia

Long-eared owl
Asio otus
Short-eared owl
Asio flammeus
Boreal owl
Aegolius funerius
Saw-whet owl
Aegolius acadicus

Screech owl
Otus asio

FOREST BIRDS

Spruce grouse
Canachites canadensis
Ruffed grouse
Bonasa umbellus
American woodcock
Philohela minor
Whip-poor-will
Caprimulgus vociferus
Pileated woodpecker
Dryocopus pileatus
Yellow-bellied sapsucker
Sphyrapicus varius
Great crested flycatcher
Myiarchus crinitus
Least flycatcher
Empidonax minimus
Eastern wood pewee
Contopus virens
Olive-sided flycatcher
Nuttallornis borealis
Common raven
Corvus corax
Common crow
Corvus brachyrhynchos
Black-billed magpie
Pica pica
Canada jay
Perisoreus canadensis
Boreal chikadee
Parus hudsonicus
White-breasted nuthatch
Sitta carolinensis

Red-breasted nuthatch
Sitta canadensis
Brown creeper
Certhia familiaris
Winter wren
Troglodytes troglodytes
Hermit thrush
Hylocichla guttata
Veery
Hylocichla fuscescens
Ruby-crowned kinglet
Regulus calendula
Solitary vireo
Vireo solitarius
Red-eyed vireo
Vireo olivaceus
Black and white warbler
Mniotilta varia
Magnolia warbler
Dendroica magnolia
Cape May warbler
Dendroica tigrina
Black-throated blue warbler
Dendroica caerulescens
Myrtle warbler
Dendroica coronata

Blackburnian warbler
Dendroica fusca
Bay-breasted warbler
Dendroica castanea
Northern waterthrush
Seiurus noveboracensis
Connecticut warbler
Oporornis agilis
Canada warbler
Wilsonia canadensis
American redstart
Setophaga ruticilla
Pine grosbeak
Pinicola enucleator
Pine siskin
Spinus pinus

FIELD, SHRUB AND FOREST-EDGE BIRDS

Greater prairie chicken
Tympanuchus cupido
Sharp-tailed grouse
Pedioecetes phasianellus
Sage grouse
Centrocercus urophasianus
Hungarian partridge
Perdix perdix
Ring-necked pheasant
Phasianus colchicus
Killdeer
Charadrius vociferus
Upland plover
Bartramia longicauda
Horned lark
Eremophila alpestris
Carolina wren
Thryothorus ludovicianus
Semipalmated plover
Charadrius semipalmatus
Brown thrasher
Toxostoma rufum
Northern shrike
Lanius excubitor
Loggerhead shrike
Lanius ludovicianus
Chestnut-sided warbler
Dendroica pensylvanica
Mourning warbler
Oporornis philadelphia
Bobolink
Dolichonyx oryzivorus
Western meadowlark
Sturnella neglecta
Indigo bunting
Passerina cyanea
Snow bunting
Plectrophenax nivalis
American goldfinch
Spinus tristis

Rufous-sided towhee
Pipilo erythrophthalmus
Lark bunting
Calamospiza melanocorys
Oregon junco
Junco oreganus
White-throated sparrow
Zonotrichia albicollis
White-crowned sparrow
Zonotrichia leucophrys
Clay-colored sparrow
Spizella pallida
Song sparrow
Melospiza melodia
Lapland longspur
Calcarius lapponicus
McCown's longspur
Rhynchophanes mccownii

Chestnut-collared longspur
Calcarius ornatus

GARDEN AND TOWN BIRDS

Mourning dove
Zenaidura macroura
Common nighthawk
Chordeiles minor
Chimney swift
Chaetura pelagica
Ruby-throated hummingbird
Archilochus colubris

Yellow-shafted flicker
Colaptes auratus
Red-headed woodpecker
Melanerpes erythrocephalus
Hairy woodpecker
Dendrocopos villosus
Downy woodpecker
Dendrocopos pubescens
Eastern kingbird
Tyrannus tyrannus
Western kingbird
Tyrannus verticalis
Tree swallow
Iridoprocne bicolor
Barn swallow
Hirundo rustica
Cliff swallow
Petrochelidon pyrrhonota
Purple martin
Progne subis
Black-capped chickadee
Parus atricapillus
House wren
Troglodytes aedon
American robin
Turdus migratorius
Eastern bluebird
Sialia sialis
Cedar waxwing
Bombycilla cedrorum
Common starling
Sturnus vulgaris
Yellow warbler
Dendroica petechia
House sparrow
Passer domesticus
Baltimore oriole
Icterus galbula
Common grackle
Quiscalus quiscula
Brewer's blackbird
Euphagus cyanocephalus
Rusty blackbird
Euphagus carolinus
Brown-headed cowbird
Molothrus ater
Slate-colored junco
Junco hyemalis
Chipping sparrow
Spizella passerina

MAMMALS

HARES
LEPORIDAE
Arctic hare
Lepus arcticus
Snowshoe hare
Lepus americanus
Eastern cottontail
Sylvilagus floridanus

Mountain cottontail
Sylvilagus nuttalli

White-tailed jack rabbit
Lepus townsendi

SQUIRRELS
SCIURIDAE

Arctic ground squirrel
Citellus undulatus

Franklin's ground squirrel
Citellus franklini

Richardson's ground squirrel
Citellus richardsoni

Thirteen-lined ground squirrel
Citellus tridecemlineatus

Flying squirrel
Glaucomys sabrinus

Red squirrel
Tamiasciurus hudsonicus

Western chipmunk
Eutamias minimus

Black-tailed prairie dog
Cynomys ludovicianus

Woodchuck
Marmota monax

POCKET GOPHERS
GEOMYIDAE

Eastern pocket gopher
Geomys bursarius

Western pocket gopher
Thomomys talpoides

BATS
VESPERTILIONIDAE

Big brown bat
Eptesicus fuscus

Hoary bat
Lasiurus cinereus

Least bat
Myotis subulatus

Little brown bat
Myotis lucifugus

Red bat
Lasiurus borealis

Silver-haired bat
Lasionycteris noctivagans

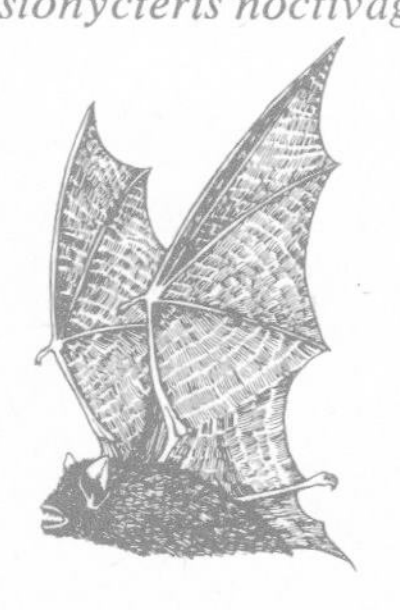

SHREWS
SORICIDAE

Arctic shrew
Sorex arcticus

Big short-tailed shrew
Blarina brevicauda

Common shrew
Sorex cinereus

Dusky shrew
Sorex obscurus

Pygmy shrew
Microsorex hoyi

Water shrew
Sorex palustris

BEAVERS
CASTORIDAE

Beaver
Castor canadensis

MICE
CRICETIDAE

Brown lemming
Lemmus trimucronatus

Long-tailed deermouse
Peromyscus maniculatus

Woodland deermouse
Peromyscus leucopus

Northern grasshopper mouse
Onychomys leucogaster

Muskrat
Ondatra zibethica

Northern lemming mouse
Synaptomys borealis

Northern red-backed vole
Clethrionomys gapperi

Tundra red-backed vole
Clethrionomys rutilus

Sagebrush vole
Lagurus curtatus

Heather vole
Phenacomys intermedius

Greenland varying lemming
Dicrostonyx groenlandicus

Chestnut-cheeked vole
Microtus xanthognathus

Meadow vole
Microtus pennsylvanicus

Prairie vole
Microtus ochrogaster

Richardson's vole
Microtus richardsoni

Bushy-tailed woodrat
Neotoma cinerea

POCKET MICE AND RATS
HETEROMYIDAE

Wyoming pocket mouse
Perognathus fasciatus

Kangaroo rat
Dipodomys ordi

OLD WORLD RATS AND MICE
MURIDAE

House mouse
Mus musculus

Brown rat
Rattus norvegicus

PORCUPINES
ERETHIZONTIDAE

Porcupine
Erethizon dorsatum

WOLVES AND FOXES
CANIDAE

Coyote
Canis latrans

Gray wolf
Canis lupus

Gray fox
Urocyon cinereoargenteus

Red fox
Vulpes fulva

BEARS
URSIDAE

Black bear
Ursus americanus

Grizzly bear
Ursus horribilis

RACCOONS
PROCYONIDAE

Raccoon
Procyon lotor

WEASELS, FERRETS AND MINKS
MUSTELIDAE

Badger
Taxidea taxus

Black-footed ferret
Mustela nigripes

Fisher
Martes pennanti

Marten
Martes americana

Mink
Mustela vison

Otter
Lutra canadensis

Striped skunk
Mephitis mephitis

Least weasel
Mustela rixosa

Long-tailed weasel
Mustela frenata

Short-tailed weasel
Mustela erminea

Wolverine
Gulo luscus

CATS
FELIDAE

Bobcat
Lynx rufus

Lynx
Lynx canadensis

Mountain lion
Felis concolor

ANTELOPE
ANTILOCAPRIDAE

Pronghorn
Antilocapra americana

CATTLE
BOVIDAE

Bison
Bison bison

DEER
CERVIDAE

Wapiti
Cervus canadensis

Moose
Alces alces

Mule deer
Odocoileus hemionus

White-tailed deer
Odocoileus virginianus

Woodland caribou
Rangifer caribou

BIBLIOGRAPHY

REGIONAL MAPS AND INFORMATION

Large-scale maps and other information on the Western Plains region can be obtained at moderate cost from: Department of Natural Resources, Regina; Department of Mines and Natural Resources, Norquay Bldg., Winnipeg; Department of Lands and Forests, Natural Resources Building, Edmonton; Government of Canada, Department of Energy, Mines and Resources, 601 Booth Street, Ottawa, Ont. A selection of film strips and slides is available from: National Film Board, P.O. Box 6100, Montreal 3, P.Q.

REGIONAL

BIRD, R. D.
Ecology of the Aspen Parkland of Western Canada.
Ottawa: Canada Department of Agriculture, 1961.

Conference on Land, Forest, Wildlife.
Edmonton: Alberta, Department of Lands and Forest, 1960.

FURNIVAL, G. M.
Cypress Lake Map-area, Saskatchewan.
Geological Survey of Canada, Memoir 242.

Guidebook, Cypress Hills Plateau, Alberta and Saskatchewan.
Alberta Society of Petroleum Geologists, 1965.

HARDY, W. G. (editor).
Alberta, a Natural History.
Edmonton: M. G. Hurtig, 1967.

KENDREW, W. G. and CURRIE, B. W.
The Climate of Central Canada.
Ottawa: Queen's Printer, 1955.

MACOUN, J.
Manitoba and the Great North West.
Guelph: World Publishing Company, 1882.

SPRY, I. M.
The Palliser Expedition: 1857-1860.
Toronto: Macmillan Company of Canada, 1963.

WARKENTIN, J.
The Western Interior of Canada: 1612-1917.
Toronto: McClelland and Stewart, 1964.

GEOLOGY

ATWOOD, WALLACE W.
Physiographic Provinces of North America.
Boston: Ginn, 1940.

BAIRD, DAVID M.
An Introduction to Geology.
Canadian Broadcasting Corporation, 1959.

CLARK, THOMAS H. and STEARN, COLIN W.
The Geological Evolution of North America.
New York: Ronald Press, 1960.

EARDLEY, A. J.
Structural Geology of North America.
New York: Harper and Row, 1962.

ENGLISH, GEORGE and JENSEN, DAVID.
Getting acquainted with Minerals.
Toronto: McGraw-Hill, 1958.

FENTON, CARROLL L. and FENTON, MILDRED A.
The Fossil Book.
New York: Doubleday, 1958.

FLINT, R. F.
Glacial and Pleistocene Geology.
New York: Wiley, 1957.

FRITZ, MADELEINE A.
Story of Ancient Life
Toronto: Pamphlet Series No. 1, Royal Ontario Museum of Palaeontology.

Geology and Economic Minerals of Canada.
Ottawa: Geological Survey of Canada, Dept. of Mines and Technical Surveys, 1957.

KAY, M. and COLBERT, E.
Stratigraphy and Life History.
New York: J. Wiley and Sons, 1965.

MCCROSSAN, R. C. and GLAISTER, R. P. (editors)
Geological History of Western Canada.
Calgary: Alberta Society of Petroleum Geologists.

PEARL, RICHARD M.
How to know the Rocks and Minerals.
New York: McGraw-Hill, 1955.

POUGH, FREDERICK H.
A Field Guide to Rocks and Minerals.
Boston: Houghton Mifflin, 1957.

RUSSELL, L. S. and LANDES, R. W.
Geology of the Southern Alberta Plains.
Ottawa: Geological Survey of Canada, Memoir 221, 1940.

RUSSELL, LORIS S.
The Mastodon.
Royal Ontario Museum Series, University of Toronto Press, 1965.

RUSSELL, L. S.
Dinosaur Hunting in Western Canada.
Royal Ontario Museum, University of Toronto Press, 1966.

SABINA, ANN P.
Rock and Mineral Collecting in Canada: Vol. I.
Ottawa: Queen's Printer, 1965.

STOCKWELL, C. H. (editor)
Geology and Economic Minerals of Canada.
Ottawa: Geological Survey of Canada, Economic Geology Series No. 1, 1963.

WESTGATE, J. A.
Surficial Geology of the Cypress Hills Area, Alberta.
Research Council of Alberta, Preliminary Report 65-2.

WILLIAMS, M. Y. and DYER, W. S.
Geology of Southern Alberta and Southwestern Saskatchewan.
Ottawa: Geological Survey of Canada, Memoir 163, 1930.

WRIGHT, H. E. and FRY, D. G. (editors)
The Quaternary of the United States.
Princeton University Press, 1965.

PLANTS

ALLEE, W. C. et al.
Principles of Animal Ecology.
Philadelphia: W. P. Saunders Company.

BIRDSEYE, CLARENCE and ELEANOR G.
Growing Woodland Plants.
New York: Oxford University Press, 1951.

BUDD, A. C.
Wild Plants of the Canadian Prairies.
Ottawa: Research Branch, Canada Dept. of Agriculture, 1964.

BULLER, REGINALD A. H.
Essays on Wheat.
New York: MacMillan, 1919.

CAMPBELL, J. B., BEST, K. F., and BUDD, A. C.
99 Range Forage Plants of the Canadian Prairies.
Ottawa: Canada Dept. of Agriculture, 1966.

CARMICHAEL, LLOYD T.
Prairie Wildflowers.
Toronto: Dent, 1960.

CARMICHAEL, LLOYD T.
Saskatchewan Wildflowers.
Regina: Saskatchewan Museum of Natural History.

CLARK, S. E., CAMPBELL, J. A. and CAMPBELL, J. B.
Native Grass Pastures in Southern Alberta, Saskatchewan and Manitoba.
Canada Department of Agriculture, Publ. 738. 1942.

COBB, BOUGHTON.
A Field Guide to the Ferns.
Boston: Houghton Mifflin, 1963.

CORMACK, R. G. H.
Trees and Shrubs of Alberta.
Edmonton: Dept. of Lands and Forests, 1964.

CRAIGIE, J. H.
Stem rust of Cereals.
Ottawa: Canada Dept. of Agriculture, 1957.

FERNALD, MERRITT L.
Gray's Manual of Botany.
New York: American Book Company, 1950.

FRANKTON, CLARENCE
Weeds of Canada.
Ottawa: Queen's Printer, 1966.

FLOCK, ELIZABETH BURNETT
Wildflowers of the Prairie Provinces.
Regina: School Aids and Textbook Publishing Co., 1960.

FRASER, J. G. C. and WHITESIDE, A. G. O.
Handbook of Canadian Spring Wheat Varieties.
Ottawa: Canada Department of Agriculture, 1956.

HUTCHINSON, SIR JOSEPH.
Essays on Crop Plant Evolution.
Cambridge: University Press, 1965.

JOHNSON, THORVALDUR.
Rust Research in Canada.
Ottawa: Research Branch, Canada Dept. of Agriculture, 1961.

LEMMON, ROBERT S. and JOHNSON, CHARLES C.
Wildflowers of North America.
New York: Doubleday, 1961.

MCCORMICK, JACK.
The Life of the Forest.
New York: McGraw-Hill, 1966.

MOSS, E. H.
Flora of Alberta.
University of Toronto Press, 1959.

Native Trees of Canada.
Ottawa: Queen's Printer, Bulletin 61, Department of Northern Affairs and National Resources, 1956.

PETERSON, ROGER TORY and MCKENNY, MARGARET
A Field Guide to Wildflowers.
Boston: Houghton Mifflin, 1968.

PETRIDES, GEORGE A.
A Field Guide to Trees and Shrubs.
Boston: Houghton Mifflin, 1958.

POHL, R. W.
How to know the Grasses.
Dubuque, Iowa: Wm. C. Brown Co., 1954.

RICKETT, HAROLD WILLIAM.
The New Field Book of American Wild Flowers.
New York: Putnam's, 1963.

ROWE, J. S.
Forest Regions of Canada.
Ottawa: Queen's Printer, Bulletin 123, Dept. of Northern Affairs and National Resources, 1966.

TAYLOR, NORMAN.
A Guide to the Wild Flowers.
New York: Garden City Books.

TIFFANY, L. F.
Algae, The Grass of many Waters.
New York: Charles C. Thomas, 1958.

WEAVER, J. E. and ALBERTSON, F. W.
Grasslands of the Great Plains: Their Nature and Use.
Lincoln, Nebraska: Johnson Publishing Company, 1956.

WHERRY, E. T.
Wild Flower Guide.
New York: Doubleday, 1948.

ANIMALS

Birds of the Cypress Hills Provincial Park.
Regina: Saskatchewan Dept. of Natural Resources.

BECK, W. K.
A Guide to Saskatchewan Mammals.
Regina: Saskatchewan Natural History Society, 1958.

BORRER, DONALD J. and DELONG, DWIGHT, M.
An Introduction to the Study of Insects.
New York: Holt, Rinehart, Winston.

BOURLIERE, FRANCOIS.
The Natural History of Mammals.
New York: Alfred A. Knopf, 1964.

BURT, WILLIAM H.
A Field Guide to the Mammals.
Boston: Houghton Mifflin, 1964.

CAMERON, AUSTIN W.
Canadian Mammals.
Ottawa: National Museum of Canada, 1964.

COLBERT, E. H.
Dinosaurs.
New York: Dutton & Co., 1961.

CONANT. ROGER.
A Field Guide to Reptiles and Amphibians.
Boston: Houghton Mifflin, 1958.

COOK, F. R.
A Guide to the Amphibians and Reptiles of Saskatchewan.
Regina: Museum of Natural History, 1966.

DORST, JEAN.
The Migration of Birds.
Boston: Houghton Mifflin, 1963.

DRIMMER, FREDERICK.
The Animal Kingdom.
New York: Greystone, 1954.

GODFREY, W. E.
Birds of the Cypress Hills and Flotten Lake Regions, Saskatchewan.
Ottawa: National Museum of Canada, Bulletin 120, 1950.

GODFREY, W. EARL.
The Birds of Canada.
Ottawa: National Museum of Canada, 1966.

HALLIDAY, HUGH M.
Wildlife Trails across Canada.
Toronto: Thomas Allen, 1956.

IMMS, A. D.
A General Textbook of Entomology.
(Revised by O. W. Richards and R. G. Davies).
London: Methuen, 1960.

KORTRIGHT, FRANCIS H.
Ducks, Geese and Swans of North America.
Washington: Wildlife Management Inst., 1942.

LINDUSKA, J. P. (editor)
Waterfowl tomorrow.
Washington, D.C.: U. S. Dept. of Interior, Bureau of Sports Fisheries and Wildlife, 1964.

LOGIER, E. B. S. and TORER, G. C.
Check-list of the Amphibians and Reptiles of Canada and Alaska.
Contributions of Royal Ontario Museum of Zoology and Palaeontology, No. 41, 1955.

LUTZ, FRANK E.
Field Book of Insects.
New York: Putnam's, 1934.

Mammals of Cypress Hills Provincial Park.
Regina: Saskatchewan Dept. of Natural Resources.

METCALF, C. L., FLINT, W. R. and METCALF, R. L.
Destructive and Useful Insects.
New York: McGraw-Hill, 1951.

MITCHENER, A. V.
Field Crop Insects.
Winnipeg: Line Elevators Farm Service, 1956.

NIERING, W. A.
The Life of the Marsh.
New York: McGraw-Hill, 1966.

NOVAKOWSKI, N. S.
Whooping Crane Population Dynamics.
Ottawa: Canadian Wildlife Service Report Series No. 1, Department of Indian Affairs and Northern Development, 1966.

OLIVER, JAMES
The Natural History of North American Amphibians and Reptiles.
New York: Van Nostrand, 1955.

PALMER, RALPH S.
The Mammal Guide.
New York: Doubleday, 1954.

PETERSON, ROGER TORY.
A Field Guide to the Birds.
Boston: Houghton Mifflin, 1947.

RAND, A. L.
Mammals of the eastern Rockies and western Plains of Canada.
National Museum of Canada, Bulletin 108, 1948.

ROE, F. G.
The North American Buffalo.
Toronto: University of Toronto Press, 1951.

RUSSELL, L. S.
Dinosaur hunting in western Canada.
Toronto: Royal Ontario Museum, Life Sciences, Contribution 70, 1966.

SALT, W. R. and WILK, A. L.
The Birds of Alberta.
Edmonton: Queen's Printer, 1964.

SWINTON, W. E.
Dinosaurs of Canada.
Toronto: Royal Ontario Museum Series, No. 5, 1965.

TAVERNER, P. A.
Birds of Canada.
Ottawa: Queen's Printer, 1934.

TIETZ, HARRISON M.
North American Insects.
Minneapolis: Burgess.

URQUHART, F. A.
Introducing the Insect.
Toronto: Clarke, Irwin, 1949.

MISCELLANEOUS

ANDERSON, MARGARET D.
Through the Microscope.
New York: The Natural History Press, Garden City, 1965.

COKER, R. E.
Streams, Lakes, Ponds.
The University of North Carolina Press, Chapel Hill, 1954.

DICE, L. R.
Natural communities.
Ann Arbor: University of Michigan Press, 1952.

FARB, PETER.
The Face of North America.
New York: Harper and Row, 1963.

LEGGET, R. F. (editor)
Soils in Canada.
Royal Society of Canada, Special Publ. No. 3, 1961.

HYNES, H. B. N.
The Biology of Polluted Waters.
Liverpool: Liverpool University Press, 1960.

JACKSON, D. E. (editor)
Algae and Man.
New York: Plenum Press, 1964.

KEITH, L. B.
Wildlife's Ten-year Cycle.
Madison: University of Wisconsin Press, 1963.

KLOTS, ELSIE B.
The New Field Book of Freshwater Life.
New York: Putnam's, 1966.

LAYCOCK, A. H.
Water Deficiency Patterns in the Prairie Provinces.
Regina: Prairie Provinces Water Board, Report No. 8, 1964.

MCALESTER, A.
The History of Life.
New York: Prentice-Hall, 1968.

MORGAN, ANN H.
Field Book of Ponds and Streams.
New York: Putnam's, 1930.

MOSS, H. C.
A Guide to understanding Saskatchewan Soils.
Saskatoon: Univ. of Saskatchewan, 1965.

NEEDHAM, J. G. and NEEDHAM, P. R.
A Guide to the Study of Freshwater Biology.
San Francisco: Holden-Day, 1962.

Exploratory Soil Surveys of Northern Alberta.
Research Council of Alberta, 1958-1965.

REID, GEORGE K.
Ecology of Inland Waters and Estuaries.
New York: Reinhold, 1961.

RUDD, R. L.
Pesticides and the Living Landscape.
Madison: University of Wisconsin Press, 1964.

RUTTNER, F.
Fundamentals of Limnology.
(Translated by D. G. Frey and F. E. J. Fry)
University of Toronto Press, 1963.

SANDERSON, IVAN T.
The Continent we live on.
New York: Random House, 1961.

TOOGOOD, J. A. and NEWTON, J. D.
Water Erosion in Alberta.
Edmonton: Faculty of Agriculture, University of Alberta, Bulletin No. 56, 1955.

Saskatchewan Department of Natural Resources Bulletins:
- No. 3—Fisheries Research in Saskatchewan.
- No. 4—Sharp-tailed Grouse in Saskatchewan.
- No. 5—Fisheries Resources of Saskatchewan.
- No. 6—Wildlife Research in Saskatchewan.
- No. 7—Fish of Saskatchewan.
- No. 8—Forest Resources of Saskatchewan.
- No. 9—Moose in Saskatchewan.

The Audubon Nature Encyclopedia.
Philadelphia: Curtis Books, 1965.

INDEX

P

Q

R

S

T

U

V

W

Y

ACKNOWLEDGEMENTS

The author and editors wish to acknowledge with gratitude the advice and assistance of: Dr. D. A. Rennie, University of Saskatchewan, John Goodale, Floral, Saskatchewan, L. J. Chapman, Ontario Research Foundation, W. W. Pettapiece, University of Alberta–on soils; Dr. P. W. Riegert, Canada Dept. of Agriculture, Saskatoon, Dr. D. R. Robertson, Manitoba Dept. of Agriculture and Conservation–on insects; Dr. J. W. White and Dr. D. R. Knott, University of Saskatchewan, P. O. Moen, Dept. of Conservation and Development, Regina, Dr. N. C. Stoskopf, University of Guelph, Professor J. R. Maze, University of Toronto–on agriculture and plant science; Dr. A. G. Edmund, Royal Ontario Museum, F. G. Bard, Saskatchewan Museum of Natural History–on fossils; Dr. E. J. Crossman, Royal Ontario Museum–on fishes; A. Penman, Metropolitan Corporation of Greater Winnipeg, G. C. Mitchell, Saskatchewan Water Resources Commission, Tom Harper, Department of Natural Resources, Regina, T. E. Weber, Dept. of Highways, Winnipeg–on conservation; Professor C. R. Forsberg, University of Saskatchewan, A. L. Riegert, Dept. of Public Health, Regina, Mrs. Douglas Smith, Edmonton, L. M. Kay, Dept. of Health, Winnipeg, Derrick Carrol, Saskatoon City Engineer–on pollution; Frank Ternan, Imperial Oil Company–on petroleum; L. C. Goldman, U.S. Bureau of Sport Fisheries and Wildlife–on whooping cranes; Dr. N. S. Novakowski, Dept. of Indian Affairs and Northern Development, Ottawa–on Wood Buffalo Park; R. J. Zaph, Park Superintendent, W. T. Galliver, Alberta Dept. of Lands and Forests, B. C. Shier, Saskatchewan Dept. of Industry and Commerce–on the Cypress Hills. Our thanks also to the following: Hans Moeller, National Film Board, F. G. Wagner, Prairie Farm Rehabilitation Administration, Mabel H. Ledgard, Saskatchewan Provincial Photo Library–for pictorial references; H. W. Braithwaite, Saskatoon Dairy Pool, Mrs. Georgena Swan, Meadow Lake, Sask.–for regional information; Miss Libby Oughton for compiling the index.

This book was produced entirely in Canada by: Mono Lino Typesetting Co. Limited / *Typesetting;* Herzig Somerville Limited / *Film Separation;* Ashton-Potter Limited / *Printing;* T. H. Best Printing Co. Limited / *Binding. Typefaces: Times New Roman and Helvetica. Paper: 65 lb. Georgian Offset Smooth.*

PICTURE CREDITS

Order of appearance in the text of pictures listed here is left to right, top to bottom.

Cover/Fred Lahrman
1/National Parks Service (Dalton Muir)
2/Cyril G. Hampson
4/NPS (DM)
8/Bill Brooks
10/Harold Whyte
20/Saskatchewan Government
27/Alberta Government
29/HW, HW
39/Wayne Pettapiece
40/J.B. Miller
44/BB
45/BB
50/AG
54/National Air Photo Library
57/J.R. Maze
68/Gene Aliman
72/AG
75/Manitoba Government
76/D.W. Schmidt, National Film Board (Textfilms), NFB (T), NFB (T)
77/CGH
80/R. Huntington
84/JBM
89/Doug Wilkinson
90/National Film Board (Stills), Gord Edmund, DWS
91/GE
92/BB
93/GE, GE, GE, BB
94/CGH
97/DWS
100/Dave Hancock, CGH, NFB (T), CGH
101/NFB(T), NFB(T), NFB(T), CGH, NFB(T), CGH
108/CGH, DH,
109/CGH
110/NFB (S)
111/NFB (S)
112/CGH
115/FL
116/CGH
117/BB
119/Mrs. H. Sutton
121/NPS (DM)
122/NPS (DM), NPS (DM)
123/NPS (DM), CGH, NPS (DM), NPS (DM)
124/NFB(S), NPS (DM)
125/DWS
126/FL
127/N.S. Novakowski, FL, U.S. Bureau of Sport Fisheries and Wildlife (Luther C. Goldman), U.S. BSF&W (LCG)
128/NPS (DM)
132/NFB (S)
136/Prairie Farm Rehabilitation Administration